Data Acquisition and Conversion Handbook

A Technical Guide to A/D and D/A Converters and Their Applications

Edited by Eugene L. Zuch

Published by

DATEL INTERSIL

11 CABOT BOULEVARD
MANSFIELD, MASSACHUSETTS 02048

PREFACE

In recent years Datel-Intersil has published many technical articles on the subject of data acquisition and conversion in the industry trade journals. Since many engineers have requested reprints of these articles, it was decided to compile them into a useful, coherent reference handbook on data conversion and make it available at moderate cost. This handbook is the result of that effort.

The book also contains a 23 page basic introduction to data conversion entitled "Principles of Data Acquisition and Conversion" and a useful "Glossary of Data Conversion Terms" which defines the 200 most common terms used in data conversion technology today.

The following authors have contributed to this work: Peter Bradshaw, George F. Bryant, Lawrence D. Copeland, Lee Evans, Dave Fullagar, Ralph Johnston, James B. Knitter, Wayne E. Marshall, John M. Mills, Eugene L. Murphy, Bill O'Neill, Skip Osgood, Dick Wilenken, and Eugene L. Zuch.

This handbook was conceived several years ago as a result of the encouragement of John H. Gallagher, and was supported by Arthur Pappas, Nicholas Tagaris, and James Zaros, all officers and founders of Datel Systems, Inc. (now Datel-Intersil).

August, 1979   Eugene L. Zuch
Mansfield, Mass.

i

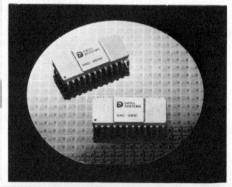

Contents

1. Principles of Data Acquisition and Conversion

Principles of
Data Acquisition and Conversion

by Eugene L. Zuch, Datel-Intersil Inc.

Data Acquisition Systems

Introduction

Data acquisition and conversion systems interface between the real world of physical parameters, which are analog, and the artificial world of digital computation and control. With current emphasis on digital systems, the interfacing function has become an important one; digital systems are used widely because complex circuits are low cost, accurate, and relatively simple to implement. In addition, there is rapid growth in use of minicomputers and microcomputers to perform difficult digital control and measurement functions.

Computerized feedback control systems are used in many different industries today in order to achieve greater productivity in our modern industrial society. Industries which presently employ such automatic systems include steel making, food processing, paper production, oil refining, chemical manufacturing, textile production, and cement manufacturing.

The devices which perform the interfacing function between analog and digital worlds are analog-to-digital (A/D) and digital-to-analog (D/A) converters, which together are known as data converters. Some of the specific applications in which data converters are used include data telemetry systems, pulse code modulated communications, automatic test systems, computer display systems, video signal processing systems, data logging systems, and sampled-data control systems. In addition, every laboratory digital multimeter or digital panel meter contains an A/D converter.

Besides A/D and D/A converters, data acquisition and distribution systems may employ one or more of the following circuit functions:

Basic Data Distribution Systems

Transducers
Amplifiers
Filters
Nonlinear Analog Functions
Analog Multiplexers
Sample-Holds

The interconnection of these components is shown in the diagram of the data acquisition portion of a computerized feedback control system in Figure 1.

The input to the system is a *physical parameter* such as temperature, pressure, flow, acceleration, and position, which are analog quantities. The parameter is first converted into an electrical signal

by means of a *transducer*; once in electrical form, all further processing is done by electronic circuits.

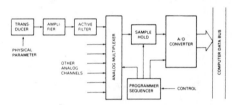

Figure 1. Data Acquisition System

Next, an *amplifier* boosts the amplitude of the transducer output signal to a useful level for further processing. Transducer outputs may be microvolt or millivolt level signals which are then amplified to 1 to 10 volt levels. Furthermore, the transducer output may be a high impedance signal, a differential signal with common-mode noise, a current output, a signal superimposed on a high voltage, or a combination of these. The amplifier, in order to convert such signals into a high level voltage, may be one of several specialized types.

The amplifier is frequently followed by a low pass *active filter* which reduces high frequency signal components, unwanted electrical interference noise, or electronic noise from the signal. The amplifier is sometimes also followed by a special *nonlinear analog function* circuit which performs a nonlinear operation on the high level signal. Such operations include squaring, multiplication, division, RMS conversion, log conversion, or linearization.

The processed analog signal next goes to an *analog multiplexer* which sequentially switches between a number of different analog input channels. Each input is in turn connected to the output of the multiplexer for a specified period of time by the multiplexer switch. During this connection time a *sample-hold* circuit acquires the signal voltage and then holds its value while an *analog-to-digital converter* converts the value into digital form. The resultant digital word goes to a computer data bus or to the input of a digital circuit.

Thus the analog multiplexer, together with the sample-hold, time shares the A/D converter with a number of analog input channels. The timing and control of the complete data acquisition system is done by a digital circuit called a *programmer-sequencer*, which in turn is under control of the computer. In some cases the computer itself may control the entire data acquisition system.

While this is perhaps the most commonly used data acquisition system configuration, there are alternative ones. Instead of multiplexing high-level signals, low-level multiplexing is sometimes used with the amplifier following the multiplexer. In such cases just one amplifier is required, but its gain may have to be changed from one channel to the next during multiplexing. Another method is to amplify and convert the signal into digital form at the transducer location and send the digital information in serial form to the computer. Here the digital data must be converted to parallel form and then multiplexed onto the computer data bus.

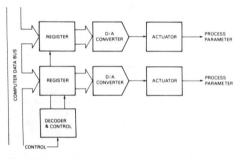

Figure 2. Data Distribution System

Basic Data Acquisition System

The data distribution portion of a feedback control system, illustrated in Figure 2, is the reverse of the data acquisition system. The computer, based on the inputs of the data acquisition system, must close the loop on a process and control it by means of output control functions. These control outputs are in digital form and must therefore be converted into analog form in order to drive the process. The conversion is accomplished by a series of *digital-to-analog converters* as shown. Each D/A converter is coupled to the computer data bus by means of a register which stores the digital word until the next update. The registers are activated sequentially by a *decoder and control circuit* which is under computer control.

The D/A converter outputs then drive *actuators* which directly control the various process parameters such as temperature, pressure, and flow. Thus the loop is closed on the process and the result is a complete automatic process control system under computer control.

Quantizing Theory

Introduction

Analog-to-digital conversion in its basic conceptual form is a two-step process: quantizing and coding. Quantizing is the process of transforming a continuous analog signal into a set of discrete output states. Coding is the process of assigning a digital code word to each of the output states. Some of the early A/D converters were appropriately called quantizing encoders.

Quantizer Transfer Function

The nonlinear transfer function shown in Figure 3 is that of an ideal quantizer with 8 output states; with output code words assigned, it is also that of

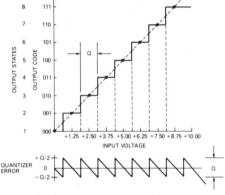

Figure 3. Transfer Function of Ideal 3-Bit Quantizer

a 3-bit A/D converter. The 8 output states are assigned the sequence of binary numbers from 000 through 111. The analog input range for this quantizer is 0 to +10V.

There are several important points concerning the transfer function of Figure 3. First, the *resolution* of the quantizer is defined as the number of output states expressed in bits; in this case it is a 3-bit quantizer. The number of output states for a binary coded quantizer is 2^n, where n is the number of bits. Thus, an 8-bit quantizer has 256 output states and a 12-bit quantizer has 4096 output states.

As shown in the diagram, there are $2^n - 1$ analog decision points (or threshold levels) in the transfer function. These points are at voltages of +0.625,

+1.875, +3.125, +4.375, +5.625, +6.875, and
+8.125. The decision points must be precisely set
in a quantizer in order to divide the analog voltage
range into the correct quantized values.

The voltages +1.25, +2.50, +3.75, +5.00, +6.25,
+7.50, and +8.75 are the center points of each
output code word. The analog decision point voltages
are precisely halfway between the code word center
points. The quantizer staircase function is the best
approximation which can be made to a straight line
drawn through the origin and full scale point; notice
that the line passes through all of the code word
center points.

Quantizer Resolution and Error

At any part of the input range of the quantizer, there
is a small range of analog values within which the
same output code word is produced. This small range
is the voltage difference between any two adjacent
decision points and is known as the analog quantization size, or *quantum*, Q. In Figure 3, the quantum is 1.25V and is found in general by dividing the
full scale analog range by the number of output
states. Thus

$$Q = \frac{FSR}{2^n}$$

where FSR is the full scale range, or 10V in this
case. Q is the smallest analog difference which can
be resolved, or distinguished, by the quantizer. In
the case of a 12-bit quantizer, the quantum is much
smaller and is found to be

$$Q = \frac{FSR}{2^n} = \frac{10V}{4096} = 2.44 \text{ mV}$$

If the quantizer input is moved through its entire
range of analog values and the difference between
output and input is taken, a sawtooth error function
results, as shown in Figure 3. This function is called
the quantizing error and is the irreducible error
which results from the quantizing process. It can
be reduced only by increasing the number of output
states (or the resolution) of the quantizer, thereby
making the quantization finer.

For a given analog input value to the quantizer,
the output error will vary anywhere from 0 to
$\pm Q/2$; the error is zero only at analog values
corresponding to the code center points. This error
is also frequently called *quantization uncertainty*
or *quantization noise*.

The quantizer output can be thought of as the analog input with quantization noise added to it. The

noise has a peak-to-peak value of Q but, as with
other types of noise, the average value is zero. Its
RMS value, however, is useful in analysis and can
be computed from the triangular waveshape to be
$Q/2\sqrt{3}$.

Sampling Theory

Introduction

An analog-to-digital converter requires a small, but
significant, amount of time to perform the quantizing
and coding operations. The time required to make
the conversion depends on several factors: the converter resolution, the conversion technique, and the
speed of the components employed in the converter.
The conversion speed required for a particular
application depends on the time variation of the
signal to be converted and on the accuracy desired.

Aperture Time

Conversion time is frequently referred to as *aperture time*. In general, aperture time refers to the
time uncertainty (or time window) in making a
measurement and results in an amplitude uncertainty (or error) in the measurement if the signal
is changing during this time.

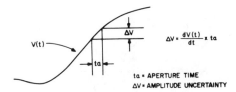

Figure 4. Aperture Time and Amplitude Uncertainty

As shown in Figure 4, the input signal to the A/D
converter changes by ΔV during the aperture time
t_a in which the conversion is performed. The error
can be considered an amplitude error or a time
error; the two are related as follows

$$\Delta V = t_a \frac{dV(t)}{dt}$$

where $dV(t)/dt$ is the rate of change with time of
the input signal.

It should be noted that ΔV represents the maximum
error due to signal change, since the actual error
depends on how the conversion is done. At some
point in time within t_a, the signal amplitude corresponds exactly with the output code word produced.

For the specific case of a sinusoidal input signal, the maximum rate of change occurs at the zero crossing of the waveform, and the amplitude error is

$$\Delta V = t_a \frac{d}{dt} (A \sin \omega t)_{t=o} = t_a A \omega$$

The resultant error as a fraction of the peak to peak full scale value is

$$\epsilon = \frac{\Delta V}{2A} = \pi f t_a$$

From this result the aperture time required to digitize a 1 kilohertz signal to 10 bits resolution can be found. The resolution required is one part in 2^{10} or 0.001.

$$t_a = \frac{\epsilon}{\pi f} = \frac{0.001}{3.14 \times 10^3} = 320 \times 10^{-9}$$

The result is a required aperture time of just 320 nanoseconds!

One should appreciate the fact that 1 KHz is not a particularly fast signal, yet it is difficult to find a 10 bit A/D converter to perform this conversion at any price! Fortunately, there is a relatively simple and inexpensive way around this dilemma by using a sample-hold circuit.

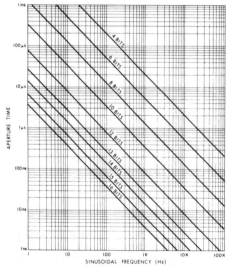

Figure 5. Graph for Aperture Error for Sinusoidal Signals

Sample-Holds and Aperture Error

A sample-hold circuit samples the signal voltage and

then stores it on a capacitor for the time required to perform the A/D conversion. The aperture time of the A/D converter is therefore greatly reduced by the much shorter aperture time of the sample-hold circuit. In turn, the aperture time of the sample-hold is a function of its bandwidth and switching time.

Figure 5 is a useful graph of Equation 5. It gives the aperture time required for converting sinusoidal signals to a maximum error less than one part in 2^n where n is the resolution of the converter in bits. The peak to peak value of the sinusoid is assumed to be the full scale range of the A/D converter. The graph is most useful in selecting a sample-hold by aperture time or an A/D converter by conversion time.

Sampled-Data Systems and the Sampling Theorem

In data acquisition and distribution systems, and other sampled-data systems, analog signals are sampled on a periodic basis as illustrated in Figure 6. The train of sampling pulses in 6(b) represents a fast-acting switch which connects to the analog signal for a very short time and then disconnects for the remainder of the sampling period.

The result of the fast-acting sampler is identical with multiplying the analog signal by a train of sampling pulses of unity amplitude, giving the modulated pulse train of Figure 6(c). The amplitude of the original signal is perserved in the modulation envelope of the pulses. If the switch type sampler is replaced by a switch and capacitor (a sample-hold circuit), then the amplitude of each sample is stored between samples and a reasonable reconstruction of the original analog signal results, as shown in 6(d).

The purpose of sampling is the efficient use of data processing equipment and data transmission facilities. A single data transmission link, for example, can be used to transmit many different analog channels on a sampled basis, whereas it would be uneconomical to devote a complete transmission link to the continuous transmission of a single signal.

Likewise, a data acquisition and distribution system is used to measure and control the many parameters of a process control system by sampling the parameters and updating the control inputs periodically. In data conversion systems it is common to use a single, expensive A/D converter of high speed and precision and then multiplex a number of analog inputs into it.

An important fundamental question to answer about sample-data systems is this: "How often must I sample an analog signal in order not to lose information from it?" It is obvious that all useful information can be extracted if a slowly varying signal is sampled at a rate such that little or no change takes place between samples. Equally obvious is the fact that information is being lost if there is a significant change in signal amplitude between samples.

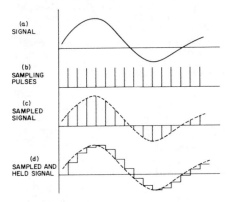

Figure 6. Signal Sampling

The answer to the question is contained in the well-known Sampling Theorem which may be stated as follows: *If a continuous, bandwidth-limited signal contains no frequency components higher than fc, then the original signal can be recovered without distortion if it is sampled at a rate of at least 2fc samples per second.*

Frequency Folding and Aliasing

The Sampling Theorem can be demonstrated by the frequency spectra illustrated in Figure 7. Figure 7(a) shows the frequency spectrum of a continuous bandwidth-limited analog signal with frequency components out to fc. When this signal is sampled at a rate fs, the modulation process shifts the original spectrum out to fs, 2fs, 3fs, etc. in addition to the one at the origin. A portion of this resultant spectrum is shown in Figure 7(b).

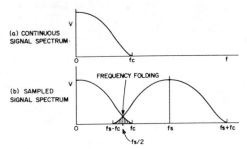

Figure 7. Frequency Spectra Demonstrating the Sampling Theorem

If the sampling frequency fs is not high enough, part of the spectrum centered about fs will fold over into the original signal spectrum. This undesirable effect is called *frequency folding*. In the process of recovering the original signal, the folded part of the spectrum causes distortion in the recovered signal which cannot be eliminated by filtering the recovered signal.

From the figure, if the sampling rate is increased such that $f_s - f_c > f_c$, then the two spectra are separated and the original signal can be recovered without distortion. This demonstrates the result of the Sampling Theorem that $f_s > 2f_c$. Frequency folding can be eliminated in two ways: first by using a high enough sampling rate, and second by filtering the signal before sampling to limit its bandwidth to $f_s/2$.

One must appreciate the fact that in practice there is always some frequency folding present due to high frequency signal components, noise, and non-ideal pre-sample filtering. The effect must be reduced to negligible amounts for the particular application by using a sufficiently high sampling rate. The required rate, in fact, may be much higher than the minimum indicated by the Sampling Theorem.

The effect of an inadequate sampling rate on a sinusoid is illustrated in Figure 8; an *alias frequency* in the recovered signal results. In this case, sampling at a rate slightly less than twice per cycle gives the low frequency sinusoid shown by the dotted line in the recovered signal. This alias frequency can be significantly different from the original frequency. From the figure it is easy to see that if the sinusoid is sampled at least twice per cycle, as required by the Sampling Theorem, the original frequency is preserved.

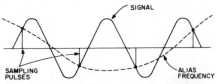

Figure 8. Alias Frequency Caused by Inadequate Sampling Rate

Coding for Data Converters

Natural Binary Code

A/D and D/A converters interface with digital systems by means of an appropriate digital code. While there are many possible codes to select, a few standard ones are almost exclusively used with data converters. The most popular code is *natural binary*, or *straight binary*, which is used in its fractional form to represent a number

$$N = a_1 2^{-1} + a_2 2^{-2} + a_3 2^{-3} + \ldots + a_n 2^{-n}$$

where each coefficient "a" assumes a value of zero or one. N has a value between zero and one.

A binary fraction is normally written as 0.110101, but with data converter codes the decimal point is omitted and the code word is written 110101. This code word represents a fraction of the full scale value of the converter and has no other numerical significance.

The binary code word 110101 therefore represents the decimal fraction $(1 \times 0.5) + (1 \times 0.25) + (1 \times 0.125) + (1 \times 0.0625) + (0 \times 0.03125) + (1 \times 0.015625) = 0.828125$ or 82.8125% of full scale for the converter. If full scale is $+10V$, then the code word represents $+8.28125V$. The natural binary code belongs to a class of codes known as positive weighted codes since each coefficient has a specific weight, none of which is negative.

The leftmost bit has the most weight, 0.5 of full scale, and is called the *most significant bit*, or MSB; the rightmost bit has the least weight, 2^{-n} of full scale, and is therefore called the *least significant bit*, or LSB. The bits in a code word are numbered from left to right from 1 to n.

The LSB has the same analog equivalent value as Q discussed previously, namely

$$\text{LSB (Analog Value)} = \frac{\text{FSR}}{2^n}$$

Table 1 is a useful summary of the resolution, number of states, LSB weights, and dynamic range for data converters from one to twenty bits resolution.

RESOLUTION BITS n	NUMBER OF STATES 2^n	LSB WEIGHT 2^{-n}	DYNAMIC RANGE dB
0	1	1	0
1	2	0.5	6
2	4	0.25	12
3	8	0.125	18.1
4	16	0.0625	24.1
5	32	0.03125	30.1
6	64	0.015625	36.1
7	128	0.0078125	42.1
8	256	0.00390625	48.2
9	512	0.001953125	54.2
10	1 024	0.0009765625	60.2
11	2 048	0.00048828125	66.2
12	4 096	0.000244140625	72.2
13	8 192	0.0001220703125	78.3
14	16 384	0.00006103515625	84.3
15	32 768	0.000030517578125	90.3
16	65 536	0.0000152587890625	96.3
17	131 072	0.00000762939453125	102.3
18	262 144	0.000003814697265625	108.4
19	524 288	0.0000019073486328125	114.4
20	1 048 576	0.00000095367431640625	120.4

Table 1. Resolution, Number of States, LSB Weight, and Dynamic Range for Data Converters

The *dynamic range* of a data converter in dB is found as follows:

$$\text{DR (dB)} = 20 \log 2^n = 20n \log 2$$
$$= 20n \ (0.301) = 6.02n$$

where DR is dynamic range, n is the number of bits,

and 2^n the number of states of the converter. Since 6.02 dB corresponds to a factor of two, it is simply necessary to multiply the resolution of a converter in bits by 6.02. A 12-bit converter, for example, has a dynamic range of 72.2 dB.

An important point to notice is that the maximum value of the digital code, namely all 1's, does not correspond with analog full scale, but rather with one LSB less than full scale, or FS $(1-2^{-n})$. Therefore a 12 bit converter with a 0 to $+10V$ analog range has a maximum code of 1111 1111 1111 and a maximum analog value of $+20V (1-2^{-12}) = +9.99756V$. In other words, the maximum analog value of the converter, corresponding to all one's in the code, never quite reaches the point defined as analog full scale.

Other Binary Codes

Several other binary codes are used with A/D and D/A converters in addition to straight binary. These codes are *offset binary*, *two's complement*, *binary coded decimal* (BCD), and their complemented versions. Each code has a specific advantage in certain applications. BCD coding for example is used where digital displays must be interfaced such as in digital panel meters and digital multimeters. Two's complement coding is used for computer arithmetic logic operations, and offset binary coding is used with bipolar analog measurements.

Not only are the digital codes standardized with data converters, but so are the analog voltage ranges. Most converters use unipolar voltage ranges of 0 to $+5V$ and 0 to $+10V$ although some devices use the negative ranges 0 to $-5V$ and 0 to $-10V$. The standard bipolar voltage ranges are $\pm2.5V$, $\pm5V$ and $\pm10V$. Many converters today are pin-programmable between these various ranges.

FRACTION OF FS	$+10V$ FS	STRAIGHT BINARY	COMPLEMENTARY BINARY
$+FS - 1$ LSB	$+9.961$	1111 1111	0000 0000
$+\frac{3}{4}$ FS	$+7.500$	1100 0000	0011 1111
$+\frac{1}{2}$ FS	$+5.000$	1000 0000	0111 1111
$+\frac{1}{4}$ FS	$+2.500$	0100 0000	1011 1111
$+\frac{1}{8}$ FS	$+1.250$	0010 0000	1101 1111
$+1$ LSB	$+0.039$	0000 0001	1111 1110
0	0.000	0000 0000	1111 1111

Table 2. Binary Coding for 8 Bit Unipolar Converters

Table 2 shows straight binary and complementary binary codes for a unipolar 8 bit converter with a 0 to $+10V$ analog FS range. The maximum analog value of the converter is $+9.961V$, or one LSB less than $+10V$. Note that the LSB size is 0.039V as shown near the bottom of the table. The *complementary binary* coding used in some converters is simply the logic complement of straight binary.

When A/D and D/A converters are used in bipolar operation, the analog range is offset by half scale, or by the MSB value. The result is an analog shift of the converter transfer function as shown in Figure 9. Notice for this 3-bit A/D converter transfer function that the code 000 corresponds with −5V, 100 with 0V, and 111 with +3.75V. Since the output coding is the same as before the analog shift, it is now appropriately called offset binary coding.

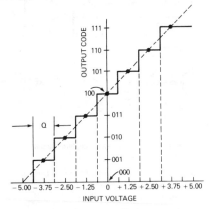

Figure 9. Transfer Function for Bipolar 3-Bit A/D Converter

Table 3 shows the offset binary code together with *complementary offset binary, two's complement,* and *sign-magnitude binary* codes. These are the most popular codes employed in bipolar data converters.

FRACTION OF FS	±5V FS	OFFSET BINARY	COMP. OFF. BINARY	TWO'S COMPLEMENT	SIGN-MAG BINARY
+FS - 1 LSB	+4.9976	1111 1111	0000 0000	0111 1111	1111 1111
+¾ FS	+3.7500	1110 0000	0001 1111	0110 0000	1110 0000
+½ FS	+2.5000	1100 0000	0011 1111	0100 0000	1100 0000
+½ FS	+1.2500	1010 0000	0101 1111	0010 0000	1010 0000
0	0.0000	1000 0000	0111 1111	0000 0000	1000 0000*
−¼ FS	−1.2500	0110 0000	1001 1111	1110 0000	0010 0000
−½ FS	−2.5000	0100 0000	1011 1111	1100 0000	0100 0000
−¾ FS	−3.7500	0010 0000	1101 1111	1010 0000	0110 0000
−FS + 1 LSB	−4.9976	0000 0001	1111 1110	1000 0001	0111 1111
−FS	−5.0000	0000 0000	1111 1111	1000 0000	−

*NOTE: Sign Magnitude Binary has two code words for zero as shown here.

	SIGN-MAG BINARY
0+	1000 0000 0000
0−	0000 0000 0000

Table 3. Popular Bipolar Codes Used with Data Converters.

The two's complement code has the characteristic that the sum of the positive and negative codes for the same analog magnitude always produces all zero's and a carry. This characteristic makes the two's complement code useful in arithmetic computations. Notice that the only difference between two's complement and offset binary is the complementing of the MSB. In bipolar coding, the MSB becomes the sign bit.

The sign-magnitude binary code, infrequently used, has identical code words for equal magnitude analog values except that the sign bit is different. As shown in Table 3 this code has two possible code words for zero: 1000 0000 or 0000 0000. The two are usually distinguished as 0+ and 0−, respectively. Because of this characteristic, the code has maximum analog values of ±(FS−1 LSB) and reaches neither analog +FS or −FS.

BCD Codes

Table 4 shows BCD and complementary BCD coding for a 3 decimal digit data converter. These are the codes used with integrating type A/D converters employed in digital panel meters, digital multimeters, and other decimal display applications. Here four bits are used to represent each decimal digit. BCD is a positive weighted code but is relatively inefficient since in each group of four bits, only 10 out of a possible 16 states are utilized.

FRACTION OF FS	+10V FS	BINARY CODED DECIMAL	COMPLEMENTARY BCD
+FS - 1 LSB	+9.99	1001 1001 1001	0110 0110 0110
+¾ FS	+7.50	0111 0101 0000	1000 1010 1111
+½ FS	+5.00	0101 0000 0000	1010 1111 1111
+¼ FS	+2.50	0010 0101 0000	1101 1010 1111
+⅛ FS	+1.25	0001 0010 0101	1110 1101 1010
+1 LSB	+0.01	0000 0000 0001	1111 1111 1110
0	0.00	0000 0000 0000	1111 1111 1111

Table 4. BCD and Complementary BCD Coding.

The LSB analog value (or quantum, Q) for BCD is

$$LSB(Analog\,Value) = Q = \frac{FSR}{10^d}$$

where FSR is the full scale range and d is the number of decimal digits. For example if there are 3 digits and the full scale range is 10V, the LSB value is

$$LSB\,(Analog\,Value) = \frac{10V}{10^3} = .01V = 10mV$$

BCD coding is frequently used with an additional overrange bit which has a weight equal to full scale and produces a 100% increase in range for the A/D converter. Thus for a converter with a decimal full scale of 999, an overrange bit provides a new full scale of 1999, twice that of the previous one. In this case, the maximum output code is 1 1001 1001 1001. The additional range is commonly referred to as ½ digit, and the resolution of the A/D converter in this case is 3½ digits.

Likewise, if this range is again expanded by 100%, a new full scale of 3999 results and is called 3¾ digits resolution. Here two overrange bits have been added and the full scale output code is 11 1001

1001 1001. When BCD coding is used for bipolar measurements another bit, a sign bit, is added to the code and the result is *sign-magnitude BCD* coding.

Amplifiers and Filters

Operational and Instrumention Amplifiers

The front end of a data acquisition system extracts the desired analog signal from a physical parameter by means of a transducer and then amplifies and filters it. An amplifier and filter are critical components in this initial signal processing.

The amplifier must perform one or more of the following functions: boost the signal amplitude, buffer the signal, convert a signal current into a voltage, or extract a differential signal from common mode noise.

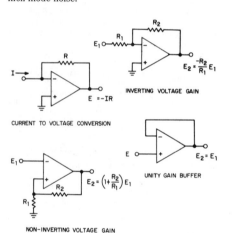

Figure 10. Operational Amplifier Configurations

To accomplish these functions requires a variety of different amplifier types. The most popular type of amplifier is an *operational amplifier* which is a general purpose gain block with differential inputs. The op amp may be connected in many different closed loop configurations, of which a few are shown in Figure 10. The gain and bandwidth of the circuits shown depend on the external resistors connected around the amplifier. An operational amplifier is a good choice in general where a single-ended signal is to be amplified, buffered, or converted from current to voltage.

In the case of differential signal processing, the *instrumentation amplifier* is a better choice since it maintains high impedance at both of its differential inputs and the gain is set by a resistor located elsewhere in the amplifier circuit. One type of instru-

mentation amplifier circuit is shown in Figure 11. Notice that no gain-setting resistors are connected to either of the input terminals. Instrumentation ampli-

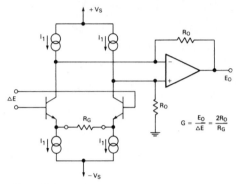

Figure 11. Simplified Instrumentation Amplifier Circuit

fiers have the following important characteristics.

1. High impedance differential inputs.
2. Low input offset voltage drift.
3. Low input bias currents.
4. Gain easily set by means of one or two external resistors.
5. High common-mode rejection ratio.

Common Mode Rejection

Common-mode rejection ratio is an important parameter of differential amplifiers. An ideal differential input amplifier responds only to the voltage difference between its input terminals and does not respond at all to any voltage that is common to both input terminals (common-mode voltage). In nonideal amplifiers, however, the common-mode input signal causes some output response even though small compared to the response to a differential input signal.

The ratio of differential and common-mode responses is defined as the common-mode rejection ratio. *Common-mode rejection ratio of an amplifier is the ratio of differential voltage gain to common-mode voltage gain and is generally expressed in dB.*

$$\text{CMRR} = 20 \log_{10} \frac{A_D}{A_{CM}}$$

where A_D is differential voltage gain and A_{CM} is common-mode voltage gain. CMRR is a function of frequency and therefore also a function of the impedance balance between the two amplifier input terminals. At even moderate frequencies CMRR can be significantly degraded by small unbalances in the source series resistance and shunt capacitance.

Other Amplifier Types

There are several other special amplifiers which are useful in conditioning the input signal in a data acquisition system. An *isolation amplifier* is used to amplify a differential signal which is superimposed on a very high common-mode voltage, perhaps several hundred or even several thousand volts. The isolation amplifier has the characteristics of an instrumentation amplifier with a very high common-mode input voltage capability.

Another special amplifier, the *chopper stabilized amplifier*, is used to accurately amplify microvolt level signals to the required amplitude. This amplifier employs a special switching stabilizer which gives extremely low input offset voltage drift. Another useful device, the *electrometer amplifier*, has ultra-low input bias currents, generally less than one picoampere and is used to convert extremely small signal currents into a high level voltage.

Filters

A *low pass filter* frequently follows the signal processing amplifier to reduce signal noise. Low pass filters are used for the following reasons: to reduce man-made electrical interference noise, to reduce electronic noise, and to limit the bandwidth of the analog signal to less than half the sampling frequency in order to eliminate frequency folding. When used for the last reason, the filter is called a *pre-sampling filter* or *anti-aliasing filter*.

Man-made electrical noise is generally periodic, as for example in power line interference, and is sometimes reduced by means of a special filter such as a *notch filter*. Electronic noise, on the other hand, is random noise with noise power proportional to bandwidth and is present in transducer resistances, circuit resistances, and in amplifiers themselves. It is reduced by limiting the bandwidth of the system to the minimum required to pass desired signal components.

No filter does a perfect job of eliminating noise or other undesirable frequency components, and therefore the choice of a filter is always a compromise. Ideal filters, frequently used as analysis examples, have flat passband response with infinite attenuation at the cutoff frequency, but are mathematical filters only and not physically realizable.

In practice, the systems engineer has a choice of cutoff frequency and attenuation rate. The attenuation rate and resultant phase response depend on the particular filter characteristic and the number of poles in the filter function. Some of the more popular filter characteristics include Butterworth, Chebychev, Bessel, and elliptic. In making this choice, the effect of overshoot and nonuniform phase delay must be carefully considered. Figure 12 illusrtates some practical low pass filter response characteristics.

Passive RLC filters are seldom used in signal processing applications today due chiefly to the undesirable characteristics of inductors. Active filters are generally used now since they permit the filter characteristics to be accurately set by precision, stable resistors and capacitors. Inductors, with their undesirable saturation and temperature drift characteristics, are thereby eliminated. Also, because active filters use operational amplifiers, the problems of insertion loss and output loading are also eliminated.

Settling Time

Definition

A parameter that is specified frequently in data acquisition and distribution systems is *settling time*. The term settling time originates in control theory but is now commonly applied to amplifiers, multiplexers, and D/A converters.

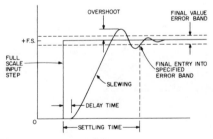

Figure 13. Amplifier Settling Time

Settling time is defined as *the time elapsed from the application of a full scale step input to a circuit to the time when the output has entered and remained within a specified error band around its final value.* The method of application of the input step may vary depending on the type of circuit, but the definition still holds. In the case of a D/A con-

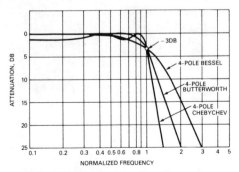

Figure 12. Some Practical Low Pass Filter Characteristics

verter, for example, the step is applied by changing the digital input code whereas in the case of an amplifier the input signal itself is a step change.

The importance of settling time in a data acquisition system is that certain analog operations must be performed in sequence, and one operation may have to be accurately settled before the next operation can be initiated. Thus a buffer amplifier preceding an A/D converter must have accurately settled before the conversion can be initiated.

Settling time for an amplifier is illustrated in Figure 13. After application of a full scale step input there is a small delay time following which the amplifier output slews, or changes at its maximum rate. *Slew rate* is determined by internal amplifier currents which must charge internal capacitances.

As the amplifier output approaches final value, it may first overshoot and then reverse and under-shoot this value before finally entering and re-maining within the specified error band. Note that settling time is measured to the point at which the amplifier output *enters* and *remains* within the error band. This error band in most devices is specified to either ±0.1% or ±0.01% of the full scale transition.

Amplifier Characteristics

Settling time, unfortunately, is not readily predict-able from other amplifier parameters such as band-width, slew rate, or overload recovery time, al-though it depends on all of these. It is also dependent on the shape of the amplifier open loop gain charac-teristic, its input and output capacitance, and the dielectric absorption of any internal capacitances. An amplifier must be specifically designed for optimized settling time, and settling time is a para-meter that must be determined by testing.

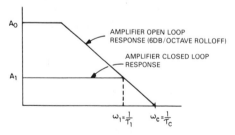

Figure 14. Amplifier Single-Pole Open Loop Gain Characteristic

One of the important requirements of a fast settling amplifier is that it have a single-pole open loop gain characteristic, i.e., one that has a smooth 6 dB per octave gain roll-off characteristic to beyond the unity gain crossover frequency. Such a desirable charac-teristic is shown in Figure 14.

It is important to note that an amplifier with a single-pole response can never settle faster than the time indicated by the number of closed loop time constants to the given accuracy. Figure 15 shows output error as a function of the number of time constants τ where

$$\tau = \frac{1}{\omega} = \frac{1}{2\pi f}$$

and f is the closed loop 3 dB bandwidth of the amplifier.

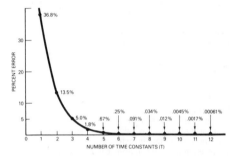

Figure 15. Output Settling Error as a Function of Number of Time Constants

Actual settling time for a good quality amplifier may be significantly longer than that indicated by the number of closed loop time constants due to slew rate limitation and overload recovery time. For example, an amplifier with a closed loop bandwidth of 1 MHz has a time constant of 160 nsec. which indicates a settling time of 1.44 μsec. (9 time con-stants) to 0.01% of final value. If the slew rate of this amplifier is 1V/μsec., it will take more than 10 μsec. to settle to 0.01% for a 10V change.

Figure 16. Ultra-Fast Settling Hybrid Operational Amplifier

If the amplifier has a nonuniform gain roll-off char-acteristic, then its settling time may have one of two undesirable qualities. First, the output may reach the vicinity of the error band quickly but then take a long time to actually enter it; second, it may overshoot the error band and then oscillate back and forth through it before finally entering and remaining inside it.

Modern fast settling operational amplifiers come in many different types including modular, hybrid, and monolithic amplifiers. Such amplifiers have settling times to 0.1% or 0.01% of 2 μsec. down to 100 nsec. and are useful in many data acquisition and conversion applications. An example of an ultra-fast settling operational amplifier of the hybrid type is shown in Figure 16.

Digital-To-Analog Converters

Introduction

Digital-to-analog converters are the devices by which computers communicate with the outside world. They are employed in a variety of applications from CRT display systems and voice synthesizers to automatic test systems, digitally controlled attenuators, and process control actuators. In addition, they are key components inside most A/D converters. D/A converters are also referred to as DAC's and are termed *decoders* by communications engineers.

The transfer function of an ideal 3-bit D/A converter is shown in Figure 17. Each input code word produces a single, discrete analog output value, generally a voltage. Over the output range of the converter 2^n different values are produced including zero; and the output has a one-to-one correspondence with input, which is not true for A/D converters.

There are many different circuit techniques used to implement D/A converters, but a few popular

ones are widely used today. Virtually all D/A converters in use are of the *parallel type* where all bits change simultaneously upon application of an input code word; *serial type* D/A converters, on the other hand, produce an analog output only after receiving all digital input data in sequential form.

Weighted Current Source D/A Converter

The most popular D/A converter design in use today is the weighted current source circuit illustrated in Figure 18. An array of switched transistor current sources is used with binary weighted currents. The binary weighting is achieved by using emitter resistors with binary related values of R, 2R, 4R, 8R, ... 2^nR. The resulting collector currents are then added together at the current summing line.

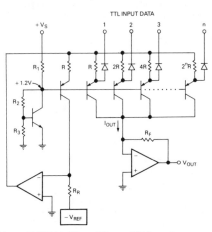

Figure 18. Weighted Current Source D/A Converter

The current sources are switched on or off from standard TTL inputs by means of the control diodes connected to each emitter. When the TTL input is high the current source is on; when the input is low it is off, with the current flowing through the control diode. Fast switching speed is achieved because there is direct control of the transistor current, and the current sources never go into saturation.

To interface with standard TTL levels, the current sources are biased to a base voltage of +1.2V. The emitter currents are regulated to constant values by means of the control amplifier and a precision voltage reference circuit together with a bipolar transistor.

The summed output currents from all current sources that are on go to an operational amplifier summing junction; the amplifier converts this output current into an output voltage. In some D/A

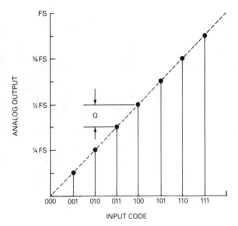

Figure 17. Transfer Function of Ideal 3-Bit D/A Converter

converters the output current is used to directly drive a resistor load for maximum speed, but the positive output voltage in this case is limited to about $+1$ volt.

The weighted current source design has the advantages of simplicity and high speed. Both PNP and NPN transistor current sources can be used with this technique although the TTL interfacing is more difficult with NPN sources. This technique is used in most monolithic, hybrid, and modular D/A converters in use today.

A difficulty in implementing higher resolution D/A converter designs is that a wide range of emitter resistors is required, and very high value resistors cause problems with both temperature stability and switching speed. To overcome these problems, weighted current sources are used in identical groups, with the output of each group divided down by a resistor divider as shown in Figure 19.

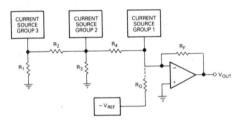

Figure 19. Current Dividing the Outputs of Weighted Current Source Groups

The resistor network, R_1 through R_4, divides the output of Group 3 down by a factor of 256 and the output of Group 2 down by a factor of 16 with respect to the output of Group 1. Each group is identical, with four current sources of the type shown in Figure 18, having binary current weights of 1, 2, 4, 8. Figure 19 also illustrates the method of achieving a bipolar output by deriving an offset current from the reference circuit which is then subtracted from the output current line through resistor R_0. This current is set to exactly one half the full scale output current.

R-2R D/A Converter

A second popular technique for D/A conversion is the R-2R ladder method. As shown in Figure 20, the network consists of series resistors of value R and shunt resistors of value 2R. The bottom of each shunt resistor has a single-pole double-throw electronic switch which connects the resistor to either ground or the output current summing line.

The operation of the R-2R ladder network is based on the binary division of current as it flows down the ladder. Examination of the ladder configuration reveals that at point A looking to the right, one measures a resistance of 2R; therefore the reference input to the ladder has a resistance of R. At the reference input the current splits into two equal parts since it sees equal resistances in either direction. Likewise, the current flowing down the ladder to the right continues to divide into two equal parts at each resistor junction.

The result is binary weighted currents flowing down each shunt resistor in the ladder. The digitally controlled switches direct the currents to either the summing line or ground. Assuming all bits are on as shown in the diagram, the output current is

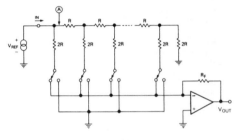

Figure 20. R-2R Ladder D/A Converter

As in the previous circuit, the output current summing line goes to an operational amplifier which converts current to voltage.

$$I_{OUT} = \frac{V_{REF}}{R} \left[\tfrac{1}{2} + \tfrac{1}{4} + \tfrac{1}{8} + \ldots + \frac{1}{2^n} \right]$$

which is a binary series. The sum of all currents is then

$$I_{OUT} = \frac{V_{REF}}{R} \left(1 - 2^{-n} \right)$$

where the 2^{-n} term physically represents the portion of the input current flowing through the 2R terminating resistor to ground at the far right.

The advantage of the R-2R ladder technique is that only two values of resistors are required, with the resultant ease of matching or trimming and excellent temperature tracking. In addition, for high speed applications relatively low resistor values can be used. Excellent results can be obtained for high resolution D/A converters by using laser-trimmed thin film resistor networks.

Multiplying and Deglitched D/A Converters

The R-2R ladder method is specifically used for *multiplying type* D/A converters. With these converters, the reference voltage can be varied over the full range of $\pm V_{max}$ with the output the product of the reference voltage and the digital input word. Multiplication can be performed in 1, 2, or 4 algebraic quadrants.

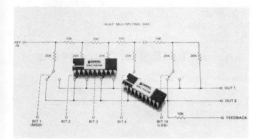

Figure 21. CMOS 14-Bit Multiplying D/A Converters

If the reference voltage is unipolar, the circuit is a one-quadrant multiplying DAC; if it is bipolar, the circuit is a two-quadrant multiplying DAC. For four-quadrant operation the two current summing lines shown in Figure 20 must be subtracted from each other by operational amplifiers.

In multiplying D/A converters, the electronic switches are usually implemented with CMOS devices. Multiplying DAC's are commonly used in automatic gain controls, CRT character generation, complex function generators, digital attenuators, and divider circuits. Figure 21 shows two 14-bit multiplying CMOS D/A converters.

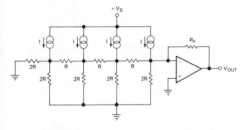

Figure 22. D/A Converter Employing R-2R Ladder with Equal Value Switched Current Sources

Another important D/A converter design takes advantage of the best features of both the weighted current source technique and the R-2R ladder technique. This circuit, shown in Figure 22, uses equal value switched current sources to drive the junctions of the R-2R ladder network. The advantage of the equal value current sources is obvious since all emitter resistors are identical and switching speeds are also identical. This technique is used in many ultra-high speed D/A converters.

One other specialized type D/A converter used primarily in CRT display systems is the *deglitched* D/A converter. All D/A converters produce output spikes, or *glitches*, which are most serious at the major output transitions of ¼ FS, ½ FS, and ¾ FS as illustrated in Figure 23(a).

Glitches are caused by small time differences between some current sources turning off and others turning on. Take, for example, the major code transition at half scale from 0111 .... 1111 to 1000 .... 0000. Here the MSB current source turns on while all other current sources turn off. The small difference in switching times results in a narrow half scale glitch. Such a glitch produces distorted characters on CRT displays.

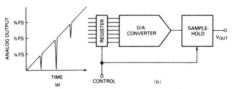

Figure 23. Output Glitches (a) and Deglitched D/A Converter (b)

Glitches can be virtually eliminated by the circuit shown in Figure 23(b). The digital input to a D/A converter is controlled by an input register while the converter output goes to a specially designed sample-hold circuit. When the digital input is updated by the register, the sample-hold is switched into the hold mode. After the D/A has changed to its new output value and all glitches have settled out, the sample-hold is then switched back into the tracking mode. When this happens, the output changes smoothly from its previous value to the new value with no glitches present.

Figure 24 shows a modular deglitched D/A converter which contains the circuitry just described.

Voltage Reference Circuits

An important circuit required in both A/D and D/A converters is the voltage reference. The accuracy and stability of a data converter ultimately depends upon the reference; it must therefore produce a constant output voltage over both time and temperature.

Figure 24. Modular Deglitched D/A Converter

The compensated zener reference diode with a buffer-stabilizer circuit is commonly used in most data converters today. Although the compensated zener may be one of several types, the compensated *subsurface*, or *buried*, zener is probably the best choice. These new devices produce an avalanche breakdown which occurs beneath the surface of the silicon, resulting in better long-term stability and noise characteristics than with earlier surface breakdown zeners.

These reference devices have reverse breakdown voltages of about 6.4 volts and consist of a forward biased diode in series with the reversed biased zener. Because the diodes have approximately equal and opposite voltage changes with temperature, the result is a temperature stable voltage. Available devices have temperature coefficients from 100 ppm/°C to less than 1 ppm/°C.

Some of the new IC voltage references incorporate active circuitry to buffer the device and reduce its dynamic impedance; in addition, some contain temperature regulation circuitry on the chip to achieve ultra-low tempcos.

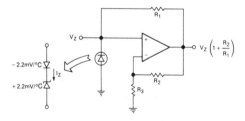

Figure 25. A Precision, Buffered Voltage Reference Circuit

A popular buffered reference circuit is shown in Figure 25; this circuit produces an output voltage

higher than the reference voltage. It also generates a constant, regulated current through the reference which is detemined by the three resistors.

Some monolithic A/D and D/A converters use another type of reference device known as the *bandgap reference*. This circuit is based on the principle of using the known, predictable base-to-emitter voltage of a transistor to generate a constant voltage equal to the extrapolated bandgap voltage of silicon. This reference gives excellent results for the lower reference voltages of 1.2 or 2.5 volts.

Analog-To-Digital Converters

Counter Type A/D Converter

Analog-to-digital converters, also called ADC's or *encoders*, employ a variety of different circuit techniques to implement the conversion function. As with D/A converters, however, relatively few of these circuits are widely used today. Of the various techniques available, the choice depends on the resolution and speed required.

One of the simplest A/D converters is the *counter*, or *servo*, type. This circuit employs a digital counter to control the input of a D/A converter. Clock pulses are applied to the counter and the output of the D/A is stepped up one LSB at a time. A comparator compares the D/A output with the analog input and stops the clock pulses when they are equal. The counter output is then the converted digital word.

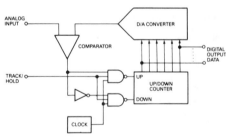

Figure 26. Tracking Type A/D Converter

While this converter is simple, it is also relatively slow. An improvement on this technique is shown in Figure 26 and is known as a *tracking* A/D converter, a device commonly used in control systems. Here an up-down counter controls the DAC, and the clock pulses are directed to the pertinent counter input depending on whether the D/A output must increase or decrease to reach the analog input voltage.

The obvious advantage of the tracking A/D converter is that it can continuously follow the input signal and give updated digital output data if the signal does not change too rapidly. Also, for small input changes, the conversion can be quite fast. The converter can be operated in either the track or hold modes by a digital input control.

Sucessive-Approximation A/D Converters

By far, the most popular A/D conversion technique in general use for moderate to high speed applications is the *successive-approximation* type A/D. This method falls into a class of techniques known as *feedback type* A/D converters, to which the counter type also belongs. In both cases a D/A converter is in the feedback loop of a digital control circuit which changes its ouput until it equals the analog input. In the case of the successive-approximation converter, the DAC is controlled in an optimum manner to complete a conversion in just n-steps, where n is the resolution of the converter in bits.

The operation of this converter is analogous to weighing an unknown on a laboratory balance scale using standard weights in a binary sequence such as 1, ½, ¼, ⅛, ... ⅟n kilograms. The correct procedure is to begin with the largest standard weight and proceed in order down to the smallest one.

The largest weight is placed on the balance pan first; if it does not tip, the weight is left on and the next largest weight is added. If the balance does tip, the weight is removed and the next one added. The same procedure is used for the next largest weight and so on down to the smallest. After the nth standard weight has been tried and a decision made, the weighing is finished. The total of the standard weights remaining on the balance is the closest possible approximation to the unknown.

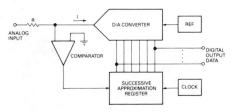

Figure 27. Successive Approximation A/D Converter

In the successive-approximation A/D converter illustrated in Figure 27, a successive-approximation register (SAR) controls the D/A converter by implementing the weighing logic just described. The SAR first turns on the MSB of the DAC and the comparator tests this output against the analog input. A decision is made by the comparator to leave the bit on or turn it off after which bit 2 is turned on and a second comparison made. After n-

comparisons the digital output of the SAR indicates all those bits which remain on and produces the desired digital code. The clock circuit controls the timing of the SAR. Figure 28 shows the D/A converter output during a typical conversion.

The conversion efficiency of this technique means that high resolution conversions can be made in very short times. For example, it is possible to perform

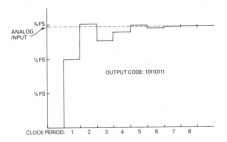

Figure 28. D/A Output for 8-Bit Successive Approximation Conversion

a 10 bit conversion in 1 μsec. or less and a 12 bit conversion in 2 μsec. or less. Of course the speed of the internal circuitry, in particular the D/A and comparator, are critical for high speed performance.

The Parallel (Flash) A/D Converter

For ultra-fast conversions required in video signal processing and radar applications where up to 8 bits resolution is required, a different technique is employed; it is known as the *parallel* (also *flash*, or *simultaneous*) method and is illustrated in Figure 29.

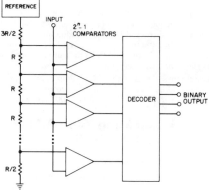

Figure 29. 4-Bit Parallel A/D Converter

This circuit employs 2^n-1 analog comparators to directly implement the quantizer transfer function of an A/D converter.

The comparator trip-points are spaced 1 LSB apart by the series resistor chain and voltage reference. For a given analog input voltage all comparators biased below the voltage turn on and all those biased above it remain off. Since all comparators change state simultaneously, the quantization process is a one-step operation.

A second step is required, however, since the logic output of the comparators is not in binary form. Therefore an ultra-fast decoder circuit is employed to make the logic conversion to binary. The parallel technique reaches the ultimate in high speed because only two sequential operations are required to make the conversion.

The limitation of the method, however, is in the large number of comparators required for even moderate resolutions. A 4-bit converter, for example, requires only 15 comparators, but an 8-bit converter needs 255. For this reason it is common practice to implement an 8-bit A/D with two 4-bit stages as shown in Figure 30.

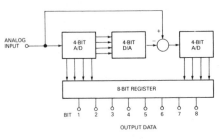

Figure 30. Two-Stage Parallel 8-Bit A/D Converter

The result of the first 4-bit conversion is converted back to analog by means of an ultra-fast 4-bit D/A and then subtracted from the analog input. The resulting residue is then converted by the second 4-bit A/D, and the two sets of data are accumulated in the 8-bit output register.

Converters of this type achieve 8-bit conversions at rates of 20 MHz and higher, while single stage 4-bit conversions can reach 50 to 100 MHz rates.

Integrating Type A/D Converters

Indirect A/D Conversion

Another class of A/D converters known as integrating type operates by an indirect conversion method. The unknown input voltage is converted into a time period which is then measured by a clock and counter. A number of variations exist on the basic principle such as *single-slope*, *dual-slope*, and *triple-slope* methods. In addition there is another technique —completely different— which is known as the *charge-balancing* or *quantized feedback* method.

The most popular of these methods are dual-slope and charge-balancing; although both are slow, they have excellent linearity characteristics with the capability of rejecting input noise. Because of these characteristics, integrating type A/D converters are almost exclusively used in digital panel meters, digital multimeters, and other slow measurement applications.

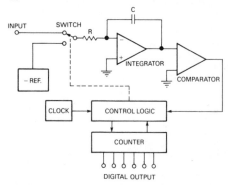

Figure 31. Dual Slope A/D Converter

Dual-Slope A/D Conversion

The dual-slope technique, shown in Figure 31, is perhaps best known. Conversion begins when the unknown input voltage is switched to the integrator input; at the same time the counter begins to count clock pulses and counts up to overflow. At this point the control circuit switches the integrator to the negative reference voltage which is integrated until the output is back to zero. Clock pulses are counted during this time until the comparator detects the zero crossing and turns them off.

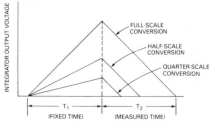

Figure 32. Integrator Output Waveform for Dual Slope A/D Converter

The counter output is then the converted digital word. Figure 32 shows the integrator output waveform where T_1 is a fixed time and T_2 is a time proportional to the input voltage. The times are related as follows:

$$T_2 = T_1 \frac{E_{IN}}{V_{REF}}$$

The digital output word therefore represents the ratio of the input voltage to the reference.

Dual-slope conversion has several important features. First, conversion accuracy is independent of the stability of the clock and integrating capacitor so long as they are constant during the conversion period. Accuracy depends only on the reference accuracy and the integrator circuit linearity. Second, the noise rejection of the converter can be infinite if T_1 is set to equal the period of the noise. To reject 60 Hz power noise therefore requires that T_1 be 16.667 msec. Figure 33 shows digital panel meters which employ dual slope A/D converters.

Figure 33. Digital Panel Meters Which Employ Dual Slope A/D Converters

Charge-Balancing A/D Conversion

The charge-balancing, or quantized feedback, method of conversion is based on the principle of generating a pulse train with frequency proportional to the input voltage and then counting the pulses for a fixed period of time. This circuit is shown in Figure 34. Except for the counter and timer, the circuit is a *voltage-to-frequency* (V/F) converter which generates an output pulse rate proportional to input voltage.

The circuit operates as follows. A positive input voltage causes a current to flow into the operational integrator through R_1. This current is integrated, producing a negative going ramp at the output. Each time the ramp crosses zero the comparator output triggers a precision pulse generator which puts out a constant width pulse.

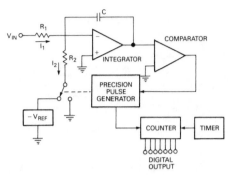

Figure 34. Charge-Balancing A/D Converter

The pulse output controls switch S_1 which connects R_2 to the negative reference for the duration of the pulse. During this time a pulse of current flows out of the integrator summing junction, producing a fast, positive ramp at the integrator output. This process is repeated, generating a train of current pulses which exactly balances the input current—hence the name charge balancing. This balance has the following relationship:

$$f = \frac{1}{\tau} \frac{V_{IN}}{V_{REF}} \frac{R_2}{R_1}$$

where τ is the pulse width and f the frequency.

A higher input voltage therefore causes the integrator to ramp up and down faster, producing higher frequency output pulses. The timer circuit sets a fixed time period for counting. Like the dual-slope converter, the circuit also integrates input noise, and if the timer is synchronized with the noise frequency, infinite rejection results. Figure 35 shows the noise rejection characteristic of all integrating type A/D converters with rejection plotted against the ratio of integration period to noise period.

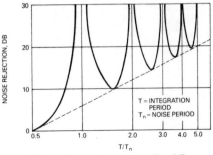

Figure 35. Noise Rejection for Integrating Type A/D Converters

Analog Multiplexers

Analog Multiplexer Operation

Analog multiplexers are the circuits that time-share an A/D converter among a number of different analog channels. Since the A/D converter in many cases is the most expensive component in a data acquisition system, multiplexing analog inputs to the A/D is an economical approach. Usually the analog multiplexer operates into a sample-hold circuit which holds the required analog voltage long enough for A/D conversion.

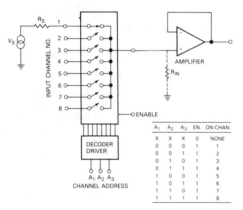

Figure 36. Analog Multiplexer Circuit

As shown in Figure 36, an analog multiplexer consists of an array of parallel electronic switches connected to a common output line. Only one switch is turned on at a time. Popular switch configurations include 4, 8, and 16 channels which are connected in single (single-ended) or dual (differential) configurations.

The multiplexer also contains a decoder-driver circuit which decodes a binary input word and turns on the appropriate switch. This circuit interfaces

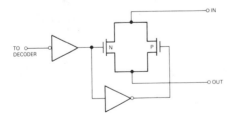

Figure 37. CMOS Analog Switch Circuit

with standard TTL inputs and drives the multiplexer switches with the proper control voltages. For the 8-channel analog multiplexer shown, a one-of-eight decoder circuit is used.

Most analog multiplexers today employ the CMOS switch circuit shown in Figure 37. A CMOS driver controls the gates of parallel-connected P-channel and N-channel MOSFET's. Both switches turn on together with the parallel connection giving relatively uniform on-resistance over the required analog input voltage range. The resulting on-resistance may vary from about 50 ohms to 2K ohms depending on the multiplexer; this resistance increases with temperature. A representative group of monolithic CMOS analog multiplexers is shown in Figure 38.

Figure 38. A Group of Monolithic CMOS Analog Multiplexers

Analog Multiplexer Characteristics

Because of the series resistance, it is common practice to operate an analog multiplexer into a very high load resistance such as the input of a unity gain buffer amplifier shown in the diagram. The load impedance must be large compared with the switch on-resistance and any series source resistance in order to maintain high transfer accuracy. *Transfer error* is the input to output error of the multiplexer with the source and load connected; error is expressed as a percent of input voltage.

Transfer errors of 0.1% to 0.01% or less are required in most data acquisition systems. This is readily achieved by using operational amplifier buffers with typical input impedances from 10^8 to 10^{12} ohms. Many sample-hold circuits also have very high input impedances.

Another important characteristic of analog multiplexers is *break-before-make* switching. There is a small time delay between disconnection from the previous channel and connection to the next channel which assures that two adjacent input channels are never instantaneously connected together.

Settling time is another important specification for analog multiplexers; it is the same definition previously given for amplifiers except that it is measured from the time the channel is switched on. *Throughput rate* is the highest rate at which a multiplexer can switch from channel to channel with the output settling to its specified accuracy. *Crosstalk* is the ratio of output voltage to input voltage with all channels connected in parallel and off; it is generally expressed as an input to output attenuation ratio in dB.

As shown in the representative equivalent circuit of Figure 39, analog multiplexer switches have a

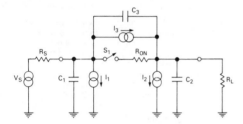

Figure 39. Equivalent Circuit of Analog Multiplexer Switch

number of leakage currents and capacitances associated with their operation. These parameters are specified on data sheets and must be considered in the operation of the devices. Leakage currents, generally in picoamperes at room temperature, become troublesome only at high temperatures. Capacitances affect crosstalk and settling time of the multiplexer.

Analog Multiplexer Applications

Analog multiplexers are employed in two basic types of operation: high-level and low-level. In *high-level multiplexing*, the most popular type, the analog signal is amplified to the 1 to 10V range ahead of the multiplexer. This has the advantage of reducing

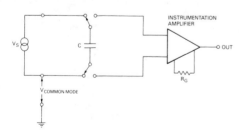

Figure 40. Flying Capacitor Multiplexer Switch

the effects of noise on the signal during the remaining analog processing. In *low-level multiplexing* the signal is amplified after multiplexing; therefore great care must be exercised in handling the low-level signal up to the multiplexer. Low-level multiplexers generally use two-wire differential switches in order to minimize noise pick-up. Reed relays, because of essentially zero series resistance and absence of switching spikes, are frequently employed in low-level multiplexing systems. They are also useful for high common-mode voltages.

A useful specialized analog multiplexer is the *flying-capacitor* type. This circuit, shown as a single channel in Figure 40 has differential inputs and is particularly useful with high common-mode voltages. The capacitor connects first to the differential analog input, charging up to the input voltage, and is then switched to the differential output which goes to a high input impedance instrumentation amplifier. The differential signal is therefore transferred to the amplifier input without the common mode voltage and is then further processed up to A/D conversion.

In order to realize large numbers of multiplexed channels, you can connect analog multiplexers in parallel using the enable input to control each device. This is called *single-level multiplexing*. You can also connect the output of several multiplexers to the inputs of another to expand the number of channels; this method is *double-level multiplexing*.

Sample-Hold Circuits

Operation of Sample-Holds

Sample-hold circuits, discussed earlier, are the devices which store analog information and reduce the aperture time of an A/D converter. A sample-hold is simply a voltage-memory device in which an input voltage is acquired and then stored on a high quality capacitor. A popular circuit is shown in Figure 41.

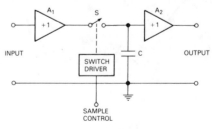

Figure 41. Popular Sample-Hold Circuit

A₁ is an input buffer amplifier with a high input impedance so that the source, which may be an analog multiplexer, is not loaded. The output of A_1 must be capable of driving the hold capacitor with stability and enough drive current to charge it rapidly. S_1 is an electronic switch, generally an FET, which is rapidly switched on or off by a driver circuit which interfaces with TTL inputs.

C is a capacitor with low leakage and low dielectric absorption characteristics; it is a polystyrene, polycarbonate, polypropylene, or teflon type. In the case of hybrid sample-holds, the MOS type capacitor is frequently used.

A_2 is the output amplifier which buffers the voltage on the hold capacitor. It must therefore have extremely low input bias current, and for this reason an FET input amplifier is required.

There are two modes of operation for a sample-hold: *sample* (or tracking) *mode*, when the switch is closed; and *hold mode*, when the switch is open. Sample-holds are usually operated in one of two basic ways. The device can continuously track the input signal and be switched into the hold mode only at certain specified times, spending most of the time in tracking mode. This is the case for a sample-hold employed as a deglitcher at the output of a D/A converter, for example.

Alternatively, the device can stay in the hold mode most of the time and go to the sample mode just to acquire a new input signal level. This is the case for a sample-hold used in a data acquisition system following the multiplexer.

The Sample-Hold as a Data Recovery Filter

A common application for sample-hold circuits is *data recovery*, or *signal reconstruction, filters*. The problem is to reconstruct a train of analog samples into the original signal; when used as a recovery filter, the sample-hold is known as a *zero-order hold*. It is a useful filter because it fills in the space between samples, providing data smoothing.

As with other filter circuits, the gain and phase components of the transfer function are of interest. By an analysis based on the impulse response of a sample-hold and use of the Laplace transform, the transfer function is found to be

$$G_0(f) = \frac{1}{f_s} \left[\frac{\sin \pi \left(\dfrac{f}{f_s} \right)}{\pi \left(\dfrac{f}{f_s} \right)} \right] \epsilon^{-j\pi f/f_s}$$

where f_s is the sampling frequency. This function contains the familiar (sin x) /x term plus a phase term, both of which are plotted in Figure 42.

The sample-hold is therefore a low pass filter with a cut-off frequency slightly less than $f_s/2$ and a linear phase response which results in a constant delay time of T/2, where T is the time between samples. Notice that the gain function also has significant response lobes beyond f_s. For this reason a sample-hold reconstruction filter is frequently followed by another conventional low pass filter.

Other Sample-Hold Circuits

In addition to the basic circuit of Figure 41, there are several other sample-hold circuit configurations which are frequently used. Figure 43 shows two such circuits which are closed loop circuits as contrasted with the open loop circuit of Figure 41. Figure 43(a) uses an operational integrator and another amplifier to make a fast, accurate inverting sample-hold. A buffer amplifier is sometimes added in front of this circuit to give high input impedance. Figure 43(b) shows a high input impedance non-inverting sample-hold circuit.

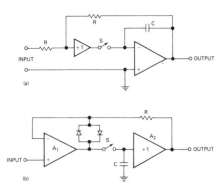

Figure 43. Two Closed Loop Sample-Hold Circuits

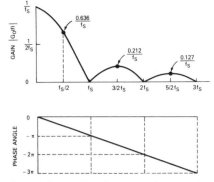

Figure 42. Gain and Phase Components of Zero-Order Hold Transfer Function

The circuit in Figure 41, although generally not as accurate as those in Figure 43, can be used with a diode-bridge switch to realize ultra-fast acquisition sample-holds, such as those shown in Figure 44.

Figure 44. Ultra-Fast Sample-Hold Modules Which Employ Diode-Bridge Switches

Sample-Hold Characteristics

A number of parameters are important in characterizing sample-hold performance. Probably most important of these is *acquisition time*. The definition is similar to that of settling time for an amplifier. It is the time required, after the sample-command is given, for the hold capacitor to charge to a full-scale voltage change and remain within a specified error band around final value.

Several hold-mode specifications are also important. *Hold-mode droop* is the output voltage change per unit time when the sample switch is open. This droop is caused by the leakage currents of the capacitor and switch, and the output amplifier bias current. *Hold-mode feedthrough* is the percentage of input signal transferred to the output when the sample switch is open. It is measured with a sinusoidal input signal and caused by capacitive coupling.

The most critical phase of sample-hold operation is the transition from the sample mode to the hold mode. Several important parameters characterize this transition. *Sample-to-hold offset* (or *step*) *error* is the change in output voltage from the sample

mode to the hold mode, with a constant input voltage. It is caused by the switch transferring charge onto the hold capacitor as it turns off.

Aperture delay is the time elapsed from the hold command to when the switch actually opens; it is generally much less than a microsecond. *Aperture uncertainty* (or *aperture jitter*) is the time variation, from sample to sample, of the aperture delay. It is the limit on how precise is the point in time of opening the switch. Aperture uncertainty is the time used to determine the aperture error due to rate of change of the input signal. Several of the above specifications are illustrated in the diagram of Figure 45.

Sample-hold circuits are simple in concept, but generally difficult to fully understand and apply. Their operation is full of subtleties, and they must therefore be carefully selected and then tested in a given application.

Specification of Data Converters

Ideal vs. Real Data Converters

Real A/D and D/A converters do not have the ideal transfer functions discussed earlier. There are three basic departures from the ideal: offset, gain, and linearity errors. These errors are all present at the same time in a converter; in addition they change with both time and temperature.

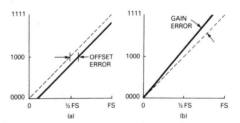

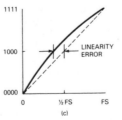

Figure 46. Offset (a), Gain (b), and Linearity (c) Errors for an A/D Converter

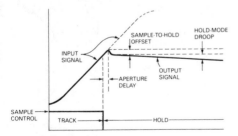

Figure 45. Some Sample-Hold Characteristics

Figure 46 shows A/D converter transfer functions which illustrate the three error types. Figure 46(a) shows *offset error*, the analog error by which the transfer function fails to pass through zero. Next, in Figure 46(b) is *gain error*, also called *scale factor error*; it is the difference in slope between the actual transfer function and the ideal, expressed as a percent of analog magnitude.

In Figure 46(c) *linearity error*, or nonlinearity, is shown; this is defined as the maximum deviation of the actual transfer function from the ideal straight line at any point along the function. It is expressed as a percent of full scale or in LSB size, such as ±½ LSB, and assumes that offset and gain errors have been adjusted to zero.

Most A/D and D/A converters available today have provision for external trimming of offset and gain errors. By careful adjustment these two errors can be reduced to zero, at least at ambient temperature. Linearity error, on the other hand, is the remaining error that cannot be adjusted out and is an inherent characteristic of the converter.

Data Converter Error Characteristics

Basically there are only two ways to reduce linearity error in a given application. First, a better quality higher cost converter with smaller linearity error can be procured. Second, a computer or microprocessor can be programmed to perform error correction on the converter. Both alternatives may be expensive in terms of hardware or software cost.

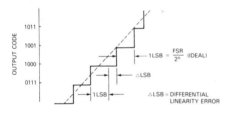

Figure 47. Defining Differential Linearity Error

The linearity error discussed above is actually more precisely termed *integral linearity error*. Another important type of linearity error is known as *differential linearity error*. This is defined as the maximum amount of deviation of any quantum (or LSB change) in the entire transfer function from its ideal size of $FSR/2^n$. Figure 47 shows that the actual quantum size may be larger or smaller than the ideal; for example, a converter with a maximum differential linearity error of $\pm\frac{1}{2}$ LSB can have a quantum size between ½ LSB and 1½ LSB anywhere in its tranfer function. In other words, any given analog step size is $(1\pm\frac{1}{2})$ LSB. Integral and differ-

ential linearities can be thought of as macro and micro-linearities, respectively.

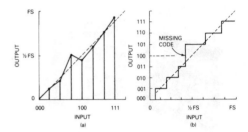

Figure 48. Nonmonotonic D/A Converter (a) and A/D Converter with Missing Code (b)

Two other important data converter characteristics are closely related to the differential linearity specification. The first is *monotonicity*, which applies to D/A converters. Monotonicity is the characteristic whereby the output of a circuit is a continuously increasing function of the input. Figure 48(a) shows a *nonmonotonic* D/A converter output where, at one point, the output decreases as the input increases. A D/A converter may go nonmonotonic if its differential linearity error exceeds 1 LSB; if it is always less than 1 LSB, it assures that the device will be monotonic.

The term *missing code*, or *skipped code*, applies to A/D converters. If the differential linearity error of an A/D converter exceeds 1 LSB, its output can miss a code as shown in Figure 48(b). On the other hand, if the differential linearity error is always less than 1 LSB, this assures that the converter will not miss any codes. Missing codes are the result of the A/D converter's internal D/A converter becoming nonmonotonic.

For A/D converters the character of the linearity error depends on the technique of conversion. Figure 49(a), for example, shows the linearity

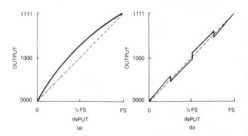

Figure 49. Linearity Characteristics of Integrating (a) and Successive Approximation (b) A/D Converters

characteristic of an integrating type A/D converter. The transfer function exhibits a smooth curvature between zero and full scale. The predominant type of error is integral linearity error, while differential linearity error is virtually nonexistent.

Figure 49(b), on the other hand, shows the linearity characteristic of a successive approximation A/D converter; in this case differential linearity error is the predominant type, and the largest errors occur at the specific transitions at ½, ¼, and ¾ scale. This result is caused by the internal D/A converter nonlinearity; the weight of the MSB and bit 2 current sources is critical in relation to all the other weighted current sources in order to achieve ±½ LSB maximum differential linearity error.

Temperature Effects

Ambient temperature change influences the offset, gain, and linearity errors of a data converter. These changes over temperature are normally specified in ppm of full scale range per degree Celsius. When operating a converter over significant temperature change, the effect on accuracy must be carefully determined. Of key importance is whether the device remains monotonic, or has no missing codes, over the temperatures of concern. In many cases the total error change must be computed, i.e., the sum of offset, gain, and linearity errors due to temperature.

The characteristic of monotonicity, or no missing codes, over a given temperature change can be readily computed from the *differential linearity tempco* specified for a data converter. Assuming the converter initially has ½ LSB of differential linearity error, the change in temperature for an increase to 1 LSB is therefore

$$\Delta T = \frac{2^{-n} \times 10^6}{2\,DLT}$$

where n is the converter resolution in bits and DLT is the specified differential linearity tempco in ppm of FSR/°C. ΔT is the maximum change in ambient temperature which assures that the converter will remain monotonic, or have no missing codes.

Selection of Data Converters

One must keep in mind a number of important considerations in selecting A/D or D/A converters.

An organized approach to selection suggests drawing up a checklist of required characteristics. An initial checklist should include the following key items:

1. Converter type
2. Resolution
3. Speed
4. Temperature coefficient

After the choice has been narrowed by these considerations, a number of other parameters must be considered. Among these are analog signal range, type of coding, input impedance, power supply requirements, digital interface required, linearity error, output current drive, type of start and status signals for an A/D, power supply rejection, size, and weight. One should list these parameters in order of importance to efficiently organize the selection process.

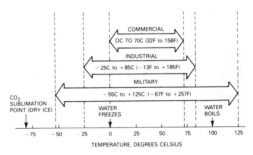

Figure 50. Standard Operating Temperature Ranges for Data Converters

In addition, the required operating temperature range msut be determined; data converters are normally specified for one of three basic ranges known in the industry as commercial, industrial, or military. These temperature ranges are illustrated in Figure 50. Further, the level of reliability must be determined in terms of a standard device, a specially screened device, or a military standard 883 device.

And finally, not to be forgotten are those important specifications, price and delivery, to which the reputation of the manufacturer must be added.

2. A/D and D/A Converters

Where and when to use which data converter

A broad shopping list of monolithic, hybrid, and discrete-component devices is available; the author helps select the most appropriate

With the commercial availability of data-converter products—the result of both hybrid (multichip) and monolithic (single-chip) technologies—users of analog-to-digital (A/D) and digital-to-analog (D/A) converters now have an impressive array of designs from which to choose. In addition, the older discrete-component designs still remain a viable choice for many high-performance applications, particularly those where broad operating characteristics and specialized features are important. Unfortunately, rather than helping the users to match the proper products to their needs, data-converter manufacturers confuse the issue by arguments over the relative merits of the different technologies. A closer look at the various types of data converters may help to clear up some of this confusion.

How data converters are used

Data converters are the basic interfaces between the physical world of analog parameters and the computational world of digital data processing. They are used in many industries in a wide variety of applications, including data telemetry, automatic process control, test and measurement, computer display, digital panel meters and multimeters, and voice communications, as well as in remote data recording and video signal processing.

As a typical example of the use of A/D and D/A converters, Fig. 1 illustrates how an entire industrial process can be controlled by a single digital computer, which may be located at a considerable distance from the process site. To communicate with the process, data inputs to the computer must be converted into digital form and the outputs reconverted into analog form.

Physical parameters of temperature, pressure, and flow are sensed by appropriate transducers and amplified to higher voltage levels by operational or instrumentation amplifiers. The various amplifier outputs are then fed into an analog multiplexer for sequential switching to the next stage—a sample-hold circuit that "freezes" the input voltage of a sequentially switched input for a fixed period of time, long enough for the following A/D converter to make a complete conversion cycle. In this manner, a single A/D converter is time-shared over a large number of analog input channels. Each channel is sampled peri-

odically at a rate that is relatively fast when compared with any change in the process.

After receiving data from the process, the computer calculates the existing "state" of the process and compares it with the "desired state" stored in its memory. From this comparison, corrections are determined for the process variables. This information is fed to D/A converters that convert the digital data into analog form, and are then used to supply inputs to the process to bring it to the desired state.

Types of data converters

Of the many different techniques that have been employed to perform data conversion, only a few are in wide use. Most D/A converter designs utilize a parallel-input circuit. In this scheme, the converter accepts a parallel binary input code and delivers an analog output voltage by means of binary weighted switches that act simultaneously upon application of the digital input. In the opening illustration, a representative parallel-input D/A-converter circuit is presented (A) in which binary weighted pnp-transistor current sources are controlled by emitter-connected diodes. For simplicity, a 4-bit converter is shown. The inputs operate from transistor–transistor logic (TTL) levels. The output current changes rapidly with a change in the digital input code. Since a voltage output is desired in most cases, the current from the pnp transistors is fed to an operational amplifier current-to-voltage converter. An internal voltage reference, which may be a Zener-diode or band-gap reference circuit, completes the circuit.

The most common A/D-conversion technique is the successive-approximation method, used in 70–80 percent of all present-day applications. As shown in the opening illustration, this circuit (B) incorporates the parallel-input D/A converter circuit previously described along with a successive-approximation register, a comparator, and a clock. The D/A converter's output, controlled by the successive-approximation register, is compared, one bit at a time, against the input signal, starting with the largest or most significant bit. A complete conversion is always accomplished in n steps for an n-bit converter, regardless of the input signal value. Successive-approximation A/D converters have the desirable characteristics of high conversion speed as well as excellent accuracy and stability, provided the circuit is well designed.

The next most popular A/D-conversion method is the dual-slope technique found in most digital panel meters and digital multimeters and commonly used in measurement and numeric display systems, also shown in the opening illustration (C). This converter circuit operates on an indirect principle, whereby the input voltage is

Eugene L. Zuch   Datel Systems, Inc.

The most common D/A and A/D conversion techniques are the parallel-input scheme for D/A conversion (A), the successive-approximation A/D conversion technique (B), the popular dual-slope A/D conversion circuit (C), and the parallel, or flash, A/D conversion circuit for ultrahigh speeds (D).

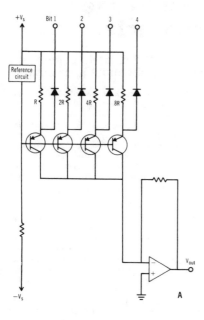

A

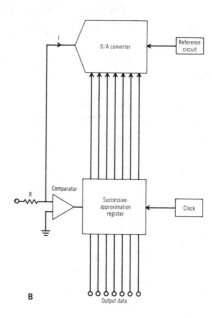

B

C

D

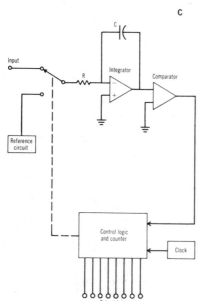

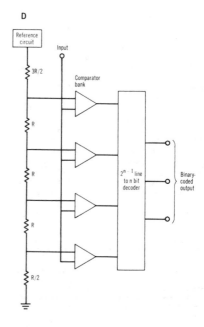

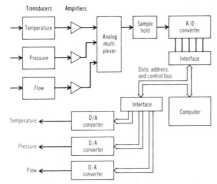

|1| A/D and D/A conversion products are a process-control system's basic interface elements between its physical variables and digital controlling computers.

converted to a time period measured by means of a reference and a counter. First, the input voltage is integrated for a fixed period of time, determined by the circuit's clock and counter. The integrator is then switched to the reference, causing integration in the opposite direction, until the output is back to zero, as determined by the comparator. The resultant digital-word output of the counter is proportional to the input voltage. The dual-slope method is very accurate, as its accuracy and stability depend only on the accuracy and stability of the circuit's reference. Its disadvantage is a much slower conversion time than with successive-approximation converters.

A third A/D-conversion method is the less frequently used ultrahigh-speed parallel, or flash, technique. As shown in the opening illustration, this circuit (D) employs $2^n - 1$ comparators to make an n-bit conversion. The comparators are biased by a tapped resistor connected to the reference voltage. The input signal is fed to the other comparator inputs all tied together. The result is a circuit that acts as a quantizer with 2^n levels, where n is the number of bits. For a given input-voltage level, all comparators biased below that level trip ON, and those biased above it remain OFF. The $2^n - 1$ digital outputs from the comparator must then be decoded into binary outputs. Since the complete conversion cycle occurs in only two steps, very-high-speed conversions are possible. The limitation of this technique is that it is difficult to realize high resolution, because of the large number of comparators required.

A comparison of technologies

Traditionally, data converters have been of the discrete-component type, first becoming available in instrument cases and later in compact, encapsulated modules. The advantage of this approach is that optimum components of all types can be combined. For example, for very high levels of speed and precision, a high-speed comparator may be combined with precision, high-speed current switches utilizing very-low-temperature-coefficient resistors and a very-low-temperature-coefficient reference. The result of such flexible component selection has been the development of some very impressive high-performance discrete-component converters over the past several years. For example, Table I shows that

12-bit current-output D/A converters are available with settling times as low as 50 ns, with voltage-output units achieving settling times down to 600 ns. Resolution can be as high as 16 bits. Excellent stabilities are also possible; ultralow drifts of 1 ppm/°C are achievable.

Equally impressive performance is also obtainable from discrete-component A/D converters. The fastest are the parallel types with resolutions of 8 bits at a 17-MHz conversion rate. Successive-approximation A/D converters offer rapid conversion times at various resolutions. As can be seen in Table II, conversion times of 0.80, 1.0, 2.0, and 10 μs at respective resolutions of 8, 10, 12, and 14 bits are possible. Slower but higher-resolution 14-bit dual-slope and 16-bit successive-approximation A/D converters with excellent stabilities are also available.

Hybrid converters

Although hybrid-converter design is almost as flexible as that of discrete-component converters, it does have two limitations: Not all of the semiconductor components used in a hybrid converter are readily available in chip form. Moreover, the number of chips used in a hybrid converter must be kept to a minimum for the converter to be economically producible. Minimizing the chip count minimizes the number of bonds required, which in turn minimizes labor content and maximizes both end-product yield and reliability.

Three factors have played a role in the emergence of new low-cost high-performance hybrid converters. The first is the availability of low-cost quad-current switches in chip form, which has simplified the circuitry required for the binary weighted current sources used. Second, new monolithic successive-approximation registers have minimized the logic circuitry required. And third, stable thin-film resistors with tight temperature tracking characteristics, and trimmable with fast laser trimming techniques, have made it possible to achieve economical 12-bit, and higher, resolutions. In fact, the excellent tracking characteristics of thin-film resistors (tracking within 1–2 ppm/°C is considered routine) provides hybrid converters with an advantage over modular discrete-component units.

As can be seen in Table I, hybrid devices include 8-, 10-, 12-, and 16-bit D/A converters with excellent performance characteristics. The 12-bit D/A converters have temperature coefficients as low as 10 ppm/°C, and some certain input registers. Most hybrid D/A converters do not require external output amplifiers.

Hybrid A/D converters with resolutions of 8, 10, and 12 bits are available, with respective conversion times of 0.9, 6.0, and 8.0 μs. An attractive feature of such A/D converters is their low price; for example, 12-bit models are now selling for under $100. Such units are complete converters and, except for calibration adjustments, require no external circuitry.

Monolithic converters

Monolithic data converters are generally a step below discrete and hybrid units in performance. In addition, various external components are usually required for proper operation, although this may not be viewed as a serious limitation since the attractive low prices of monolithic converters may more than compensate for the cost of the added components.

One of the obvious fabrication difficulties is making stable monolithic resistors for 10- and 12-bit monolithic

I. Representative D/A converters

Resolution (bits)	Settling Time (μs)	Output Type	Gain TC (ppm/°C)	Comments
Discrete-component converters				
10	0.025	Current	15	Ultrafast
10	0.25	Voltage	60	Ultrafast
12	0.05	Current	20	Ultrafast
12	2	Voltage	20	Fast; contains input register
12	5	Voltage	7	Low drift
12	0.60	Voltage	35	Ultrafast; deglitched
14	2	Voltage	10	Fast; low drift
16	25	Voltage	1	Ultralow drift
Hybrid converters				
8	2	Voltage	—	Contains input register
10	3	Voltage	—	Fast
12	3	Voltage	10	Fast
12	3	Voltage	20	Contains input register
16	50	Current	7	High resolution; requires external output amplifier
Monolithic converters				
8	0.085	Current	—	Fast; requires external reference
8	0.50	Current	—	Companding type for communication applications
10	1.5	Voltage	60	Complete unit; includes reference and output amplifier
10	0.50	Current	—	Multiplying type made from CMOS technology; requires external reference and output amplifier
10	0.25	Current	60	Uses thin-film resistors; has internal reference, but requires external output amplifier
12	0.50	Current	—	Multiplying type made from CMOS technology; does not have 12-bit linearity; requires external reference and output amplifier
12	0.30	Current	—	Bipolar type with true 12-bit linearity; requires external reference and output amplifier

II. Representative A/D converters

Resolution (bits)	Conversion Time (μs)	Conversion Type	Gain TC (ppm/°C)	Comments
Discrete-component converters				
5	0.01	Parallel	—	Ultrafast; 100-MHz rate
8	0.80	Successive approximation	20	Very fast; 1.2-MHz rate
8	0.06	Parallel	100	Ultrafast; 17-MHz rate
10	1	Successive approximation	20	Very fast; 1-MHz rate
12	2	Successive approximation	30	Very fast; 500-kHz rate
14	10	Successive approximation	6	Fast
16	400	Successive approximation	8	High resolution; very low drift
14	230 000	Dual slope	8	High resolution; low drift; Ratiometric with front-end isolation
Hybrid converters				
8	0.9	Successive approximation	—	Fast
10	6	Successive approximation	30	Fast
12	8	Successive approximation	20	Fast
Monolithic converters				
8	40	Successive approximation	—	Requires external reference and clock
8	1800	Charge balancing	—	CMOS; requires external reference and other components
10	40	Successive approximation	—	CMOS; requires external comparator, reference, and other components
10	6000	Charge balancing	—	CMOS; requires external reference and other components
12	24 000	Charge balancing	—	CMOS; requires external reference and other components
13	40 000	Dual slope	—	CMOS; has auto-zero circuit; requires external reference and other components
3½-digit BCD	40 000	Dual slope	—	CMOS; has auto-zero circuit; requires external reference and other components

converters. It is possible to use diffused resistors for 8-bit, and sometimes 10-bit, converters, but tracking requirements at the 12-bit level are severe, necessitating the use of thin-film resistors and the additional step of depositing the thin-film resistors onto the monolithic chip.

Monolithic-converter designers have been quite successful in employing ingenious circuit techniques to achieve what would have been difficult to do in a straightforward manner. This is one of the challenging aspects of monolithic circuitry. For example, although monolithic 12-bit successive-approximation A/D converters are quite difficult to make, equivalent accuracy can be readily achieved by use of the slower dual-slope conversion technique. A number of low-cost 12-bit monolithic units are on the market that offer good performance characteristics. They utilize either the dual-slope or charge-balancing technique.

Charge balancing involves switching, in discrete time intervals, the output of a current source fed into the summing junction of an operational integrator. The switching is controlled by a comparator, which is controlled, in turn, by the output of the operational integrator. The input signal, which is also fed into the operational integrator's summing junction, determines the switching current's pulse rate. As the input signal increases in magnitude, the switched current's pulse rate (controlled by the comparator) increases in proportion to the input signal, until a current balance is achieved at the operational integrator's summing junction.

Whereas earlier monolithic devices used a two-chip approach to separate the analog and digital portions of the circuit, newer converters are one-chip units. Never-

A brief look backwards

High-performance data converters first became available in 1955, when the Epsco Corp. unveiled its Datrac B-611 A/D converter (one of the historical exhibits of last year's ELECTRO in Boston). This vacuum-tube-based instrument, together with its companion power supply, weighed 150 pounds (68 kg) and cost $8500. Yet it offered impressive performance, even by today's standards: 11-bit resolution at a 44-kHz.conversion rate.

The development of early converters was spurred in part by the then infant U.S. space program, which used them for high-speed pulse-code-modulation (PCM) data-telemetry and computer data-reduction applications, and also for digitizing radar signals.

By 1958–1959, packaged transistors replaced vacuum tubes to produce 12-bit A/D converters that were substantially smaller in size than their predecessors. At least three such converters were introduced at that time—by Adage, Epsco, and Packard-Bell; they ranged in conversion times from 13 to 48 μs. Selling price was still quite high (about $5000) and by 1960, only about 2000 of these converters were in use.

A breakthrough occurred in 1966 when Epsco introduced its Datrac 3, a small hand-held 12-bit discrete-component A/D converter constructed on just two circuit boards in a metal-case module. The unit had 24-μs conversion and sold for $1200. Similar devices soon followed and, by 1968, the Redcor Corp. had introduced the first encapsulated discrete-component 12-bit A/D converter with 50-μs conversion at a price of $600.

The next year saw rapid improvement in discrete-component-converter performance, with 12-bit A/D-converter conversion times dropping down to 12 μs. During that same period, the Beckman Instrument Co. unveiled a new-generation data converter—the first hybrid converter, an 8-bit D/A unit made from multiple monolithic IC chips and a thick-film resistor network. An 8-bit D/A with a thin-film resistor network was produced in 1970 by Micro Networks.

Monolithic data converters were also being developed in the late '60s. In 1968, Fairchild Semiconductor was able to build a monolithic 10-bit D/A converter based on its model μA722, although this unit was a basic building block requiring an external reference, resistor network, and output amplifier. By 1970, Analog Devices had manufactured the industry's first monolithic quad-current switches, to be used as building blocks for hybrid A/D and D/A converters up to 16 bits in resolution. It was also in 1970 that Precision Monolithics produced the first complete D/A converter in monolithic form—a 6-bit unit that included a reference and an output amplifier, and required no additional components for operation (model DAC-01).

Meanwhile, discrete-component converters continued to be improved in performance characteristics. By 1971, conversion times for 12-bit A/D units had dropped to just 4 μs, though prices still hovered around the $600–$700 mark. Hybrid-converter prices continued to drop, with an 11-bit D/A converter (Beckman Instruments' model 848) selling for $155 in 1971 and a 12-bit unit (Micro Networks' model MN312) dropping to $100 by the next year. Monolithic units also continued to be improved. In 1972, Motorola announced an 8-bit monolithic D/A converter (model MC1408), and Precision Monolithics produced a 10-bit unit (model DAC-02) the next year.

By 1975, the price of hybrid data converters such as Datel Systems' 12-bit model ADC-HY12B A/D converter had dropped below $100. At the same time, 10-bit monolithic D/A converters were selling for as low as $20. And performance of discrete-component A/D converters such as Datel's ADC-EH12B3—a 12-bit 2-μs unit—has reached a new high at a record low price of $300, half the former price.

Monolithic-converter prices have continued to drop (now down to about $10 for a 10-bit D/A unit requiring external components) while performance is up (300-ns for a 12-bit D/A converter from Precision Monolithics requiring only an external reference and an op amp).

theless, external components, such as an integrating capacitor, a reference, and some compensation parts, are needed for proper operation.

CMOS circuitry has been used to fabricate monolithic converters with BCD coding, for digital panel meters and small instruments. Among the other popular monolithic A/D converter types is an 8-bit design that employs a variation of the successive-approximation technique. This device is made with an ion-implanted p-channel MOS technology. Instead of the conventional eight switches, it uses 255 switches connected to a 256-series-resistor chain. In hybrid or discrete form, this would be a gross waste of components, but not so in monolithic form. This approach results in a monotonic 8-bit A/D converter.

Another successful monolithic approach has been to use bipolar technology to make an 8-bit D/A converter with a companding characteristic for use in voice PCM systems. A typical device has eight inputs, which select eight chords (straight-line approximations to a curve), each with 16 equal steps. As part of an A/D converter, this device compresses a signal (provides high gain at low signal levels and vice versa). When used as a D/A converter, it expands the signal according to a standardized logarithmic curve.

Tables I and II list some representative monolithic D/A and A/D converters. A large number of 8-bit devices are on the market, chiefly because of their low prices and satisfactory performance levels. Several 10-bit D/A

converters are also available, one of which can be obtained with a reference and an output amplifier. And one multiplying-type 10-bit unit can have a variable reference applied to it. The CMOS 12-bit monlithic D/A converter model available at this time is a multiplying type, and does not provide full 12-bit linearity. Another bipolar 12-bit D/A converter has been introduced that has true 12-bit linearity, and requires an external reference and output amplifier. ◆

The author wishes to acknowledge the help of the following in tracing some early-model data converters: Nicholas Tagaris, John Gallagher, and James Zaros of Datel Systems; Richard Tatro of Micro Networks; Richard Snyder of Beckman Instruments; Donn Soderquist of Precision Monolithics.

Eugene L. Zuch (M) is product marketing manager for data conversion products at Datel Systems, Inc., Canton, Mass. where he has been employed since 1973. He has held technical marketing positions for the last seven years. Before this, he was a design engineer involved in the development of analog and data-conversion circuitry. Mr. Zuch holds B.S. and M.S. degrees in electrical engineering from the Massachusetts Institute of Technology, and a B.S. degree in management from that school's Sloan School of Management. He is a registered professional engineer and a member of Tau Beta Pi and Eta Kappa Nu. He has written extensively on the subject of data conversion for various electronics trade magazines.

Know your converter codes. When you work with a/d and d/a converters, there are many input and output codes to choose from. Here are some characteristics of each.

The right digital code can help simplify system design when analog-to-digital and digital-to-analog converters are used in the system.

While some custom a/d and d/a converters use special codes, off-the-shelf units employ one of a few common codes adopted by the industry as "standard" (Table 1). Understanding which code to use, and where, is the key to a simpler system design. And the added benefits with a standard code include lower cost of the converter and a wider choice of vendors.

Many designers are perplexed about application. There are unipolar codes—straight binary, complementary binary and binary coded decimal (BCD). There are bipolar codes—sign-magnitude binary, sign-magnitude BCD, offset binary, one's complement and two's complement. Other decimal codes include excess-three, 2421, 5421, 5311 and 74-2-1. And there are also reflective codes—such as the Grey code; and error-detecting codes—like the Hamming.

All codes used in converters are based on the binary numbering system. Any number can be represented in binary by the following

$$N = a_n2^n + a_{n-1}2^{n-1} + \ldots + a_22^2 + a_12^1 + a_02^0,$$

where each coefficient a assumes a value of one or zero. A fractional binary number can be represented as

$$N = a_12^{-1} + a_22^{-2} + a_32^{-3} + \ldots + a_n2^{-n}.$$

A specific binary fraction is then written, for example, as 0.101101. In most converters it is this fractional binary number that is used for the basic converter code. Conventionally the fractional notation is assumed and the decimal point dropped.

The left-most digit has the most weight, 0.5, and is commonly known as the most-significant-bit (MSB). Thus the right-most digit would have the least weight, $1/2^n$, and is called the least-significant-bit (LSB).

This coding scheme is convenient for converters, since the full-scale range used is simply interpreted in terms of a fraction of full scale. For instance, the fractional code word 101101 has a value of $(1 \times 0.5) + (0 \times 0.25) + (1 \times$

Eugene Zuch, Senior Engineer, Datel Systems, 1020 Turnpike St., Canton, Mass. 02021.

Table 1. Summary of coding for a/d and d/a converters

	D/a converters	A/d converters
Unipolar	Straight binary	Straight binary
	BCD	BCD
	Complementary binary	Straight bin, invert. analog
	Complementary BCD	BCD, inverted analog
Bipolar	Offset binary	Offset binary
	Complementary off. binary	Two's complement
	Two's complement	Offset bin, invert. analog
		Two's compl, invert. analog
		Sign +mag. binary
		Sign +mag. BCD

0.125) + (1 × 0.0625) + (0 × 0.03125) + (1 × 0.015625), or 0.703125 of full-scale value. If all the bits are ONEs, the result is not full scale but rather $(1 - 2^{-n}) \times$ full scale. Thus a 10-bit d/a converter with all bits ON has an input code of 1111 1111 11. If the unit has a +10-V full-scale output range, the actual analog output value is

$$(1 - 2^{-10}) \times 10 \text{ V} = +9.990235 \text{ V}.$$

The quantization size, or LSB size, is full scale divided by 2^n—which in this case is 9.77 mV.

Analyzing digital codes

The four most common unipolar codes are straight binary, complementary binary, binary-coded decimal (BCD) and complementary BCD. Of these four, the most popular is straight-binary, positive-true. Positive-true coding means that a logic ONE is defined as the more positive of the two voltage levels for the logic family.

Negative-true logic defines things the other way—the more negative logic level is called ONE and the other level ZERO. Thus, for standard TTL, positive true logic makes the +5-V output logic ONE and 0 V a ZERO. In negative true logic the +5 V is ZERO and 0 V is ONE.

All four of the codes are defined (Table 2) in terms of the fraction of their full-scale values. Full-scale ranges of +5 and +10 V are shown with 12-bit codes.

Table 2. Unipolar codes—12 bit converter
Straight binary and complementary binary

Scale	+ 10 V FS	+5 V FS	Straight binary	Complementary binary
+FS − 1 LSB	+9.9976	+4.9988	1111 1111 1111	0000 0000 0000
+7/8 FS	+8.7500	+4.3750	1110 0000 0000	0001 1111 1111
+3/4 FS	+7.5000	+3.7500	1100 0000 0000	0011 1111 1111
+5/8 FS	+6.2500	+3.1250	1010 0000 0000	0101 1111 1111
+1/2 FS	+5.0000	+2.5000	1000 0000 0000	0111 1111 1111
+3/8 FS	+3.7500	+1.8750	0110 0000 0000	1001 1111 1111
+1/4 FS	+2.5000	+1.2500	0100 0000 0000	1011 1111 1111
+1/8 FS	+1.2500	+0.6250	0010 0000 0000	1101 1111 1111
0+1 LSB	+0.0024	+0.0012	0000 0000 0001	1111 1111 1110
0	0.0000	0.0000	0000 0000 0000	1111 1111 1111

BCD and complementary BCD

Scale	+ 10 V FS	+5 V FS	Binary coded decimal	Complementary BCD
+FS−1 LSB	+9.99	+4.95	1001 1001 1001	0110 0110 0110
+7/8 FS	+8.75	+4.37	1000 0111 0101	0111 1000 1010
+3/4 FS	+7.50	+3.75	0111 0101 0000	1000 1010 1111
+5/8 FS	+6.25	+3.12	0110 0010 0101	1001 1101 1010
+1/2 FS	+5.00	+2.50	0101 0000 0000	1010 1111 1111
+3/8 FS	+3.75	+1.87	0011 0111 0101	1100 1000 1010
+1/4 FS	+2.50	+1.25	0010 0101 0000	1101 1010 1111
+1/8 FS	+1.25	+0.62	0001 0010 0101	1110 1101 1010
0+1 LSB	+0.01	+0.00	0000 0000 0001	1111 1111 1110
0	0.00	0.00	0000 0000 0000	1111 1111 1111

D/a and a/d converters: The operating basics

The basic transfer characteristic of an ideal d/a converter forms the plot shown in Fig. A. The d/a takes an input digital code and converts it to an analog output voltage or current. This form of discrete input and discrete output (quantized) gives the transfer function a straight line through the tops of the vertical bars. In general the analog values are completely arbitrary and a large number of binary digital codes can be used. Analog full-scale can be defined as −25.2 to 85.7 V as easily as 0 to 10 V.

In practice, though, the industry has settled on several codes and very simple ranges for most major applications. For instance, the transfer characteristics in Fig. A are for a d/a converter that uses a 3-bit unipolar binary code and an output defined only in terms of its full-scale value.

The ideal a/d converter (Fig. B) has a staircase transfer characteristic. Here an analog input voltage or current is converted into a digital word. The analog input is quantized into n levels for a converter with n bits resolution. For the ideal converter, the true analog value corresponding to a given output code word is centered between two decision levels. There are $2^N − 1$ analog decision levels. The quantitization size, Q, is equal to the full-scale range of the converter divided by 2^n.

For the ideal d/a converter, there is a one-to-one correspondence between input and output, but for the a/d there is not, because any analog input within a range of Q will give the same output code word. Thus, for a given code word, the corresponding input analog value could have errors of from 0 to ±Q/2. This quantization error can be reduced only by an increase in converter resolution.

Although the analog input or output ranges are arbitrary, some of the standardized ranges include 0 to +5, 0 to +10, 0 to −5 and 0 to −10 V for unipolar converters, and −2.5 to +2.5, −5 to 5 and −10 to +10 V for bipolar units. Many units on the market are programmable types in which external pin connections determine the range of operation.

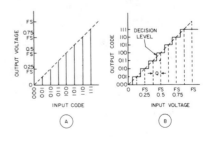

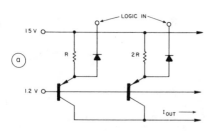

1. **Weighted current-source configurations** for straight binary (a) and complementary binary (b) coding gener- ate output current in different directions. The resistor weighting determines the output code.

Complementary-binary, positive-true coding is also used in d/a converters. This scheme is used because of the weighted current source configuration employed in many converter designs.

Fig. 1 shows two commonly used weighted-current-source designs. The pnp version (Fig. 1a) delivers a positive output current with straight binary positive-true coding. When the logic input is ONE, or +5 V, the current source is on, since the input diode is back-biased. Thus the current from each ON weighted current source is summed at the common-collector connection and flows to the output. A ZERO input holds the cathode of the input diode at ground and steals the emitter current from the transistor, keeping it off.

The use of an npn current source (Fig. 1b) produces a negative output current with complementary binary positive-true coding. The pnp transistors operate in the same way as before, but each collector is connected to the emitter of an npn weighted current source, which is turned on or off by the pnp transistor. This basic method finds common use in IC quad current-source circuits.

Complementary binary, positive-true, coding is identical to straight binary negative true; these are just two definitions of the same code. Straight-binary, negative-true, coding is commonly used to interface equipment with many minicomputer input/output busses. Unipolar a/d converters most frequently use the straight binary positive-true coding. They also use straight-binary inverted-analog where the full-scale code word corresponds to the negative full scale analog value.

Another popular code used in many converters is BCD. Table 2 shows three-decade BCD and complementary BCD codes used with converters that have full-scale ranges of +5 or +10 V. BCD is an 8421 weighted code, with four bits used to code each decimal digit. This code is relatively inefficient, since only 10 of the 16 code states for each decade are used. It is, however, a very useful code for interfacing decimal displays and switches with digital systems.

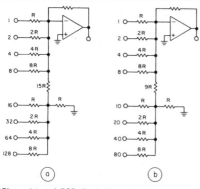

2. **Binary (a) and BCD (b) ladder networks** in d/a converters use the same weighting in the resistor quads but different divider ratios.

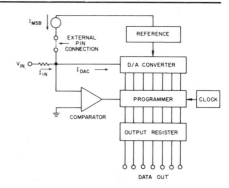

3. **Most a/d converters for bipolar operation** are offset by a current equal to the value of the MSB. The half-scale then becomes 100 . . . 0.

With d/a converters, it is especially convenient to have input decimal codes for use with such equipment as digitally programmed power supplies. And, with a/d converters, BCD is particularly popular for the dual-slope type for direct connection to numeric displays.

BCD coding in converters can be achieved in two ways: binary-to-BCD code conversion or direct weighting of internal resistor ladders and current sources. Today it is almost always done by resistor weighting schemes (Fig. 2). Each of the weighted resistors gets switched to a voltage source and thus generates the weighted current for the amplifier. Fig. 2a shows an 8-bit binary ladder network. Due to temperature-tracking constraints, groups of four resistors are used. Then the total resistance variation won't exceed 8-to-1.

In between the groups of four resistors is a current divider composed of two resistors that give a division ratio of 16 to 1 between resistor quads. The BCD ladder configuration is similar, with the same values in each of the groups of four resistors. In this case, however, the current divider has a ratio of 10 to 1 between resistor quads. Thus, because of the difference in internal weighting, BCD-coded converters cannot be pinstrapped for another code; they must be ordered only for BCD use.

Codes can be made bipolar

Most converters have provision for both unipolar and bipolar operation by external pin connection. The unipolar analog range is offset by one-half of full scale, or by the value of MSB current source, to get bipolar operation (Fig. 3). The current source, equal to the MSB current, is

derived from the internal voltage reference, so it will track the other weighted current sources with temperature.

For bipolar operation, this current source is connected to the converter's comparator input. Since the current flows in a direction opposite from that of the other weighted sources, its value is subtracted from the input range. With the weighted currents flowing away from the comparator input, the normal input voltage range is positive. Thus the offsetting can change a 0 to +10-V input range into a −5 to +5-V bipolar range.

If the analog range is offset for a converter with straight binary coding, the new coding becomes offset binary. This is the simplest code for a converter to implement, since no change in the coding is required. Table 3 shows offset binary coding for a bipolar converter with a ±5-V input range. All ZEROs in the code correspond to minus full scale. The code word that was originally half-scale becomes the analog zero, 1000 0000 0000. And all ONEs correspond to +5 V less one LSB. Successive-approximation a/d converters also have a serial, straight-binary output. This serial output is the result of the sequential conversion process, and it also becomes offset binary when the converter is connected for bipolar operation.

Three other types of binary codes are shown in Table 3, along with the offset binary. Of all four, the two most commonly used are offset binary and two's complement. Some converters use the sign-magnitude binary, but the one's complement is rarely used.

The two's complement code is the most popular because most digital arithmetic is performed in it; thus most interfacing problems are elim-

Table 3. Bipolar codes—12 bit converter

Scale	±5 V FS	Offset binary	Two's complement	One's complement	Sign-mag binary
+FS−1 LSB	+4.9976	1111 1111 1111	0111 1111 1111	0111 1111 1111	1111 1111 1111
+3/4 FS	+3.7500	1110 0000 0000	0110 0000 0000	0110 0000 0000	1110 0000 0000
+1/2 FS	+2.5000	1100 0000 0000	0100 0000 0000	0100 0000 0000	1100 0000 0000
+1/4 FS	+1.2500	1010 0000 0000	0010 0000 0000	0010 0000 0000	1010 0000 0000
0	0.0000	1000 0000 0000	0000 0000 0000	0000 0000 0000*	1000 0000 0000*
−1/4 FS	−1.2500	0110 0000 0000	1110 0000 0000	1101 1111 1111	0010 0000 0000
−1/2 FS	−2.5000	0100 0000 0000	1100 0000 0000	1011 1111 1111	0100 0000 0000
−3/4 FS	−3.7500	0010 0000 0000	1010 0000 0000	1001 1111 1111	0110 0000 0000
−FS+1 LSB	−4.9976	0000 0000 0001	1000 0000 0001	1000 0000 0000	0111 1111 1111
−FS	−5.0000	0000 0000 0000	1000 0000 0000	—	—

*Note: One's complement and sign magnitude binary have two code words for zero as given below; these are designated zero plus and zero minus:

	One's complement	Sign-mag binary
0+	0000 0000 0000	1000 0000 0000
0−	1111 1111 1111	0000 0000 0000

Table 4. Inverted analog offset binary coding comparison

Scale	Normal analog offset binary	Inverted analog offset binary	Normal analog comp. offset binary
+ FS		0000 0000 0000	
+FS − 1 LSB	1111 1111 1111	0000 0000 0001	0000 0000 0000
+1/2 FS	1100 0000 0000	0100 0000 0000	0011 1111 1111
0	1000 0000 0000	1000 0000 0000	0111 1111 1111
−1/2 FS	0100 0000 0000	1100 0000 0000	1011 1111 1111
− FS +1 LSB	0000 0000 0001	1111 1111 1111	1111 1111 1110
− FS	0000 0000 0000		1111 1111 1111

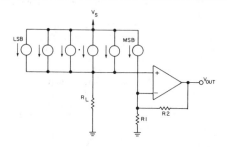

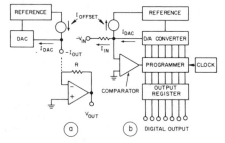

4. **For two's complement coding** in a d/a, the MSB current-source must go to the opposite terminal from the other weighted sources to avoid output glitches.

5. **The inverted-analog d/a converter** (a) and the inverted-analog a/d converter (b) have negative-going analog output and input values, respectively.

inated. The easiest way to characterize the two's-complement code is to look at the sum of a positive and negative number of the same magnitude; the result is all ZEROs plus a carry.

Visually the only difference between two's complement and offset binary is the left-most bit. In two's complement code it is the complement of the left-most bit in offset binary.

This left-most bit is normally called the MSB; in offset binary it is, in effect, the sign bit, and is so called in the other codes. Thus two's-complement coding is derived from offset binary when the sign bit is complemented and brought out as an additional output.

Coding has its limitations

Both two's-complement and offset-binary codes have magnitudes (if we temporarily forget about the sign bit) that increase from minus full scale to zero, and, with a sign change, from zero to plus full scale. Both codes have a single definition of zero. On the other hand, one's-complement and sign-magnitude codes have magnitudes that increase from zero to plus full scale and from zero to minus full scale. Both of these codes have two

code words for zero, as shown in Table 3. Because of the extra code word used for zero, the range of these codes is one LSB less than for offset-binary and two's-complement coding.

For positive numbers, one's-complement is the same as two's-complement. The negative number in one's-complement is obtained when the positive number is complemented. Sign-magnitude coding is identical to offset binary for positive numbers; negative numbers are obtained by use of the positive number with a complemented sign bit.

D/a converters don't usually use two's-complement coding. This is because it's hard to invert the MSB weighted current source. If the logic input is inverted, there is an extra digital delay in switching the current source, and this causes large output transients when the current is switched on and off.

The other alternative is to change the direction of the MSB current instead of inverting the digital input. This is also difficult to do and can introduce switching delays.

One satisfactory way of inverting the MSB is shown in Fig. 4. Here a voltage output d/a converter that uses two's-complement coding has the MSB current switched into the negative amplifier input terminal, while the other weighted currents are switched into the load resistor and positive input terminal. Thus opposite-polarity output voltages are produced, and there are no additional switching delays in the MSB.

One other code in Table 1 is the sign-magnitude BCD. This code, used mostly in dual-slope a/d converters, usually requires 13 bits for a three-decade digital display. Of the 13 bits, 12 are for the BCD code and one for the sign bit. An additional output bit for an overrange indication is generally supplied.

Another scheme in Table 1 is inverted analog code. This is also called negative reference coding. While most converters use zero to plus full scale as analog values; the inverted configuration uses zero to minus full scale values. The coding then increases in magnitude when the analog level increases in magnitude from zero to minus full scale. For bipolar coding, normal analog has an increasing code as the analog value goes from minus full scale to plus full scale; inverted analog coding does the opposite—the code increases as the analog value goes from plus full scale to minus.

Why the need for this code? Fig. 5a shows a d/a converter that delivers a negative output current. With bipolar operation and use of the offset current source, the converter provides a code ZERO that corresponds to plus full scale output current. However, if a current-to-voltage converter is used at the output, an inversion takes place, and a normal analog output voltage results.

In Fig. 6b, a d/a converter with positive output current is used in an a/d converter. Since the d/a output current is summed with the offset and input current at the comparator input, a negative input voltage is needed to balance these currents. The analog input thus goes from plus full scale to minus full scale for an increasing output code. Normal analog coding is achieved by use of an inverting amplifier ahead of the analog input terminal.

Inverted analog coding is compared with the normal offset binary coding in Table 4. This comparison shows that if the inverted analog offset binary code is rotated around the zero of the analog voltage, a normal analog offset binary output results. If inverted analog offset binary is compared with normal analog complementary offset binary, the two codes will appear identical except for an offset of one LSB. The relationship between these two codes can be expressed as:

Normal analog complementary binary + 1 LSB = Inverted analog offset binary.

Therefore a converter that uses one of these codes can also be used for the other with an external offset adjustment of 1 LSB. ∎∎

INTERPRETATION OF DATA CONVERTER ACCURACY SPECIFICATIONS

Cognizance of accuracy factors involved when interfacing data converters into system applications permits designers to meet overall error budget constraints. Transfer functions; quantization noise; offset, gain, and linearity errors; and temperature effects must be interpreted to satisfy specification requirements

Eugene L. Zuch   Datel Systems, Incorporated, Canton, Massachusetts

Analog-to-digital and digital-to-analog converters are widely utilized to interface between the physical world of analog measurements and the computational world of digital computers. Dating from the early 1950s, the application of data converters has increased enormously as the use of minicomputers and microcomputers has grown. Typical applications of data converters involve the areas of process control and measurement where the inputs and outputs of the system must be in analog form, yet the computation and control functions are performed digitally. In such a system, input variables such as temperature, flow, pressure, and velocity must be converted into electrical form by a transducer, then amplified and converted into digital form by an analog-to-digital converter for the computer to process.

Since the computer not only measures and determines the state of a process, but also controls it, its computations must be employed to close the loop around the system. This is done by causing the computer to actuate inputs to the process itself, thus controlling its state. Because the actuation is done by analog control parameters, the output of the digital computer must be converted into analog form by a digital-to-analog converter. Such a closed loop feedback control system is shown in Fig 1.

Interfacing by analog-to-digital (A-D) and digital-to-analog (D-A) converters performs a vital role. At the present time, it is estimated that at least 15% of all microcomputers function in such control and measurement applications where data converters are required; this percentage is expected to grow to about 40% within a few years. For the designer of such computer controlled systems, it is fortunate that a broad choice of data converters exists. In fact, a virtual supermarket of A-D and D-A converters of all prices, sizes, and performance specifications is available. This spectrum of converters encompasses those from simple 8-bit monolithic devices costing a few dollars, through better performing hybrid devices with higher resolution, to higher cost discrete module converters with the best performance characteristics.

Design selection involves not only price and size, but also many facets of performance: resolution, linearity, temperature coefficient, speed, and various self-contained options. In the realm of A-D converters (ADCs), there is also the choice between basic conversion methods, such as successive approximation, dual-slope integrating, and parallel (or flash) techniques. Furthermore, there exists a choice between three competing technologies: monolithic, hybrid, and modular, each with its own specific advantages. Since A-D and D-A converters are basically analog circuits that have digital inputs or outputs, the computer systems engineer who may be mostly familiar with digital techniques must become familiar

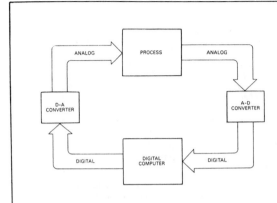

Fig 1 Computer controlled feedback control system. Computer closes loop around process to control its state. However, two interfaces are required: A-D converter and D-A converter

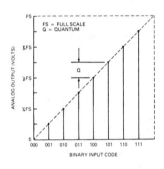

Fig 2 Ideal DAC transfer function. This I/O graph is shown for 3-bit DAC which has one-to-one correspondence between input and output

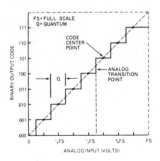

Fig 3 Ideal ADC transfer function. I/O graph illustrates 3-bit ADC which has quantized characteristic

with the many analog specifications describing data converter performance in order to choose the correct converter for a specific requirement.

Data Converter Transfer Functions

Fig 2 shows the transfer function of an ideal 3-bit D-A converter (DAC). This converter is assumed to be of the parallel type, as are virtually all DACs in use today. A parallel DAC responds simultaneously to all digital input lines whereas a serial DAC responds sequentially to each digital input. The transfer function representing a 3-bit DAC is a discontinuous function; its analog output voltage or current changes only in discrete analog steps, or quanta, rather than continuously. However, a one-to-one correspondence exists between the binary input code and the analog output value. For each input code there is one, and only one, possible output value. Analog step magnitude, or quantum, is shown as Q.

The horizontal axis is the input binary code, in this case a 3-bit code, increasing from 000 to 111. The number of output states, or quanta, is 2^n, where n is the number of bits in the code. For a 3-bit DAC, the number of states is 2^3 or 8; for a 12-bit DAC, the number of states is 2^{12} or 4096.

Fig 3 illustrates the transfer function for an ideal 3-bit ADC. This transfer function is also discontinuous but without the one-to-one correspondence between input and output. An ADC produces a quantized output from a continuously variable analog input. Therefore, each output code word corresponds to a small range (Q) of analog input values. The ADC also has 2^n output states and $2^n - 1$ transition points between states; Q is the analog difference between these transition points.

For both ADCs, Q represents the smallest analog difference that the converter can resolve. Thus, it is the resolution of the converter expressed in analog units. Resolution for an A-D or D-A converter, however, is commonly expressed in bits, since this defines the number of

TABLE 1

Summary of Data Converter Characteristics

Resolution (n)	States (2ⁿ)	Binary Weight (2⁻ⁿ)	Q for 10 V FS	S/N Ratio (dB)	Dynamic Range (dB)	Max Output for 10 V FS (V)
4	16	0.0625	0.625 V	34.9	24.1	9.3750
6	64	0.0156	0.156 V	46.9	36.1	9.8440
8	256	0.00391	39.1 mV	58.9	48.2	9.9609
10	1024	0.000977	9.76 mV	71.0	60.2	9.9902
12	4096	0.000244	2.44 mV	83.0	72.2	9.9976
14	16384	0.0000610	610 μV	95.1	84.3	9.9994
16	65536	0.0000153	153 μV	107.1	96.3	9.9998

states of the converter. A converter with a resolution of 12 bits, then, ideally resolves 1 part in 4096 of its analog range.

For an ideal ADC or DAC, Q has the same value anywhere along the transfer function. This value is $Q = FSR/2^n$, where FSR is the converter's full-scale range—the difference between the maximum and minimum analog values. For example, if a converter has a unipolar range of 0 to 10 V or a bipolar range of -5 to 5 V, FSR in both cases is 10 V. Q is also referred to as one least significant bit (LSB), since it represents the smallest code change the converter can produce, with the last bit in the code changing from 0 to 1 or 1 to 0.

Notice in the transfer functions of both A-D and D-A converters that the output never reaches full scale. This results because full scale is a nominal value that remains the same regardless of the resolution of the converter. For example, assume that a DAC has an output range of 0 to 10 V; then 10 V is nominal full scale. If the converter has an 8-bit resolution, its maximum output is $255/256 \times 10$ V $= 9.961$ V. If the converter has 12-bit resolution, its maximum output voltage is $4095/4096 \times 10$ V $= 9.9976$ V.

In both cases, maximum output is one bit less than indicated by the nominal full-scale voltage. This is true because analog zero is one of the 2^n converter states; therefore, there are only $2^n - 1$ steps above zero for either an A-D or D-A converter. To actually reach full scale would require $2^n + 1$ states, necessitating an additional coding bit. For simplicity and convenience then, data converters always have the analog range defined as nominal full scale rather than actual full scale for the particular resolution implemented.

In the transfer functions of Figs 2 and 3, a straight line is passed through the output values in the case of the DAC and through the code center points in the case of the ADC. For the ideal converter, this line passes precisely through zero and full scale. Table 1 summarizes the characteristics of the ideal A-D or D-A converter for the most commonly applied resolutions.

Quantization Noise and Dynamic Range

Even an ideal A-D or D-A converter has an irreducible error, which is quantization uncertainty or quantization noise. Since a data converter cannot distinguish an analog difference less than Q, its output at any point may be in error by as much as $\pm Q/2$.

Fig 4(a) shows an ideal ADC and an ideal DAC that digitize and then reconstruct an analog slow-voltage ramp signal. The ADC and output register are both triggered together so that the DAC is updated in synchronism with the A-D conversions. The DAC output ramp is identical with the analog input ramp except for the discrete steps in its output (not counting time delay). If the output ramp is subtracted from the input ramp as shown, the difference is the quantization noise—a natural result of the conversion process. This noise [Fig 4(b)] is simply the difference between the transfer function and the straight line shown in Fig 3. Quantization noise from an ideal converter is therefore a triangular waveform with a peak-to-peak value of Q.

As with most noise sources, the average value is zero, but the rms value is determined from the triangular shape to be E_n (rms) $= Q/\sqrt{12}$. Thus, a data conversion system can be thought of as a simple signal processor that adds noise to the original signal by virtue of the quantization process. Since this noise is an inherent part of the conversion process, it cannot be eliminated except with a converter of infinite resolution. The best that can be done, even with ideal converters, is to reduce it to a level consistent with desired system accuracy. This is done by using a converter with sufficiently high resolution.

In many computerized signal processing applications, it is necessary to determine the signal-to-noise (S/N) ratio, which is a power ratio expressed in decibels. It can be found from the ratio of peak-to-peak signal to rms noise as follows.

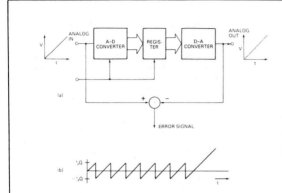

Fig 4 Signal digitization and reconstruction (a) and quantization noise (b). Quantization noise is shown as difference between input and output for ideal data conversion system

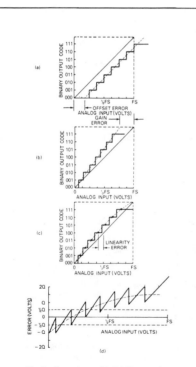

Fig 5 Errors in nonideal A-D converters. Transfer functions are shown for ADCs with offset error (a), gain error (b), and linearity error (c). ADC with all three errors present will have quantization error as shown in (d)

$$\text{s/n Ratio (dB)} = 10 \log \left[\frac{2^n Q}{Q/\sqrt{12}} \right]^2 = 20 \log 2^n + 20 \log \sqrt{12}$$
$$= 6.02n + 10.8 \qquad (1)$$

The s/n ratio increases by a factor of about 6 dB for each additional bit of resolution.

Dynamic range of a data converter, another useful term, is found from the ratio of FSR to Q. This ratio is the same as the number of converter states.

$$\text{Dynamic Range (dB)} = 20 \log 2^n = 20n \log 2 = 6.02n \qquad (2)$$

Therefore, simply multiplying the number of bits of resolution by 6 dB gives the dynamic range. s/n ratio and dynamic range are summarized for the most popular resolutions in Table 1.

Nonideal Data Converters

Real A-D and D-A converters exhibit a number of departures from the ideal transfer functions just described. These departures include offset, gain, and linearity errors (Fig 5), all of which appear simultaneously in any given data converter. In addition, the errors change with both time and temperature. In Fig 5(a), the ADC transfer function is shifted to the right from the ideal function. This offset error is defined as the analog value by which the transfer function fails to pass through zero; it is generally specified in millivolts or in percent of full scale.

In Fig 5(b), the converter transfer function has a slope difference from the ideal function. This gain, or scale factor, error is defined as the difference in full-scale values between the ideal and actual transfer functions when the offset error is zero; gain error is expressed in percent.

An ADC transfer function in Fig 5(c) exhibits linearity error, a curvature from the ideal straight line. Linearity error, or nonlinearity, is the maximum deviation of the transfer function from a straight line drawn between zero and full scale; it is expressed in percent or in LSBs (such as $\pm\frac{1}{2}$ LSB). Fig 5(d) shows the total error of a nonideal

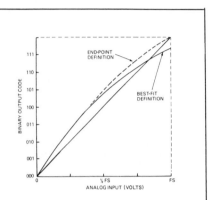

Fig 6 Comparison of linearity error definitions. Curves illustrate end-point and best-fit definitions of linearity error in an ADC

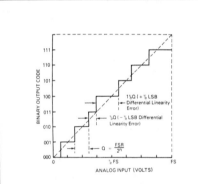

Fig 7 Definition of differential linearity error. This transfer function illustrates ±½ LSB differential linearity errors. Differential linearity error of zero means that every step in transfer function has size of precisely Q

ADC, which contains offset, gain, nonlinearity, and quantization errors. Compare this curve with that of Fig 4(b).

Fortunately, most A-D and D-A converters on the market today have provision for trimming out the initial offset and gain errors. By means of two simple external potentiometer adjustments, the offset and gain errors can be virtually reduced to zero or within the limits of measurement accuracy. Then, only the linearity error remains.

Nonlinearity

Linearity error is the most difficult error to deal with since it cannot be eliminated by adjustment. Like quantization error, it is an irreducible error. Basically, there are just two methods to reduce linearity error, both of which are expensive: either use a higher quality converter with better linearity, or perform a digital error correction routine on the data using a computer. The latter, of course, may not be feasible in many applications. There is some merit in using a more expensive converter, however. For example, suppose that an ultralinear 8-bit ADC is required. Most good quality converters have linearity errors specified to less than ±½ LSB. If a more expensive 12-bit ADC is employed with only 8 output bits used, then its linearity error of ±½ LSB out of 12 bits is the same as ±1/32 LSB out of 8 bits. This converter, therefore, becomes an ultralinear 8-bit ADC and probably at not too great an additional cost.

Actually, two types of linearity errors existing in A-D and D-A converters are integral linearity error and differential linearity error. Integral linearity error in Fig 5(c) is due to the curvature of the transfer function, resulting in departure from the ideal straight line. The definition given for integral linearity error as the maximum deviation of the transfer function from a straight line between zero and full scale is a conservative one used by most data converter manufacturers. It is an "end-point" definition, as contrasted with the normal definition of linearity error as the maximum deviation from the "best-fit" straight line.

Since determining the best-fit straight line for data converters can be a tedious process when calibrating the device, most manufacturers have opted for the more conservative definition. This means that the converter must be aligned accurately at zero and at full scale to realize the specified linearity. The end-point definition can mean a linearity that is twice as good as a best-fit definition, as illustrated in Fig 6. Notice that the curvature may be twice as great with the best-fit straight line definition.

Differential linearity error is the amount of deviation of any quantum from its ideal value. In other words, it is the deviation in the analog difference between two adjacent codes from the ideal value of $FSR/2^n$. If a data converter has ±½ LSB maximum differential linearity error, then the actual size of any quantum in its transfer function is between ½ LSB and 1½ LSB; each analog step is 1 ±½ LSB. Fig 7 illustrates the definition. The first two steps shown are the ideal value $Q = FSR/2^n$. The next step is only ½Q, and above this is 1½Q. These two steps are at the limit of the specification of ±½ LSB maximum differential linearity error. Most data converters today are specified in terms of both integral and differential linearity error. In production testing of data converters, quanta sizes are measured over the converter's full-scale range.

Two other important terms are commonly used in conjunction with the differential linearity error specification. The first is monotonicity, which applies to DACs. A monotonic DAC has an analog output that is a continuously increasing function of the input. The DAC transfer function shown in Fig 8(a) is monotonic even though it has a large differential linearity error. The transfer

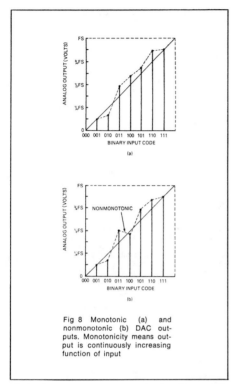

Fig 8 Monotonic (a) and nonmonotonic (b) DAC outputs. Monotonicity means output is continuously increasing function of input

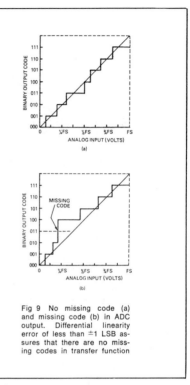

Fig 9 No missing code (a) and missing code (b) in ADC output. Differential linearity error of less than ±1 LSB assures that there are no missing codes in transfer function

function of Fig 8(b), on the other hand, is nonmonotonic since the output actually decreases at one point. In terms of differential linearity error, a DAC may go nonmonotonic if the differential linearity error is greater than ±1 LSB at some point; if the differential linearity error is less than ±1 LSB, it assures that the output is monotonic.

The term missing, or skipped, code applies to ADCs. When the differential linearity error of an ADC is greater than ±1 LSB, the output may have a missing code; if the differential linearity error is less than ±1 LSB, it assures that there are no missing codes. Fig 9(a) shows the transfer function of an ADC with a large differential linearity error but with no missing codes. In Fig 9(b), however, the differential linearity error causes a code to be skipped in the output.

For ADCs, the linearity characteristic depends on the technique of A-D conversion used; each converter type exhibits its own specific nonlinearity characteristic. Fig 10 illustrates the nonlinearity characteristics of the two most popular types of ADCs: successive approximation and dual-slope integrating. With the successive approximation ADC, and also with other feedback type ADCs that use a parallel input DAC in the feedback loop, differential linearity error is the dominant type of nonlinearity. This is due to the parallel input DAC, which is made up of

weighted current sources. The worst differential linearity errors occur at the major code transitions, such as $\frac{1}{4}$, $\frac{1}{2}$, and $\frac{3}{4}$ scale. If these differential linearity errors are small, then the integral linearity error will also be small.

The difficulty at the major transition points is that, for example, the most significant bit current source is turning on while all other current sources are turning off. This subtraction of currents must be accurate to ±$\frac{1}{2}$ LSB and is a severe constraint in high resolution DACs. This means that the weighted current sources must be precisely trimmed in manufacturing. The most difficult transition is at $\frac{1}{2}$ scale, where all bits change state (eg, for an 8-bit converter, 01111111 to 10000000), and the worst differential linearity error generally occurs here.

The next most difficult transitions occur at $\frac{1}{4}$ scale and $\frac{3}{4}$ scale, where all but one of the bits change state (eg, for an 8-bit converter, 00111111 to 01000000 and 10111111 to 11000000, respectively). Relatively smaller differential linearity errors may also occur at the $\frac{1}{8}$, $\frac{3}{8}$, $\frac{5}{8}$, and $\frac{7}{8}$ scale transitions, and so on. Fig 10(a) shows a successive approximation ADC transfer function, illustrating exaggerated differential linearity errors at $\frac{1}{4}$, $\frac{1}{2}$, and $\frac{3}{4}$ scale. If these errors are properly trimmed out in manufacturing, then both differential and integral linearity errors will be less than ±$\frac{1}{2}$ LSB.

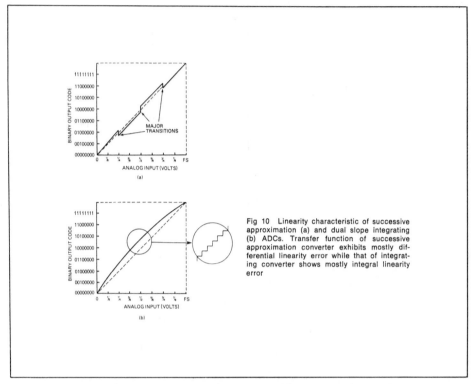

Fig 10 Linearity characteristic of successive approximation (a) and dual slope integrating (b) ADCs. Transfer function of successive approximation converter exhibits mostly differential linearity error while that of integrating converter shows mostly integral linearity error

Fig. 10(b) shows a dual-slope integrating ADC transfer function. In this case, the predominant nonlinearity is the integral linearity error; differential linearity error is almost nonexistent in integrating type ADCs, which also includes charge balancing ADCs. The curvature of the transfer function is caused by a nonideal integrator circuit. Differential linearity is determined by the time between clock pulses in the converter, and this is constant within any conversion cycle.

Temperature Induced Errors

Ambient temperature changes cause variations in offset, gain, and linearity errors. If a converter is operated at a constant temperature within its specified operating temperature range, offset and gain errors can be zeroed by external adjustment at that temperature. But if the converter must operate with changing ambient temperature, then the problem becomes acute.

Offset change with temperature is generally specified in microvolts per degree Celsius, or in parts per million of full scale per degree Celsius. Gain temperature coefficient is specified in parts per million per degree Cel-

sius, and linearity error change with temperature is expressed in parts per million of full scale per degree Celsius.

Effective aproaches to minimizing gain and offset changes with temperature are available. If a converter operates most of the time at a given temperature, then its offset and gain should be zeroed at that temperature. If, however, the ambient temperature varies between two temperatures, the converter should be calibrated midway between those two temperatures. Another approach to minimizing changes with temperature is to use a converter with a low temperature coefficient to meet the desired specification. Data converters with low temperature coefficients are, of course, more expensive, but this may be the most economical solution to the problem when all design factors are considered. Another method of minimizing gain error is based on the fact that many data converters with internal references have provision for connecting an external reference. In such a case, it is possible to connect a lower temperature coefficient external reference to the converter. This can be particularly effective where a number of converters are used together and one reference is used for all of them.

Linearity error temperature coefficient is the most troublesome specification, since it resists correction. In many applications, it is desired that the converter be

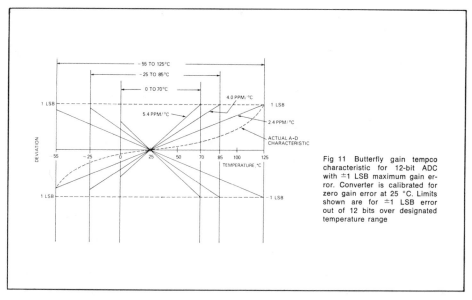

Fig 11 Butterfly gain tempco characteristic for 12-bit ADC with ±1 LSB maximum gain error. Converter is calibrated for zero gain error at 25 °C. Limits shown are for ±1 LSB error out of 12 bits over designated temperature range

monotonic, or have no missing codes, over the desired operating temperature range. From the converter differential linearity temperature coefficient, it is useful to determine the temperature range over which the converter will have guaranteed monotonicity or no missing codes. Using a conservative approach, it is assumed that the converter has a maximum initial differential linearity error of ±½ LSB. Then, if the differential linearity error changes by not more than an additional ½ LSB, a DAC will remain monotonic and an ADC will have no missing codes.

With a 12-bit ADC for example, ½ LSB is equal to 120 ppm. If the operating temperature range is 0 to 70 °C and the converter is calibrated at 25 °C, the maximum temperature change is 70 °C − 25 °C, or 45 °C. To guarantee no missing codes, the differential linearity temperature coefficient must be 120 ppm/45 °C = 2.7 ppm/°C of full scale, maximum. An even lower differential linearity temperature coefficient is required to assure no missing codes if the operating temperature range is the full −55 °C to 125 °C military range. Performing a similar computation gives 120 ppm/100 °C = 1.2 ppm/°C of full scale, maximum, for the differential linearity temperature coefficient.

Gain temperature coefficient is commonly specified by the butterfly limits shown in Fig 11. All the lines pass through zero at 25 °C, where it is assumed that the initial measurement is made. The graph of Fig 11 shows the maximum gain temperature coefficient required for a ±1 LSB gain error for a 12-bit A-D or D-A converter over three different temperature ranges. Observe that the

gain deviation curve must be within the bounds shown to meet the specification of ±1 LSB maximum change. The dotted curve shows an actual converter gain deviation that would qualify as a gain temperature coefficient of ±2.4 ppm/°C over the −55 to 125 °C operating temperature range. This represents a very low temperature coefficient for an actual converter since most available devices fall in the range of 5 to 50 ppm/°C.

Error Budget Summary

A common mistake in specifying data converters is to assume that the relative accuracy of a converter is determined only by the number of resolution bits. In fact, achievable relative accuracy is likely to be far different from the implied resolution, depending on the converter specifications and operating conditions. This simply means that the last few resolution bits may be meaningless in terms of realizable accuracy.

The best way to attack this design problem is with a systematic error budget. An error budget partitions all possible errors by source to arrive at a total error. In a given system, this must be done not only for the A-D or D-A converter, but also for the other circuits, such as transducer, amplifier, analog multiplexer, and sample and hold.

As an example, using the accuracy specifications for a typical 12-bit ADC (Table 2), an error budget can be determined based on the following assumptions: operating temperature range of 0 °C to 50 °C, maximum

TABLE 2

Accuracy Specifications for 12-Bit ADC

Characteristic	Value
Resolution	12 Bits
Differential Linearity Error	±½ LSB max
Differential Linearity Tempco	±2 ppm/°C of FSR max
Gain Tempco	±20 ppm/°C max
Offset Tempco	±5 ppm/°C of FSR max
Power Supply Sensitivity	0.002%/%

TABLE 3

Error Budget for 12-Bit ADC

Specification	Error (%)
Quantization Error (±½ LSB)	0.012
Differential Linearity Error (±½ LSB)	0.012
Differential Linearity Error over Temp (2 ppm/°C x 25)	0.005
Gain Change over Temp (20 ppm/°C x 25)	0.05
Zero Change over Temp (5 ppm/°C x 25)	0.0125
Change with Power Supply (1 x 0.002%)	0.002
Long Term Change	0.02
Total Error, Worst Case	0.1135
Total Statistical (rms) Error	0.0581

power supply voltage change of 1% with time and temperature, and maximum converter change of 0.02% with time. Table 3 shows the resulting error budget with a total worst case error of 0.1135%. It is improbable that the errors will all add in one direction. Statistical (rms) addition of the errors yields a lower value of 0.0581%; this, on the other hand, may be too optimistic since the number of error sources is small. At any rate, the maximum error will be somewhere between 0.0581% and 0.1135%, a significant difference from what might be assumed as a 12-bit or 0.024% converter. The ideal relative accuracy has been degraded by one to two resolution bits.

In applying data converters, best results are achieved by reading the data sheet carefully for accuracy specifications, computing total error by the error budget method, and then carefully aligning and testing the converter in its actual application.

Bibliography

H. Schmid, *Electronic Analog/Digital Conversions*, Van Nostrand Reinhold, New York, 1970

J. Sherwin, "Specifying D/A and A/D Converters," *Electronic Products*, Nov 1976, p 48

Signetics Corp, *Analog Data Manual*, Sunnyvale, Calif, 1977, pp 678-679

Datel Systems, Inc, "Principles of Data Acquisition and Conversion," *Modules for Data Conversion* catalog, Canton, Mass, 1978

E. Zuch, "Where and When to Use Which Data Converter," *IEEE Spectrum*, June 1977, pp 38-42

E. Zuch, "Linking the Analog World to Digital Computers," *Instruments and Control Systems*, Sept 1977, pp 87-89

Eugene L. Zuch is product marketing manager for data conversion products at Datel Systems. He has previously performed marketing and engineering functions. His educational background includes BS and MS degrees in electrical engineering from MIT and a BS in management from the MIT Sloan School of Management.

Compensate for temperature drift in data-converter circuits

Data-converter circuits must operate in a nonideal world in which temperature drift can reduce the efficacy of their design. Beating the problem requires an understanding of drift components.

Eugene L Zuch, Datel Systems Inc

Compensating for data-converter temperature drift can be a complicated process, involving (depending upon system needs and designer expertise) one or more of the following:

- Properly calibrating the chosen converter
- Choosing a converter that best suits the system's stability needs
- Mounting the chosen converter in a temperature-regulated environment
- Using a converter with provision for an external reference
- Controlling drift by means of external error correction.

Whatever technique (or combination of techniques) you use, though, its effective application requires an understanding of the sources of data-converter temperature drift.

Where does the drift come from?

Although all data-conversion devices can operate over a defined range of ambient temperature, as temperature varies within that range, the elements of a device's accuracy—its offset, gain and linearity—will change.

To compensate for this temperature drift, as well as for drift occurring over time, most data converters come with provisions for external adjustment of offset and gain errors. In near-constant temperature environments, though, and for moderate-resolution devices, the drift remains small. Thus, in such environments, calibrating a converter for offset and gain at the

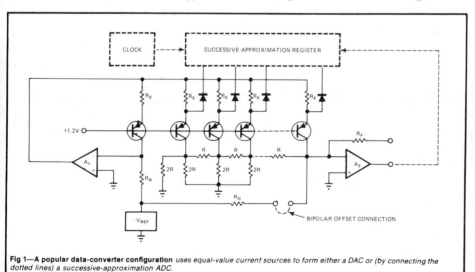

Fig 1—A popular data-converter configuration *uses equal-value current sources to form either a DAC or (by connecting the dotted lines) a successive-approximation ADC.*

Matching analog components improves temperature tracking

ambient operating temperature usually suffices. For a 12-bit ADC or DAC with 20-ppm/°C maximum gain drift, for example, the maximum gain drift over ±5°C is only ±0.42 bit. (Converters with 14-bit (or greater) resolution, however, show significant drift even for small temperature changes.)

Consider a popular data-converter configuration (Fig 1), using a D/A converter employing equal-value, switched pnp current sources. An R/2R resistor ladder provides binary weighting, and the servo loop of A_1 maintains constant current through the transistors. In conjunction with feedback resistor R_F, the output amplifier (A_2) converts the output current into a voltage.

R_0 and the reference voltage provide a one-half full-scale offset current for connection in the bipolar mode.

Connecting the circuitry represented by the dotted lines converts this circuit into a successive-approximation A/D converter, in which a clock-controlled successive-approximation register (SAR) in turn controls the D/A converter, and A_2 is a comparator rather than an op amp.

In both the D/A- and A/D-circuit versions, this circuitry's analog portion determines its temperature drift. Modern data-converter designs match discrete components in such a circuit to cancel the drift errors and furnish stable operation over temperature. In hybrid-type D/A converters, for example, identical R_Fs fabricated on the same thin-film chip track each other closely. Similarly, the R and 2R ladder resistors don't influence temperature drift so long as they track

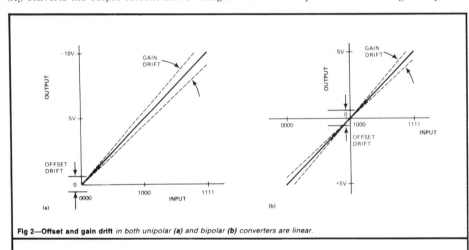

Fig 2—Offset and gain drift *in both unipolar (a) and bipolar (b) converters are linear.*

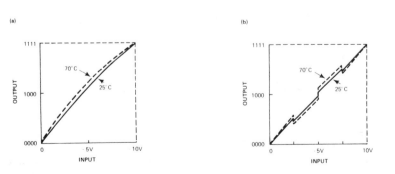

Fig 3—Linearity drift *in an integrating A/D converter (a) produces a change in the shape of the transfer function; in a successive-approximation A/D converter (b), it produces larger steps at adjacent code transitions.*

each other. The current sources vary in proportion to the reference resistor R_R, but R_F compensates for this effect, tracking R_R over changes in temperature by altering the gain of A_2. In bipolar operation, R_0 must track R_R for stable operation. Other possible temperature-drift errors result from the change in transistor beta and V_{BE}, but the transistors, too, are matched for tracking.

Ideally, then, with perfect component temperature tracking, the circuit exhibits only three sources of drift:

- Offset-voltage drift caused by A_2's input drifts
- Leakage-current change in the current sources
- Gain drift caused by the temperature coefficient of the voltage-reference source.

In practice, of course, component tracking is not perfect, thereby adding to the drift problem; in well-designed circuits, the resulting drift

TABLE 1—SOURCES OF TEMPERATURE DRIFT FOR CIRCUIT OF FIG 1	
SYMBOL	SOURCE OF DRIFT
d_o	OFFSET DRIFT DUE TO INPUT OFFSET VOLTAGE AND INPUT OFFSET CURRENT DRIFT OF OUTPUT AMPLIFIER A_2 AND LEAKAGE-CURRENT DRIFT OF TRANSISTOR CURRENT SOURCES
d_{RO}	OFFSET DRIFT DUE TO DIFFERENTIAL TEMPERATURE TRACKING OF R_0 AND R_R
d_C	CIRCUIT-GAIN DRIFT DUE TO DIFFERENTIAL TEMPERATURE TRACKING OF R_F s, TRANSISTOR V_{BE} s, TRANSISTOR BETAS AND INPUT OFFSET VOLTAGE AND CURRENT DRIFT OF SERVO AMPLIFIER A_1
d_R	GAIN DRIFT OF VOLTAGE-REFERENCE CIRCUIT
d_{RF}	GAIN DRIFT DUE TO DIFFERENTIAL TEMPERATURE TRACKING OF R_F AND R_R
d_L	GAIN DRIFT DUE TO DIFFERENTIAL TEMPERATURE TRACKING OF R AND 2R RESISTORS IN LADDER NETWORK

remains small but must nonetheless be accounted for. Component tracking is best when the resistors have equal values (and identical geometries) or are held to small resistance ratios.

Analyzing the drift

Table 1 describes the sources of temperature drift for the circuit in **Fig 1**, as well as delineating the symbols referring to each drift component. **Table 2** groups these drift components according to their contribution to +FS, −FS or zero operating points.

Analyzing the circuit's unipolar operation is simple. With an input code of 0000, all bits are OFF, and the DAC output is zero. The only offset drift, d_o, comprises the input-offset voltage, the current drifts of A_2 and the leakage current of the current sources. This last factor remains negligible at room temperature but doubles with each 10°C increase; it becomes significant at approximately 100°C. The offset temperature drift arising from d_o, shown in **Fig 2a**, shifts the converter's entire transfer function up or down with temperature. It affects all points on the transfer function.

An input code of 1111 sets the DAC's output bits ON, producing −FS output (−10V in this case). (For simplicity's sake, **Fig 2a** shows the output inverted.) At this output level, several sources of gain drift come into play. Although d_R furnishes the most significant contribution, d_C, d_{RF} and d_L, resulting from differential component tracking errors, must also be dealt with. The gain drift by itself rotates the transfer function around the origin, as shown in **Fig 2a**.

To summarize: The unipolar mode has the least drift at zero; it has the greatest drift at −FS.

Bipolar operation introduces additional drift sources. With an input code of 1000, the converter output is zero. Adjusting the current through R_0 during calibration precisely balances the offset current and MSB source current to provide zero output. Three sources of drift—d_o, d_C, and d_{RO}—combine here to move the transfer function up or

```
DIFFERENTIAL
LINEARITY IN
FRACTIONS LSB
Tran  1 =      - 0.3
Tran  2 =      - 0.1
Tran  3 =      - 0.1
Tran  4 =      - 0.1
Tran  5 =      - 0.0
Tran  6 =      - 0.0
Tran  7 =      - 0.0
Tran  8 =      - 0.0
Tran  9 =        0.0
Tran 10 =        0.0
Tran 11 =      - 0.0
```

Fig 4—A test performed on a 12-bit D/A converter at ambient temperature shows its differential-linearity error.

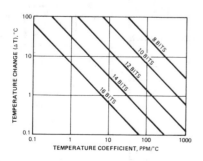

Fig 5—Use this graph to determine the range over which a particular converter remains monotonic. The method assumes an initial linearity error of ± 1/2 LSB.

Linearity drift changes transfer-function shape

down with temperature.

An input code of 1111 produces $-FS$ $(-5V)$ output. Three new drift sources—d_R, d_{RF} and d_L—add to the three present at zero. Finally, an input code of 0000 turns all bits OFF; the output is then $+5V$ or $+FS$. The only current into the output-amplifier summing junction comes from the reference through R_0. Now all drift sources except d_C and d_L are present—all current sources are OFF.

To summarize: In the bipolar mode, the least drift occurs at zero output; the worst, when all input bits are ON. When all bits are OFF, drift lies between these extremes.

A comparison of the two modes of operation shows that unipolar exhibits fewer drift sources and that in either mode the least drift occurs at zero output. Realize also that the largest source of temperature drift in either mode comes from the converter's reference.

Maintaining linearity can be difficult

Linearity drift (which changes the *shape* of the converter's transfer function) is the most difficult drift component to handle. Fig 3a illustrates the effect of this component on an integrating A/D converter: Integral linearity—the maximum deviation from an ideal straight line—is the predominant type of linearity error here. A change in temperature increases the transfer function's curvature.

In a successive-approximation A/D converter, on the other hand, the predominant linearity-error form is differential-linearity error. Illustrated in **Fig 3b**, this error is the analog size difference between actual adjacent code transitions and the ideal LSB size. Differential-linearity drift occurs primarily at major code transitions (one-half, one-quarter and three-quarter scale), as shown in exaggerated form in **Fig 3b**. This deviation increases with temperature change.

Determining an n-bit converter's worst-case differential-linearity errors requires measuring $n-1$ differences. The first measurement is the difference between the most significant bit and all other bits; the second measures the difference between the MSB plus the second bit with all other bits, and so on. Ideally, each measurement produces a 1-LSB difference. The results of such a test, performed at room temperature on a high-performance 12-bit D/A converter, appear in **Fig 4**. Repeating the measurements at the operating-temperature extremes determines the converter's differential-linearity temperature coefficient (DLTC):

$$DLTC = \Delta DL / \Delta T$$

where ΔDL is the worst-case change in differential linearity between the two temperatures and ΔT is the temperature difference.

The combination of DLTC and temperature

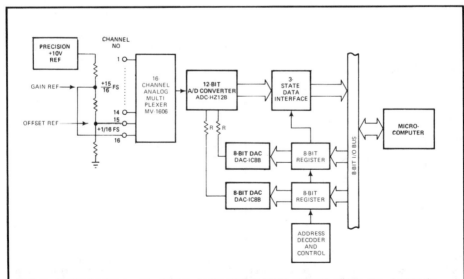

Fig 6—A self-calibrating data-converter circuit *requires two channels for the calibration process. The µC stores the correct output codes in its memory and compares them with the actual output codes.*

TABLE 2–ERROR ANALYSIS OF TEMPERATURE-DRIFT SOURCES			
OPERATING MODE	+FS	OUTPUT 0	-FS
UNIPOLAR	–	d_O	$d_O + d_R + d_C + d_{RF} + d_L$
BIPOLAR	$d_O + d_{RO} + d_R + d_{RF}$	$d_O + d_C + d_{RO}$	$d_O + d_C + d_{RO} + d_R + d_{RF} + d_L$

NOTE:
A CONVERTER WITH PNP CURRENT SOURCES (FIG 1) IS A MODEL. FOR A CONVERTER WITH NPN CURRENT SOURCES, +FS AND -FS ARE INTERCHANGED

TABLE 3–DIFFERENTIAL-LINEARITY TEMPERATURE COEFFICIENTS REQUIRED TO GUARANTEE MONOTONICITY OVER STANDARD RANGES			
RESOLUTION (BITS)	0 TO 70°C $\Delta T = 45°$	25 TO +85°C $\Delta T = 60°$	-55 TO +125°C $\Delta T = 100°$
8	43.4	32.6	19.5
10	10.8	8.1	4.9
12	2.7	2.0	1.2
14	0.68	0.51	0.31
16	0.17	0.13	0.076

*ΔT REPRESENTS THE CHANGE FROM +25°C

change can, if large enough, cause a D/A converter's output to be nonmonotonic; an A/D converter can skip output codes when the circuit's differential-linearity error exceeds 1 LSB.

To effectively use either an ADC or a DAC, then, first establish the range over which the DAC remains monotonic and the ADC produces all output codes. Use of manufacturer-provided DLTC specifications, combined with the initial linearity error, can determine this range. **Fig 5**, for example, assumes an initial differential-linearity error of ±1/2 LSB at 25°C, corresponding to most manufacturers' specifications. The graph, therefore, shows the temperature change required to produce the additional 1/2 LSB of error that causes nonmonotonic operation or missing codes.)

As an example, a 14-bit A/D converter operating over a temperature range of ±10°C on either side of room temperature requires a DLTC less than 3 ppm/°C, according to **Fig 5**.

Combating the drift

Understanding the foregoing explanation of the sources of converter temperature drift permits taking effective measures to deal with that drift. Proper converter calibration is one important tool in this task. Performing this calibration at room temperature is unsatisfactory; a device must be calibrated at the temperature at which it will operate. Seem obvious? Possibly, but designers often ignore this basic consideration.

The choice of converter can also make a significant difference. In some applications, monotonicity can prove more important than gain or offset drift; in such cases, you should choose the converter by DLTC, using **Fig 5**. While converters with low TCs cost more than common, low-cost devices, spending the additional money can prove the most economical alternative in the long run: Compare this extra cost with the engineering effort required to provide accurate compensation.

In critical applications, mounting a converter in a temperature-regulated enclosure can prove expedient. Then, heating the converter to a controlled temperature above any ambient temperature it will experience can improve TC by a factor of approximately 10 to 20. Although this alternative can also be expensive, the results can be remarkable. An ambient-temperature change of 50°C, for example, could be effectively reduced to 2.5°C.

A fourth effective tool for dealing with temperature drifts requires the use of a converter with provision for an external reference. Most converters' internal references achieve TCs ranging from ±20 to ±40 ppm/°C; more expensive references can reach the ±0.5- to ±10-ppm/°C range.

Finally, the most complex solution of all involves providing external error correction. **Fig 6** illustrates one such scheme, which requires use of an expensive external precision reference. The system converts 14 analog channels into digital data; the 15th and 16th channels furnish offset and gain correction, respectively. A voltage divider sets channel 15 to +1/16 FS (+0.0625V) and channel 16 to +15/16 FS (+9.375V)—full scale equals 10V. (These voltages correspond to 12-bit output codes of 0001 0000 0000 and 1111 0000 0000, respectively.)

Through use of a μC, the system calibrates itself near zero and then near full scale after each scan of its 14 channels. It deals with the offset first, in order to remove that error from the gain calibration. With the correct output codes for channels 15 and 16 stored in memory, the μC compares the actual converter output with this correct code, outputting a digital word to the register and 8-bit DAC, which in turn corrects the gain or offset. This DAC connects to the ADC's gain- and offset-calibration terminals through resistors. Both 8-bit devices operate in the bipolar mode and provide adjustment of ±0.2% FS. With 8-bit resolution, the range is incremented into 256 steps of 0.0016% FS (0.065-bit steps for a 12-bit converter).

The system can perform a complete correction with every scan or once for every N scans, because any temperature changes generally occur slowly. Alternatively, each scan can result in a small correction, amounting to one count out of 256, thereby minimizing the time required for calibration. After several initial scans, the con-

A device with large DLTC and ΔT can have a nonmonotonic output

verter is calibrated, and because the temperature changes slowly, this calibration technique follows those changes from then on.

Such an external error-correction scheme provides extremely stable operation in systems with a high-quality reference. But it corrects gain and offset errors, not those affecting linearity.

Author's biography

Eugene Zuch manages the market planning of data-conversion products for Datel Systems, Mansfield, MA. He earned BSEE and MSEE degrees from MIT, as well as a BS in management from the MIT Sloan School of Management. A member of IEEE, Tau Beta Pi and Eta Kappa Nu, Gene still finds time for Toastmasters International.

THE INTEGRATING A/D CONVERTER

Lee Evans, Intersil, Inc.

Integrating A/D converters have two characteristics in common. First, as the name implies, their output represents the integral or average of an input voltage over a fixed period of time. Compared with techniques which require that the input is "frozen" with a sample-and-hold, the integrating converter will give repeatable results in the presence of high frequency* noise. A second and equally important characteristic is that they use time to quantise the answer, resulting in extremely small nonlinearity errors and no possibility of missing output codes. Furthermore, the integrating converter has very good rejection of frequencies whose periods are an integral multiple of the measurement period. This feature can be used to advantage in reducing line frequency noise, for example, in laboratory instruments. (Fig. 1).

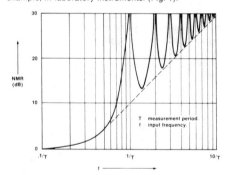

Figure 1: Normal Mode Rejection of dual-slope converter as a function of frequency.

In addition, a competitive instrument-quality product should have the following features:

1. Single Reference Voltage. This is strictly a convenience to the user, but since many designs are available with single references that contribute negligible error, products requiring dual references are rapidly becoming obsolete.

2. Auto Zero. This eliminates one trim-pot and a troublesome calibration step. Furthermore, it allows the manufacturer to use op-amps with up to 10mV offset while still achieving system offsets of only a few microvolts.

3. High Input Impedance. Recently developed monolithic FET technology allows input impedances of 1000 Mohm and leakages of a few pico amps to be achieved fairly readily.

The unique characteristics of the integrating converter have made it the natural choice for panel meters and digital voltmeter applications. For this reason, overall

*relative to the measurement period.

useage of integrating converters exceeds the combined total of all other conversion methods. Furthermore, the availability of low cost one and two chip converters will encourage digitizing at the sensor in applications such as process control. This represents a radical departure from traditional data logging techniques which in the past have relied heavily on the transmission of analog signals. The availability of one chip microprocessor system (with ROM and RAM on chip) will give a further boost to the 'conversion at the sensor' concept by facilitating local data processing. The advantage of local processing is that only essential data, such as significant changes or danger signals, will be transmitted to the central processor.

THE DUAL SLOPE TECHNIQUE - THEORY & PRACTICE

The most popular integrating converter is the "dual-slope" type, the basic operating principles of which will be described briefly. However, most of the comments relating to linearity, noise rejection, auto-zero capability, etc., apply to the whole family of integrating designs including charge balancing, triple ramps, and the 101 other techniques that have appeared in the literature. A simplified dual slope converter is shown in Figure 2.

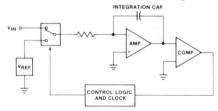

Figure 2: Simplified dual-slope converter.

The conversion takes place in three distinct phases (Fig. 3).

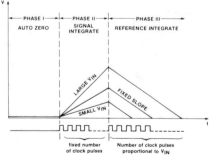

Figure 3: The three phases of a dual-slope conversion.

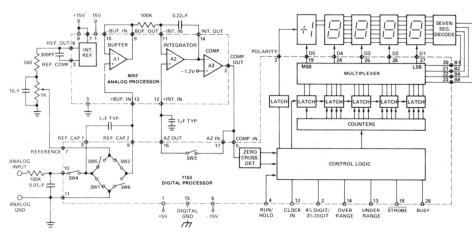

Figure 4: the 7103/8052 A/D Converter pair.

Phase 1, Auto Zero: During auto zero, the errors in the analog components (buffer offset voltages, etc.) will be automatically nulled out by grounding the input and closing a feedback loop such that error information is stored on an "auto-zero" capacitor.

Phase 2, Signal Integrate: The input signal is integrated for a fixed number of clock pulses. For a 3½-digit converter, 1,000 pulses is the usual count; for a 4½-digit converter, 10,000 is typical. On completion of the integration period, the voltage V in Fig. 3 is directly proportional to the input signal.

Phase 3, Reference Integrate: At the beginning of this phase, the integrator input is switched from V_{IN} to V_{REF}. The polarity of the reference is determined during Phase 2 such that the integrator discharges back towards zero. The number of clock pulses counted between the beginning of this cycle and the time when the integrator output passes through zero is a digital measure of the magnitude of V_{IN}.

The beauty of the dual slope technique is that the theoretical accuracy depends only on the absolute value of the reference and the equality of the individual clock pulses within a given conversion cycle. The latter can easily be held to 1 part in 10^6, so in practical terms the only critical component is the reference. Changes in the value of other components such as the integration capacitor or the comparator input offset voltage have no effect, provided they don't change during an individual conversion cycle. This is in contrast to Successive Approximation converters which rely on matching a whole string of resistor values for quantisation.

In a very real sense the designer is presented with a near perfect system; his job is to avoid introducing additional error sources in turning this text-book circuit into a real piece of hardware.

From the foregoing discussion, it might be assumed that designing a high performance dual-slope converter is as easy as falling off the proverbial log. This is not true, however, because in a practical circuit a host of pitfalls must be avoided. These include the non-ideal character-

istics of FET switches and capacitors, and the switching delay in the zero crossing detector.

ANALYZING THE ERRORS

At this point it is instructive to perform a detailed error analysis of a representative dual slope circuit, Intersil's 8052A/7103A pair. This is a 4½-digit design, where the analog circuitry is on a JFET/bipolar chip (the 8052) and the digital logic and switches on a MOS chip (7103A); the partitioning is shown in Fig. 4. The error analysis which follows relates to this specific pair - however, the principles behind the analysis apply to most integrating converters.

The analog section of the converter is shown in Fig. 5. Typical values are shown for 120KHz clock and 3 measurements/second. Each measurement is divided into three parts. In part 1, the auto-zero FET switches 1, 2 and 3 are closed for 10,000 clock pulses. The reference capacitor is charged to V_{REF} and the auto-zero capacitor is charged to the voltage that makes dV/dt of the integrator equal to zero. In each instance the capacitors are charged for 20 or more time-constants such that the voltage across them is only limited by noise.

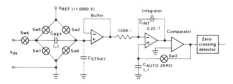

Figure 5: Analog section of a dual slope converter.

In the second phase, signal integrate, switches 1, 2 and 3 are opened and switch 4 is closed for 10,000 clock pulses. The integrator capacitor will ramp up at a rate that is proportional to V_{IN}. In the final phase, de-integrate, switch 4 is opened and, depending on the polarity of the input signal, switch 5 or 6 is closed. In either case the integrator will ramp down at a rate that is proportional to V_{REF}. The amount of time, or number of clock pulses, required to bring the integrator back to its auto-zero value is 10,000 $(\frac{V_{IN}}{V_{REF}})$. Of course, this is a description of the "ideal" cycle. Errors from this ideal cycle are caused by:

1. Capacitor droop due to leakage.
2. Capacitor voltage change due to charge "suck-out" (the reverse of charge injection) when the switches turn off.
3. Non-linearity of buffer and integrator.
4. High-frequency limitations of buffer, integrator and comparator.
5. Integrating capacitor non-linearity (dielectric absorption).
6. Charge lost by C_{REF} in charging C_{stray}.

Each of these errors will be analyzed for its error contribution to the converter.

1. Capacitor droop due to leakage.

Typical leakage (I_{Doff}) of the switches at normal operating voltage is 1 pA each and 2pA at each input of the buffer and integrator op amps. In terms of offset voltage caused by capacitor droop, the effect of the auto-zero and reference capacitors is differential, i.e., there is no offset if they droop an equal amount. A conservative typical effect of droop on offset would be 2pA discharging 1μF for 83 milliseconds (10,000 clock periods), which amounts to an averaged equivalent of .083 μV referred to the input. The effect of the droop on roll-over error (difference between equal positive and negative voltages near full scale) is slightly different. For a negative input voltage, switch 5 is closed for the de-integrate cycle. Thus the reference capacitor and auto-zero capacitor operate differentially for the entire measurement cycle. For a positive voltage, switch 6 is closed and the differential compensation of the reference capacitor is lost during de-integrate. A typical contribution to roll-over error is 3 pA discharging 1μF capacitor for 166 milliseconds, equivalent to .249 μV when averaged. These numbers are certainly insignificant for room temperature leakages but even at 100°C the contributions should be only 15 μV and 45 μV respectively. A roll-over error of 45 μV is less than 0.5 counts on this 20,000 count instrument.

2. Charge "suck-out" when the switches turn-off.

There is no problem in charging the capacitors to the correct value when the switches are on. The problem is getting the switches off without changing this value. As the gate is driven off, the gate-to-drain capacitance of the switch injects a charge on the reference or auto-zero capacitor, changing its value. The net charge injection of switch 3 turning-off can be measured indirectly by noting the offset resulting by using a .01μF auto-zero capacitor instead of 1.0μF. For this condition the offset is typically 250 μV, and since the signal ramp is a straight line instead of a parabola the main error is due to charge injection rather than leakage. This gives a net injected charge of 2.5 picocoulombs or an equivalent C_{gd} of 0.16pF. The effect of switches 1, 2, 4, 5 and 6 are more complicated since they depend on timing and some switches are going on while others are going off. A substitution of an .01 μF capacitor for reference capacitor gives less than 100 μV offset error. Thus, a conservative typical offset error for a 1.0μF capacitor is 2.5 μV. There is no contribution to roll-over error (independent of offset). Also this value does not change significantly with temperature.

3. Non-linearity of buffer and integrator.

In this converter, since the signal and reference are injected at the same point, the gain of the buffer and integrator are not of first-order importance in determining accuracy. This means that the buffer can have a very poor CMRR over the input range and still contribute zero error as long as it is constant, i.e., offset changes linearly with common mode voltage. The first error term is the non-linear component of CMRR. Careful measurement of CMRR on 30 buffers indicated roll-over errors from 5 to 30 μV. The contribution of integrator non-linearity is less than 1μV in each case.

4. High frequency limitations of amplifiers.

For a zero input signal, the buffer output will switch from zero to V_{REF} (1.0 volt) in 0.5 μseconds with an approximately linear response. The net result is to lose .25 μseconds of de-integrate period. For a 120KHz clock, this is 3% of a clock pulse or 3 μV. This is not an offset error since the delay is equal for both positive and negative references. The net result is the converter would switch from 0 to 1 at 97 μV instead of 100 μV in the ideal case.

A much larger source of delay is the comparator which contributes 3 μseconds. At first glance, this sounds absolutely ridiculous compared to the few tens of nanoseconds delay of modern IC comparators. However, they are specified with 2 to 10 mV of overdrive. By the time the 8052A comparator gets 10 mV of overdrive, the integrator will have been through zero-crossing for 20 clock pulses! Actually, the comparator has a 300MHz gain-bandwidth product which is comparable to the best IC's. The problem is that it must operate on 30 μV of overdrive instead of 10 mV. Again, this delay causes no offset error but means the converter switches from 0 to 1 at 60 μV, from 1 to 2 at 160 μV, etc. Most users consider this switching at approximately ½ LSB more desirable than the "so-called ideal" case of switching at 100 μV. If it is important that switching occur at 100 μV, the comparator delay may be compensated by including a small value resistor ($\simeq 20\Omega$) in series with the integration capacitor. (Further details of this technique are given on page 4 under the heading "Maximum Clock Frequency".)

The integrator time delay is less than 200 nsecond and contributes no measureable error.

5. Integrating capacitor dielectric absorption.

Any integrating A/D assumes that the voltage change across the capacitor is exactly proportional to the integral of the current into it. Actually, a very small percentage of this charge is "used up" in rearranging charges within the capacitor and does not appear as a voltage across the capacitor. This is dielectric absorption. Probably the most accurate means of measuring dielectric absorption is to use it in a dual-slope A/D converter with $V_{IN} \equiv V_{REF}$. In this mode, the instrument should read 1.0000 independent of other component values. In very careful measurements where zero-crossings were observed in order to extrapolate a fifth digit and all delay errors were calculated out, polypropylene capacitors gave the best results. Their equivalent readings were 0.99998. In the same test polycarbonate capacitors typically read 0.9992, polystrene 0.9997. Thus, polypropylene is an excellent choice since they are not expensive and their increased temperature coefficient is of no consequence in this circuit. The dielectric absorption of the reference and auto-zero capacitors are only important at power-on or when the circuit is recovering from an overload. Thus, smaller or cheaper capacitors can be used if very accurate readings are not required for the first few seconds of recovery.

6. Charge lost by C_{REF} in charging C_{stray}.

In addition to leakage and switching charge injection, the reference capacitor has a third method of losing charge and, therefore, voltage. It must charge C_{stray} as it swings from 0 to V_{IN} to V_{REF}. (Figure 5). However, C_{stray} only causes an error for positive inputs. To see why, let's look firstly at the sequence of events which occurs for negative inputs. During auto-zero C_{REF} and C_{stray} are both charged through the switches. When the negative signal is applied, C_{REF} and C_{stray} are in series and act as a capacitance divider. For C_{stray} = 15 pf, the divider ratio is 0.999985. When the positive reference is applied through switch #5, the same divider operates. As mentioned previously, a constant gain network contributes no error and, thus, negative inputs are measured exactly.

For positive inputs, the divider operates as before when switching from auto-zero to V_{IN}, but the negative reference is applied by closing switch #6. The reference capacitor is not used, and therefore the equivalent divider network is 1.0000 instead of .999985. At full scale, this 15 $\mu V/V$ error gives a 30 μV rollover error with the negative reading being 30 μV too low. Of course for smaller C_{stray}, the error is proportionally less.

Summary.

Error analysis of the circuit using typical values shows four types of errors. They are (1) an offset error of 2.5 μV due to charge injection, (2) a full scale rollover error of 30 μV due to C_{stray}, (3) a full scale rollover error of 5 to 30 μV due to buffer non-linearity and (4) a delay error of 40 μV for the first count. These numbers are in good agreement with actual results observed for the 8052A/7103A. Due to peak-to-peak noise of 20 μV around zero, it is possible only to say that any offsets are less than 10 μV. Also, the observed rollover error is typically ½ count (50 μV) with the negative reading larger than the positive. Finally, the transition from a reading of 0000 to 0001 occurs at 50 μV.

These figures illustrate the very high performance which can be expected from a well designed dual-slope circuit - performance figures which can be achieved with no tricky 'tweaking' of component values. Furthermore, the circuit includes desirable convenience features such as auto-zero, auto-polarity and a single reference.

MAXIMUM CLOCK FREQUENCY

Because of the 3 μS delay in the 8052 comparator, the maximum recommended clock frequency is 160KHz. In the error analysis it was shown that under these conditions half of the first reference integrate period is lost in delay. This means that the meter reading will change from 0 to 1 at 50 μV, from 1 to 2 at 150 μV, etc. As was noted earlier, most users consider this transition at midpoint to be desirable. However, if the clock frequency is increased appreciably above 160KHz, the instrument will flash 1 on noise peaks even when the input is shorted.

The clock frequency may be extended above 160KHz, however, by using a low value resistor in series with the integration capacitor. The effect of the resistor is to introduce a small pedestal voltage on to the integrator output at the beginning of the reference integrate phase (Fig. 6). By careful selection of the ratio between this

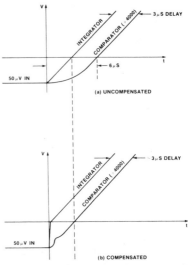

Figure 6: Integrator and comparator outputs for uncompensated (a) and compensated (b) system.

resistor and the integrating resistor (a few tens of ohms in the recommended circuit), the comparator delay can be compensated and the maximum clock frequency extended by approximately a factor of 3. At higher frequencies, ringing and second order breaks will cause significant non-linearities in the first few counts of the instrument.

NOISE

The peak-to-peak noise around zero is approximately 20 μV (pk-to-pk value not exceeded 95% of the time). Near full scale, this value increases to approximately 40 μV.

Since much of the noise originates in the auto-zero loop, some improvement in noise can be achieved by putting gain in the buffer. Pin 10 of the 8052 brings out the inverting input, so this is easily done. A gain of about 5X is optimum. Too much gain will cause the auto-zero switch to misbehave, because the amplified Vos of the buffer will exceed the switch operating range.

A low-noise version of the analog chip (8052-LN), using Bifet technology, should reduce the noise to about 3 μV pk-to-pk and even less with some gain in the buffer.

APPLICATIONS CIRCUITS

Individual applications circuits are given in the product data sheets. For reference, they are summarized below:

8052/8053 Data Sheet:
General circuit for DVM family
16 Bit binary converter
4¾ Digit DVM
4½ Digit DVM (parallel BCD)
4½ Digit DVM (multiplexed display)
8052/7101 Data Sheet:
3½ Digit LCD DPM/DVM
3½ Digit parallel BCD data acquisition system
8052/7103 Data Sheet:
4½ Digit A/D Converter
Simple 7103 to UART Interface
Complex 7103 to UART Interface
IM6100 Microprocessor to 7103 Interface
M6800 Microprocessor to 7103 Interface
Intel 8080 Microprocessor to 7103 Interface

Hybrid and Monolithic Data Conversion Circuits

Eugene L. Zuch, Datel Systems, Inc.

The first data conversion circuits made their debut over 20 years ago. Early devices, while achieving respectable performance even by today's standards, were quite bulky and expensive. And of course vacuum tubes were the active circuit elements. The development of the diffused planar transistor set the stage for the emergence of solid state data converters which quickly evolved into the form of compact modules. These modules were alone in the market for many years until in the late 1960's when the first hybrid and monolithic devices were developed. These early microelectronic devices, while leaving much to be desired in performance, nevertheless represented an important change.

The first hybrid data converters were 8 bit thick film D/A converters which were soon followed by 8 bit thin film devices. The first monolithic data converter was the μA722 circuit, a 10 bit D/A converter building block, introduced in 1968. The circuit consisted of a zener reference, 10 switched current sources, and a reference control amplifier but required an external resistor network. This device exhibited a 600 nsec. switching speed, and had 8 bit accuracy over a temperature range of 0 to 55C.

QUAD CURRENT SWITCHES

The first "quad current switches" were introduced two years after the μA722 and were an excellent conceptual and technical approach to a practical data converter building block circuit in monolithic form. These devices are now available in several circuit variations from different manufacturers and are used extensively in hybrid data converters. The basic circuit concept is illustrated in Figure 1.

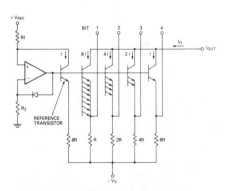

FIGURE 1. Basic Quad Current Switch Circuit

There are four NPN current source transistors and a reference transistor as shown in the diagram. The bases are all connected to a common line, and the reference transistor together with an operational amplifier form a reference control circuit which biases all of the current sources. A precision, trimmed resistor network is used to set the currents in the sources in the binary ratios of I, 2I, 4I, and 8I. To

achieve optimum tracking with temperature, the transistors are diffused with emitter areas in the binary ratios 1, 2, 4, 8, resulting in identical current density in each transistor. The transistors, therefore, have very closely matched base emitter voltage drops, and these voltages track each other with temperature change. The transistors also have matched betas with the base currents, therefore, also tracking each other.

In addition to the transistor matching which gives tight tracking characteristics, the stability of the circuit is also determined by the resistor network. This external network is generally a stable thin film nichrome device which has excellent absolute stability and tracking characteristics.

The current source collectors all connect to a common line which is the output current of the 4-bit device. Several quad current switches may be used together to achieve higher resolution. Each current source is switched on and off by current mode switching as shown in the current switching cell of Figure 2. When the digital output is low, current is sinked from the input diode which turns Q_2 off and the current source Q_1 on.

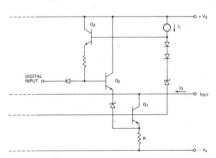

FIGURE 2. Detail Circuit of Quad Current Switching Cell

This particular circuit configuration gives standard TTL input voltage levels and results in a 40 nsec. switching time with a current output settling time of about 200 nsec. to 0.01%.

HYBRID D/A CONVERTERS

High performance 12 bit D/A converters are made possible by combining quad current switches with a precision zener reference, reference control amplifier, a thin-film resistor network, and a fast output operational amplifier as shown in Figure 3.

Three quad current switches are used with a current dividing resistor network at the outputs of two of the quads. With respect to QCS no. 1 output, QCS no. 2 output is divided down by a factor of 16 and QCS output no. 3 is divided down by a factor of 256. Due to the excellent accuracy characteristics of the quad current switches, resolutions of 12 bits and higher may be realized in this manner.

The output amplifier is a fast monolithic op amp which operates as a current to voltage converter from the current

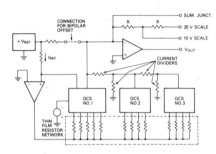

FIGURE 3. 12 Bit Hybrid D/A Converter Circuit

outputs of the quad switches. The reference control amplifier is connected differently from the one shown in Figure 1. By having the control amplifier drive the negative rail of the current sources, better immunity against negative supply voltage variations is achieved while not affecting the TTL input logic levels.

The circuit of Figure 3 is the basic design for Datel Systems' DAC-HZ12B series of high performance 12 bit D/A converters. Because of the quad current switch circuit configuration the input coding for this device is complementary binary, i.e., all zero's on the inputs produce a full scale output voltage and all one's produce zero output voltage. This coding can be changed to straight binary by using external digital inverters. In the case of the DAC-HK12B series D/A converters an internal level-controlled storage register is provided for storing a digital input word, and an inversion is done in the register to give straight binary coding.

By adding a fourth quad current switch to the circuit shown in Figure 3, additional resolutions of 13 to 16 bits can be attained. True 16 bit linearity is generally not possible, however, but a more practical specification of 16 bit resolution with 14 bit linearity is achievable over a reasonable temperature range. This performance is realized by Datel Systems model DAC-HP16B which has a companion model DAC-HP16D for 4 digit BCD applications.

An important feature designed into 12 bit hybrid D/A converters is the useful pin-programmable voltage output ranging. This is done, as shown in Figure 3, by providing a tapped feedback resistor for use with the output amplifier. The feedback resistor can thus be connected as R, 2R, or R/2 to give three possible voltage ranges. Another resistor is provided in series with the reference to permit offsetting the analog output by one half scale for bipolar operation. The final result of this is five useful output voltage ranges: 0 to +5V, 0 to +10V, ±2.5V, ±5V, and ±10V, all by simple pin connection.

Two of the primary advantages of the new hybrid D/A converters are their completeness (requiring no extra components for operation) and their operating flexibility, both at relatively low cost.

THIN FILM RESISTOR NETWORKS

Modern, low cost hybrid D/A converter designs are based on two premises: a standard circuit design with relatively few circuit components, and high volume production. The quad current switches significantly reduce the number of active circuit components required. In a similar manner thin-film resistor networks greatly reduce the number of passive circuit elements. The thin-film resistors are also an

important factor in determining the converter absolute temperature stability, tracking stability, and long term stability. When properly fabricated, these resistors result in excellent stability, surpassing that achievable in all but the most expensive discrete component converters.

The fabrication of good quality thin film resistors is a process involving many important operations. The following manufacturing steps are based Datel Systems' electron beam evaporation technique of making nickel-chromium thin-film resistor networks:

1. Oxidation of silicon substrate to form dielectric layer.
2. Deposition of nichrome thin film (<100Å) by electron beam evaporation.
3. Evaporation of barrier layer of nickel onto nichrome film.
4. Photolithographic definition and gold plating of conductor pattern.
5. Photolithographic definition and etching of resistor pattern.
6. Stabilization bake.
7. Photolithographic definition and etching of scribing grid pattern.
8. Chemical vapor deposition of silicon dioxide passivation layer.
9. Photolithographic definition and etching of bond pad openings over conductors.
10. Scribing and dicing wafer.
11. Test, inspection, and sorting of networks.

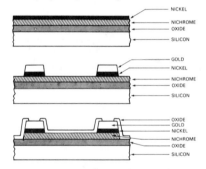

FIGURE 4. Summary of Steps in Making A Nichrome Thin-Film Resistor

Figure 4 summarizes some of the steps described above in processing a thin film resistor network. A starting three inch silicon wafer is shown together with a completely processed wafer in Figure 5; approximately 70 resistor networks are contained on this wafer. Each finished, tested resistor network is then bonded to the converter substrate.

FIGURE 5. Blank Silicon Wafer and Finished Resistor Networks

The substrate is made of alumina (AlO$_2$) and is itself a thin film component which is photolithographically defined and then electro-chemically plated with gold. Datel Systems uses thin film substrates in its hybrid products while some other companies use thick film. The main advantage of the thin film substrates is in the fine line widths which can be attained, resulting in more complex circuits. Figure 6 shows a magnified substrate mask for a 12-bit D/A converter; this conductor pattern has line widths down to 4 mils.

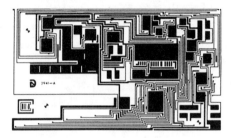

FIGURE 6. Substrate Mask (2.3 times Actual Size)
Hybrid A/D Converter

The next step in the hybrid circuit fabrication is interconnection of the resistor network with the other circuit components. This is done, at Datel Systems, by ultrasonic, thermocompression ball banding of gold wires between the bond pads. For optimum reliability the wire bonding is always between a substrate conductor and a component bond pad. Figure 7 shows a cross section of a finished hybrid circuit. A ball bond is shown on the chips whereas a wedge bond is used on the substrate.

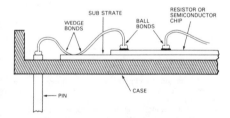

FIGURE 7. Cross-Section of Finished Hybrid Circuit

RESISTOR LASER TRIMMING

The next step in the manufacture of the hybrid converter is the functional laser trimming of the thin-film resistor network, illustrated in Figure 8. A pulsed Xenon laser trimmer is used to rapidly trim the resistors which control the most significant bit currents. The converter circuit is operated under power in a test fixture located underneath the laser beam. The trimming is observed in a magnified image on a TV monitor while the circuit operation is measured with an oscilloscope and DVM. Resistor values are initially low, and as the laser cuts away a portion of the metal film the value increases until the correct reading is obtained on the digital voltmeter.

The laser makes a precise 0.3 to 0.6 mil wide cut through

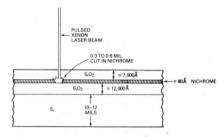

FIGURE 8. Laser Trimming a Thin-Film Resistor

the nichrome film as illustrated in Figure 8, which shows detailed dimensions of the resistor. The resistor trimming results in quad switch currents which are in the required binary ratio with each other within very close tolerance. The trimming compensates for any mismatches, as in the base emitter voltage drops for example, and results in optimum linearity of the finished converter. The trimmed current sources must have binary ratioed values within a tolerance of ±0.01% cumulative for a 12 bit converter.

It should be noted that the completed thin-film resistor is completely passivated by a 7000Å (approximately) layer of silicon dioxide. This prevents any chemical or moisture contamination of the resistor, and together with the stabilization bake performed earlier in the processing, results in excellent long term stability. When the resistor is laser trimmed the passivation layer is not affected and remains intact as shown in the illustration. This is so because the oxide layer is transparent to the wavelength of the laser light. Therefore, the laser beam passes directly through the oxide layer until it strikes the nichrome layer which is vaporized.

The nichrome resistors made in this way have absolute temperature coefficients from zero to 30 ppm/°C while achieving tracking tempcos of only 1 to 2 ppm/°C. Such tracking results in converters which have monotonic operation over a wide operating temperature range. The highest performance A/D and D/A converters are monotonic to 12 bits over a −55°C to +125°C operating range. Figure 9 shows a finished 12 bit hybrid D/A converter.

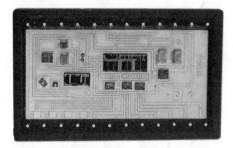

FIGURE 9. Finished Hybrid 12 Bit D/A Converter

VOLTAGE REFERENCES

One of the advantages of the hybrid microelectronic circuit design is that, like discrete component circuits, optimum components (in chip form) can be combined to achieve a given circuit design goal. This flexibility does not yet exist with monolithic circuits because of the different processes required for different types of optimum components.

A critical element in data conversion circuits is the voltage reference circuit; upon this the stability of the entire circuit depends. The reference governs, in large part, the gain stability of the circuit with both time and temperature. In the past, reference circuits generally used a compensated surface zener diode. New hybrid and monolithic circuits generally employ one of two newer reference devices: a compensated, buried (subsurface) zener diode or a bandgap voltage reference.

The buried zener exhibits both lower noise and better long term stability than the older surface zeners and as a result is becoming quite popular. Since avalanche breakdown occurs below the surface of the silicon in the bulk region, the noise and instability of the surface type zener are avoided. The breakdown voltage of the zener itself is about 5.6 volts and has a positive change with temperature of about 2 mV/°C. To compensate this, a forward biased PN junction diode is fabricated in series with the zener. Since the junction diode has a negative change of 2 mV/°C, finished devices can be tested and selected for tempcos as low as 5 ppm/°C.

A commonly used reference circuit employing a compensated buried zener reference and an operational amplifier is shown in Figure 10. The amplifier is used to both supply a constant current through the Zener reference and to buffer its output for voltages higher than the zener voltage. Another output can be taken from the zener, but is an unbuffered output.

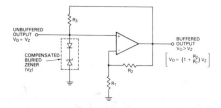

FIGURE 10. Temperature Compensated Reference Circuit

Datel Systems' DAC-HZ12BMR-1 uses such a low tempco, compensated, buried zener reference to achieve a low 10 ppm/°C gain stability over a −25°C to +85°C operating temperature range.

Another reference circuit now used in many devices, particularly monolithic data converters, is the "bandgap reference." This circuit is based on the predictable base emitter voltage change of a transistor with temperature. By using two matched transistors operating at different current densities, a stable reference voltage numerically equal to the extrapolated bandgap voltage of silicon at 0°K is achieved. This voltage is 1.205V, but in some reference circuits it is multiplied up to about 2.5V. The bandgap reference in general has not achieved the stability of the new buried Zener references, however.

One circuit which employs the bandgap reference is Datel Systems' model ADC-MC8B, an 8 bit monolithic A/D converter which can also be used as a D/A converter. The advantage of the +2.5V bandgap reference is that the entire circuit can operate from a single +5V logic supply.

SUCCESSIVE APPROXIMATION A/D CONVERTERS

The most direct approach to analog to digital conversion is using a D/A converter in a digital feedback loop as shown in Figure 11. The loop is closed at the analog comparator which compares the current output of the D/A converter against the input current developed by the analog input voltage. This comparison is made one bit at a time, and the method is, therefore, known as the successive approximation technique.

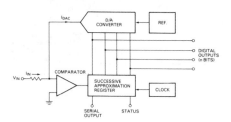

FIGURE 11. Successive Approximation A/D Converter

A clock circuit steps the converter through n comparison steps, where n is the resolution of the converter in bits. In the first clock period the D/A converter's MSB (most significant bit) output, which is one half of full scale, is compared against the input. If it is smaller than the input, the MSB current is left on and in the next clock period the next largest bit is turned on. If the MSB current is larger than the input, in the next clock period it is turned off when the next bit current is furned on. The D/A converter output at any given time is the cumulative total of all the previous bit currents which have been left on.

The comparison process is continued one bit at a time from the MSB down to the LSB (least significant bit). After the last clock period, the output of the successive approximation register contains the digital word representing the analog input. The converter also puts out an end of conversion, or status, pulse indicating that conversion is complete. In addition to the parallel data output on n digital lines, there is also a useful serial output from most converters derived from the comparison process.

The successive aproximation A/D converter with up to 12 bits resolution is made possible in hybrid form by three recent developments:

1. availability of low cost monolithic quad current switches in chip form
2. availability of low cost monolithic successive approximation registers in chip form
3. availability of fast laser trimming systems for trimming thin film resistors

The first two developments drastically reduced the number of individual monolithic chips necessary to fabricate a complete hybrid A/D converter. The third development made rapid and inexpensive trimming of the complete converter possible.

The development of the monolithic SAR (successive approximation register) was particularly significant since it eliminated a large number of digital chips. The SAR is really a special purpose digital register that contains all the storage and control logic to perform the successive approximation operation. In hybrid data converters the low parts count is extremely important for several reasons. First it reduces parts cost and labor, thus allowing the device to be produced economically in large quantities. Secondly it results in high reliability by reducing the number of total interconnections in the device. Compared to a modular converter, for example, the hybrid has less than half the total number of connections. A module, in addition to the bonds in each circuit component, has at least the same number of soldered connections.

An important advantage in the new hybrid A/D converters, in addition to low cost and small size, are the "universal operating features." Some of the operating features which result in application flexibility are:

1. Pin programmable input voltage ranges of 0 to + 5V, 0 to + 10V, ± 2.5V, ± 5V, and ± 10V.
2. Buffered (100 megohm) or unbuffered input.
3. Parallel and serial output data.
4. Short cycled operation (for less resolution at higher speed) by external pin connection.
5. Voltage reference and clock circuit outputs.

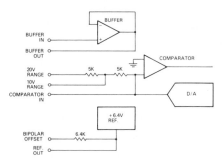

FIGURE 12. Hybrid A/D Converter Input Circuit

Some of these features are illustrated in the input circuit diagram of Figure 12. The comparator input has a tapped resistor which can be connected for input resistance values of 2.5K, 5K, or 10K, giving three different voltage ranges. If the bipolar offset pin is connected to the comparator summing junction, then the input is offset by one half scale to give bipolar operation with each of the previous voltage ranges. If high input impedance is required, the auxiliary buffer amplifier can be connected ahead of the input resistors. It should be noted, however, that the settling time of the amplifier must then be added to the conversion time of the A/D converter. The buffer output must have settled to within ±½LSB (0.012% for 12 bits) of final value before the A/D conversion cycle can be initiated.

Another way to use the buffer amplifier, if it is not used in the input circuit, is to buffer the reference output for use with external circuitry. In this way the reference can drive up to ±5 mA externally without affecting the temperature coefficient of the zener reference. External circuitry can, therefore, be made to track with the A/D converter over time and temperature.

Datel Systems' models ADC-HX12B, ADC-HZ12B, ADC-HS12B, and ADC-HF12B are all high performance hybrid 12 bit A/D converters which use the successive approximation conversion technique. Conversion times vary with these devices from 20 μsec. down to only 2 μsec.

FAST AND ULTRA-FAST HYBRID DATA CONVERTERS

A typical hybrid 12 bit A/D converter, for example the low cost ADC-HX12B, has a conversion time in the area of 20 to 25 μsec. There are some limitations in trying to achieve shorter conversion times with the circuitry just described. The limitations are in the comparator switching time and in the output settling time of the quad current switches. For accurate conversion to 12 bits, each bit output current must settle to within 0.01% of full scale before the next comparison takes place.

One of the factors that inhibits the comparator switching time and the D/A converter output settling time is the stray capacitance from the thin film resistors to the substrate conductor. Since the resistors are fabricated on a silicon wafer, this capacitance is significant because of the rather high (12) dielectric constant of silicon. The total stray capacitance seen at the QCS emitters and collectors, and also at the comparator input, significantly increases the time required for settling and switching.

One way to achieve higher conversion speed is to reduce this unwanted capacitance by fabricating the resistor network on glass instead of silicon. Glass has a dielectric constant of 4, much less than that of silicon. A nichrome thin film resistor on glass is shown in Figure 13. This nichrome-on-glass resistor network is used in Datel Systems' ADC-HZ12B 12 bit hybrid A/D converter to achieve a 12 bit conversion in 8 μsec. maximum.

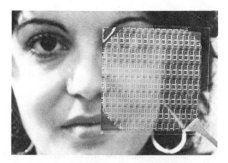

FIGURE 13. Nichrome Thin Film Resistor on Glass

For faster 12 bit conversions another circuit technique must be used. There are basic limitations in the switching speed of quad current switches which cannot be further reduced. A faster technique is to use individual PNP switched current sources as shown in Figure 14. Here all the current sources are of equal value and drive a low impedance R-2R ladder network; the impedance at every junction in the ladder is identical. The key to very fast settling time is to use higher currents driving low impedances. In addition, since each current source is switched by a single diode connected to the emitter, the switching delays are very small.

The result of the circuit of Figure 14, when used as a

D/A converter, is a current output settling time of less than 50 nsec. for 12 bit resolution. This circuit is used in Datel Systems' ultra-fast D/A converters, the DAC-HF series. As

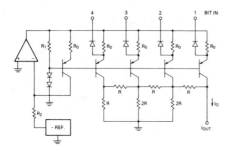

FIGURE 14. Ultra-Fast Current Output D/A Converter

with the other circuits, here the R-2R ladder network is also laser trimmed for optimum linearity. For ultra-fast 12 bit A/D conversion this D/A converter circuit can be used with a fast comparator and monolithic SAR to achieve a 2 μsec. conversion time (Datel model ADC-HF12B).

Although in lower resolution A/D converters such as 8 bit units it is possible to achieve sub-microsecond conversion times, for the ultimate in conversion speed it is necessary to employ a technique other than successive approximation. This other technique is known as the parallel, or flash, method and is illustrated in Figure 15.

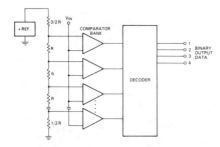

FIGURE 15. Parallel (Flash) Type A/D Converter

The parallel technique basically eliminates the n clock steps required for a complete conversion by the successive approximation converter. A bank of 2^n-1 analog comparators

8 LINE OUTPUT								BINARY OUTPUT				
1	1	1	1	1	1	1	1	1	0	0	0	OVERRANGE
0	1	1	1	1	1	1	1	0	1	1	1	
0	0	1	1	1	1	1	1	0	1	1	0	
0	0	0	1	1	1	1	1	0	1	0	1	
0	0	0	0	1	1	1	1	0	1	0	0	
0	0	0	0	0	1	1	1	0	0	1	1	
0	0	0	0	0	0	1	1	0	0	1	0	
0	0	0	0	0	0	0	1	0	0	0	1	
0	0	0	0	0	0	0	0	0	0	0	0	

TABLE I Digital Outputs for 3 Bit Parallel Converter

form an input quantizer with trip points set one LSB apart by the resistor biasing network and reference. For a given analog voltage applied to the input of the converter, all comparators biased below the input voltage will turn on and all biased above the input voltage will remain off. The logic output from the comparators is not very useful since it is a 2^n-1 line "thermometer" type scale as shown in Table 1 for a 3 bit parallel converter with an overrange bit. Therefore, a fast decoder circuit is used to convert this logic output into binary code.

The advantage of the parallel type A/D converter is that the complete conversion takes place in just two steps: the comparators switch state and the decoder switches state. With new high speed logic circuits this can be done in typically 15 nsec. The limitation is in the resolution that can be achieved with a reasonable number of comparators. The practical limit is a 4 bit converter which requires 2^n-1, or 15 comparators. The number of comparators is limited by physical placement, power consumption, and the total bias current which cumulatively flows through the resistor biasing network.

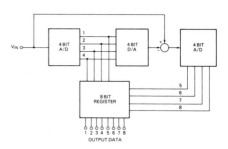

FIGURE 16. Eight-Bit, Two Step Parallel A/D Converter

To achieve 8 bit resolution, two 4 bit converters are used in a two-step approach shown in Figure 16. The first 4 bits are converted and the digital output goes to an ultra-fast 4 bit D/A converter which converts the result back to analog. The resultant analog voltage is then subtracted from the input voltage and this difference is converted into digital form by a second 4 bit parallel converter. The complete 8 bit digital word is held in an output register. Since the two steps occur at different times, the next first step can be performed while the result of the previous first step is held in the register and the second step is being done. This overlap mode of operation gives a faster conversion rate than would otherwise be possible.

The advantage of this two stage conversion is that just 30 comparators are required by the two 4 bit parallel converters as compared with 255 if a single stage 8 bit converter were used. The disadvantage is that some speed is sacrificed in the process; nevertheless, speeds as high as 20 MHz are achieved for an 8 bit conversion.

Datel Systems' HU series devices are hybrid building blocks for ultra-fast parallel type A/D converters. This is a new and very useful approach to ultra-high speed conversion since building block series may be connected in different ways to achieve a desired purpose. The ADC-HU3B is a 3-bit parallel A/D converter which is expandable. Two of these connected together make a 4-bit A/D and four connected together make a 5-bit A/D. Used as a single stage, they have a 50 MHz conversion rate.

For a two stage converter, the DAC-HU4B is an ultra-fast 4 bit D/A converter which operates directly from a 15 line input from a 4 bit A/D. Another device in this series is the SHM-HU, which is an ultra-fast sample hold for use with the ADC-HU3B.

MONOLITHIC CIRCUIT FABRICATION

Monolithic techniques have made outstanding progress in the past few years. Monolithic technology, rather than relying on a variety of different components, must rely on devices that can be readily made monolithically. The circuit design rules, therefore, have been to minimize resistors, capacitors, etc. and rely on transistors, making use of the inherent advantages of close matching, excellent thermal coupling, and the economy of using large numbers of active devices with various device geometries. The engineering ingenuity used in maximizing the use of active components has resulted in monolithic circuits which schematically look quite different from their discrete equivalents. For example, the monolithic design for an operational amplifier is quite different from a discrete-design op amp.

Monolithic circuits which are available at the present time use one or more of the following technologies: bipolar, CMOS, ion implantation, TTL, I²L, and thin film deposition. Recent progress has permitted the combination of two or more of these technologies in a single circuit, for example, bipolar and CMOS, bipolar and ion implanted FET's, and bipolar and I²L. The difficulty in making monolithic data conversion circuits has been in combining linear circuitry with digital circuitry and including precision, stable resistors.

Monolithic techniques achieved notable and rapid success with operational amplifiers, but with data conversion circuits the progress has been slower due to the above mentioned problems. Therefore, the first monolithic converters were simple 8 bit D/A converters without a reference or output amplifier. Recent progress, however, has permitted 10 and 12 bit D/A converters to be fabricated. A/D converters made with monolithic technology have been largely restricted to dual slope and charge balancing types, but some successive approximation devices are now becoming available. At the present time most monolithic data converters require a number of external parts, for example references, op amps, comparators, clock circuits, capacitors, and resistors. In spite of these limitations, monolithic circuits generally offer the lowest cost solution to a data conversion problem, and many of the earlier limitations are now being overcome.

Figure 17 illustrates two basic monolithic techniques used in data conversion circuits. The first device (Figure 16a) is a standard diffused planar NPN transistor which is the key component in monolithic bipolar circuit design. It is fabricated in the following basic steps, starting with a P type silicon wafer:

1. Photolithographic definition and diffusion of N+ buried layer. This is required to create a low collector resistance.
2. Growth of N type silicon epitaxial layer.
3. Isolation masking and diffusion (P+ type).
4. Photolithographic definition and diffusion of base region (P type).
5. Photolithographic definition and diffusion of emitter region (N+ type).
6. Photolithographic definition and evaporation of metallization layer (Aluminum).
7. Testing, dicing, and sorting of devices.

The second device is a CMOS transistor pair. These devices are formed by successive diffusions in the same manner as the NPN transistor described above. The basic differences are that the initial wafer is N type silicon and the devices themselves are unipolar transistors. One device is a P-channel MOS transistor and the other is an N-channel MOS transistor. The insulation underneath each of the two metalized gates is a stable field-oxide layer.

An important element in monolithic data converters is the resistor. Stable resistor networks are the basis for accurate and stable data conversion. For lower resolution converters, namely up to 8 bits, diffused resistors are commonly used. The diffused resistor is the most economical type to use since it requires no additional processing steps beyond those already required for a monolithic circuit. A typical diffused resistor is shown in Figure 18; it is formed by the bulk resistance of a P-type base diffusion. The value of this resistor is determined by the sheet resistivity of the diffusion and the length and width of the resistor:

$$R = Rs\ L/W$$

where Rs is the sheet resistivity.

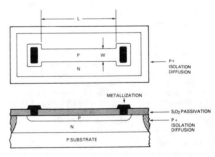

FIGURE 18. Detail of Diffused Resistor

The temperature coefficient of these resistors is large, approximately 1500 ppm/°C from 0°C to 125°C. Fortunately converter performance depends more critically upon the matching and temperature tracking of resistors than on the absolute temperature coefficient. The matching of diffused resistors to 0.5% or better and temperature tracking to 100 ppm/°C or better can be achieved in monolithic circuits.

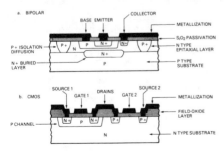

FIGURE 17. Bipolar and CMOS Monolithic Devices

The limit on using diffused resistors is generally 8 bits, although 10 bit resolution has been achieved by use of resistors with laser trimmed aluminum links. Diffused resistors, however, are no match for thin film resistors which can give less than 30 ppm/°C absolute tempco and 1 to 2 ppm/°C tracking tempco. Therefore, most 10 bit and higher resolution monolithic converters have the additional operations of depositing, photolithographic etching, and laser trimming of a thin film resistor network on part of the monolithic chip.

MONOLITHIC CONVERTER DESIGNS

A common design used in 8 bit monolithic D/A converters is shown in Figure 19. A series of collector switched NPN current sources is used with a diffused R-2R ladder network. The ladder network is connected to the emitters as shown, in order to minimize the total number of resistors; in this way only two resistors per bit are required and they have just two different values, R and 2R. Matching and tracking of the resistors is thereby simplified.

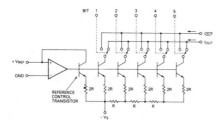

FIGURE 19. Bipolar D/A Converter with Diffused Resistor Network

A reference amplifier and reference control resistor are used to bias the current sources from an external reference voltage. Some circuits steer the collector outputs to two separate output lines which are analog logic complements of one another and are useful in a number of ways, including driving an output amplifier in push-pull.

The circuit of Figure 19 is used in Datel Systems' DAC-08B 8 bit D/A converters; these have 85 nsec. output settling time and high voltage compliance outputs (−10 to +18V). In another Datel Systems model, the DAC-IC8B, the complemented collector output is not brought out but is internally tied to the positive supply voltage. Resolution is 8 bits, and output current settling time is typically 300 nsec. An extension of this device to 10 bits resolution is model DAC-IC10-BC which uses identical circuitry but uses laser link resistor trimming of the higher order bits.

Another popular D/A conversion method uses CMOS circuitry with a precision R-2R thin-film ladder network. This circuit, illustrated in Figure 20, is particularly well suited to multiplying applications where a variable reference voltage is used. The key to multiplying operation with high precision is the low resistance CMOS switches which are in series with high resistance 2R resistors. A feedback resistor is also provided for use with an external operational amplifier. This resistor is also provided for use with an external operational amplifier. This resistor has an identical tempco with the ladder resistors since they are fabricated in the same network and, therefore, the output voltage tempco

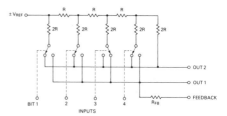

FIGURE 20. A CMOS Multiplying D/A Converter

depends on the tracking tempco rather than the absolute resistor tempco.

A detailed circuit of the CMOS switch is shown in Figure 21. It is composed of two N channel MOSFET's which are driven out of phase with each other so that one switch is on while the other is off. The switches are driven by two CMOS inverters as shown.

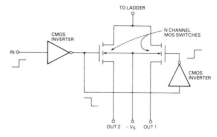

FIGURE 21. Single Pole, Double Throw CMOS Switch

This technique is used to make both monolithic and hybrid multiplying D/A converters. The advantage of a 2 or 3 chip hybrid design is that higher accuracy can be attained, with resolutions up to 14 bits. Such devices are Datel Systems' DAC-HA series, composed of 10, 12 and 14 bit multiplying D/A converters.

Monolithic A/D converters have been much more difficult to make than D/A converters, especially for resolutions higher than 8 bits. This has been particularly true for successive approximation type A/D converters where two semiconductor technologies must be combined with thin film resistor technology. The combination that looks particularly promising in the near future is the combination of bipolar linear circuitry with I²L digital circuitry and the use of nichrome thin-film resistors on the same chip.

Given the greater difficulty of making a high resolution successive approximation A/D converter in monolithic form, it is not surprising that another technique was used first. This technique is the dual slope method, which has been popular for many years in discrete component form. It is illustrated in Figure 22 and operates on an indirect conversion principle whereby the unknown input voltage is converted into a time period which is then measured by a counter.

The conversion cycle begins by switching the operational integrator to the input voltage, which is then integrated for a

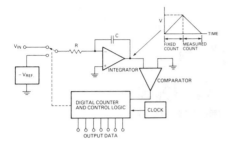

FIGURE 22. Monolithic Dual Slope A/D Converter

fixed time period. After this time, the integrator is switched to a reference voltage of opposite polarity and the integrator output integrates back to zero for a period of time which is measured by the counter. The resultant count is then the digital value of the input voltage. The important thing about the dual slope technique is that the accuracy and stability are dependent only on the reference, and not on other components in the circuit. This assumes, of course, that the operational integrator is linear. The technique is both simple and effective and is readily implemented with CMOS circuitry. Some devices also incorporate automatic zeroing circuitry to reduce the effect of offset drift with time and temperature.

The advantages of dual slope conversion are simplicity, accuracy, and noise immunity due to integration of the input signal. The chief drawback is relatively slow conversion time. Dual slope A/D converters are most commonly used in digital panel meters, digital multimeters, and other digital measuring instruments.

Another integrating conversion technique which has gained in popularity recently is the charge-balancing A/D converter. As illustrated in Figure 23, an operational integrator is enclosed in a digital feedback loop consisting of a comparator, pulse timer circuit, and a switched reference. A positive input voltage causes the integrator output voltage to cross zero volts, which is detected by the comparator and triggers the pulse timer circuit. The output pulse from the timer switches a negative reference current to the integrator input, and this current pulse is then integrated, causing the integrator output to increase in the positive direction. Therefore, every time the integrator output crosses zero another pulse is generated and integrated.

A state of equilibrium exists when the average current developed by the pulses just equals the input current. Since each current pulse is a fixed amount of charge, the name "charge-balancing" is appropriate.

If a counter is used to count the output pulses from this circuit for a fixed period of time, the circuit is then a complete A/D converter. This technique, implemented by bipolar and CMOS circuitry, is used in Datel Systems' ADC-EK series A/D converters which consist of 8, 10, and 12 bit binary devices and a 3½ digit BCD unit. If a counter is not used with the circuit then the device is the well known V/F (voltage to frequency) converter. Model VFQ-1 is a low cost monolithic V/F converter which also uses bipolar and CMOS circuitry on the same chip.

OTHER DATA ACQUISITION CIRCUITS

The devices described so far have been A/D and D/A converters. In addition to these, there are a number of other circuits which are commonly used in data acquisition applications. These circuits include sample-holds, analog multiplexers, operational and instrumentation amplifiers, and filters. All of these devices are also available in either monolithic or hybrid form; many of these products are described in the pages of this brochure.

Frequently, these various devices are combined together to make a complete "data acquisition system." Such a system has an input analog multiplexer, an instrumentation amplifier (sometimes), a sample-hold, an A/D converter, and the required control logic circuitry. These systems take care of the entire signal processing function from multiple analog inputs to the digital output which connects to a computer data bus line.

Such a system is also now available in a single hybrid package. This device is Datel Systems' model HDAS-16 and a companion device, model HDAS-8. The HDAS-16 provides 16 channels of analog multiplexing, an instrumentation amplifier with programmable gain from 1 to 1000, a sample-hold, a 12 bit A/D converter, three state output bus drivers, and all the required control logic. The HDAS-8 is identical except that it contains an 8 channel differential multiplexer. This complex hybrid circuit is fabricated on two interconnected substrates and is shown in the photograph of Figure 24.

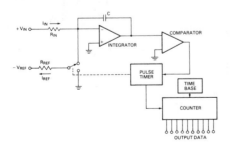

FIGURE 23. Charge Balancing A/D Converter

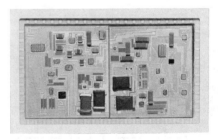

FIGURE 24. Photograph of Hybrid 12 Bit, 16 Channel Data Acquisition System

by Eugene L. Zuch
Datel Systems Inc.

an industry standard
Hybrid 12-Bit
A/D Converters

Analog to digital converters interface analog signals to digital computers and other digital control circuits. In the world of data converters the moderate speed, low cost 12-bit A/D converter is a real workhorse, serving in a broad range of applications from data acquisition systems and pulse code telemetry systems to computer-based process control systems, automatic test systems and other sampled-data systems.

System designers often require that an A/D converter provide 12-bit conversion with conversion times between 8 and 50 microseconds. Along with these basic specifications go a few other accepted parameters such as ±½ least significant

bit linearity and temperature coefficient between about 20 and 40 parts per million per degree Celsius. Twelve-bit resolution yields what most designers consider precision measurement: relative accuracy of 0.012% with 0.012% linearity.

The 0.012% accuracy figure, equal to ±½ bit accuracy, results from quantization uncertainty. Other factors such as nonlinearity, gain and offset temperature coefficients and long term drift degrade the 0.012% ideal accuracy figure. Also, the overall error budget for the complete analog portion of the external circuit may include an amplifier, analog multiplexer or sample-hold. Hence the use of a 12-bit A/D

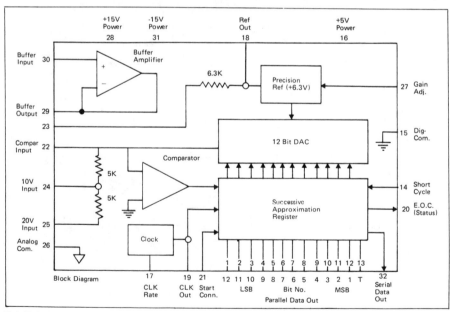

Fig 1 Block diagram shows the internal structure of a typical 12-bit hybrid analog-to-digital converter. Pin connections shown are in a standard configuration.

converter commonly results in an overall system accuracy of 0.1%.

The development of monolithic and hybrid IC technology produced dramatic changes in data conversion device technology. In the past, 12-bit A/D converters of the successive approximation type came in a standard 2"x4"x0.4" encapsulated modular package. Manufactured by a number of companies and costing between $120 and $200 each, these units still enjoy wide use.

The first moderate cost, hybrid 12-bit A/D converters, introduced in 1974, were followed by a number of devices made by different manufacturers, all housed in a standard 32-pin package with two basic pin configurations. Such standardization has been rare in the industry. Three factors weigh heavily in making these devices popular industry standards: low price (many cost less than $100), small size (about 1.1"x1.7"x0.2") and universal operating features that allow them to serve in a wide variety of applications.

These converters are quite a contrast with earlier units of equivalent performance; such units sold for $5000 in 1959 and $600 in 1968 and were considerably larger. Hybrid data converters in themselves are not really new devices since they first appeared on the market in the late 1960s, but until recently they were not produced as standard products in large volume. Early hybrid converters served in military and aerospace application where small size and high reliability were overriding considerations, and low price was not. The circuitry at that time, much more complex than today's circuitry, gave very high chip counts and relatively low production yields.

Fig 2 This A/D converter, manufactured by Datel Systems, employs thin-film hybrid technology to provide 12-bit conversion.

TABLE I HYBRID 12 BIT A/D CONVERTER SPECIFICATION SUMMARY	
Resolution	12 Bits
Nonlinearity	±1/2 LSB (0.012%)
Gain Tempco	±20ppm/°C max.
Analog Input Ranges	0 to +5V, 0 to +10V
	±2.5V, ±5V, ±10V
Coding, unipolar	Comp. Binary
Coding, bipolar	Comp. Offset Binary
Conversion Time	20 μsec. max.
Power Supply	±15VDC & +5VDC

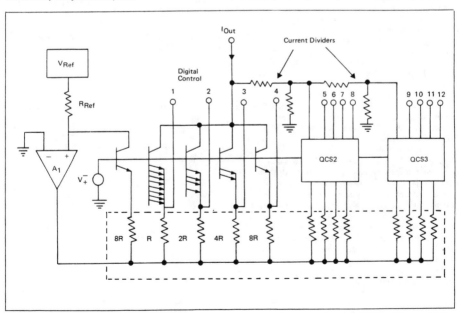

Fig 3 Quad current switches play an important role in the operation of the converter. In this circuit diagram, teh QCSs and the current divider resistors form a network providing proper current source binary weighting.

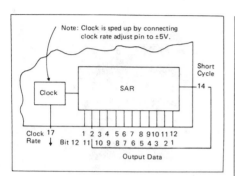

Fig 4 **External pin connections allow faster A/D conversion with lower resolution. The connection shown gives 10-bit conversion. Connecting the short cycle to ground gives full resolution (12-bit) conversion.**

Design and Operation

Several recent developments have allowed a significant reduction in number of chips required to implement a successive approximation register, and these technological advances have brought on the low cost hybrid converter. These developments include: the availability of low cost, quad current switches used to implement the converter portion of the circuit; the development of the monolithic successive approximation register; and the rapid laser trimming systems for actively trimming thin-film resistor networks.

The resulting low component count makes high yield production of a standard converter design a reality; since parts count and labor are reduced, production costs drop. In addition, reducing the parts count also reduces the number of wire bonds, thereby increasing reliability.

Fig 1 shows the block diagram of a complete 12-bit hybrid device and Fig 2 shows one such device. The circuit basically consists of a 12-bit D/A converter inside an analog/digital feedback loop. The successive approximation register (SAR) controls the converter and in turn takes inputs from the clock circuit and analog comparator. A precision low drift voltage reference circuit stabilizes the converter.

Operation of the A/D converter is straightforward. The analog input voltage connects to one of the input resistors (either directly or through the buffer amplifier at, for example, pin 25). The analog comparator compares the current flowing through the input resistor with the D/A converter's output current. A start pulse to the SAR initiates the conversion cycle, turning on the first bit (most significant bit) of the converter. This current is compared with the input current. If the MSB current is less than the input current, the MSB current is left on and in the next clock period the second bit is turned on. If the MSB current is greater than the input, it is turned off, and the second bit turned on in the next clock period.

This comparison sequence continues through all twelve bits until the cumulative total of all bit currents left on has been compared with the input current. The digital output of the SAR (which is also the input to the D/A converter) is then the digital output word equivalent to the analog input voltage. This output word is held in the SAR's output

register until initiation of the next conversion cycle. The conversion is thus completed in 12 clock periods.

Construction and Technology

The quad current switches (QCS) play an important role in the implementation of the converter (see Fig 3). Three QCSs connect to give 12 weighted currents that are summed together at the output of the circuit. The first QCS with its four weighted current sources and reference current source is shown in detail in Fig 3. The other two QCSs are identical except that their reference current sources are not used.

The voltage reference circuit sets up a constant current in the reference transistor which is controlled by amplifier A_1. By means of the reference current source, all 12 current sources are biased by maintaining a constant voltage from the transistor bases at the negative voltage rail. The biasing is independent of supply voltage variations. The voltage reference circuit consists of a low tempco compensated zener reference and an op amp circuit that maintains constant current through the zener reference.

Weighting the emitter resistors R, 2R, 4R and 8R weights the currents in the NPN transistor current sources in binary ratios of 8, 4, 2 and 1. In order that the currents track each other closely over a wide temperature range, the NPN transistors are diffused with emitter areas in binary ratios of 1, 2, 4 and 8, giving the same current density in each transistor. This identical current characteristic gives closely matched base-to-emitter voltage drops that track each other with temperature.

To get exact binary weighting of the current sources out to 12 bits, QCS2 and QCS3 both operate into precision current dividers that divide the QCS current outputs by factors of 16 and 256 respectively (compared with QCS1).

Thin-film technology. To ensure the stability of the A/D converter, the emitter, reference and current divider resistors are all fabricated in a single thin-film resistor network and then laser trimmed to the required accuracy. The resulting resistors have absolute temperature coefficients between zero and thirty parts per million/°C. Trimming the resistors while

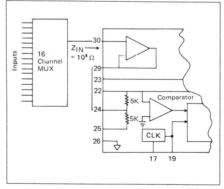

Fig 5 **This circuit multiplexes slowly changing signals without sample-hold. A throughput rate of 77 KHz can be achieved with ±1 least significant bit accuracy. This circuit multiplexes up to 16 channels. The converter's buffer amp provides it with a high-Z load.**

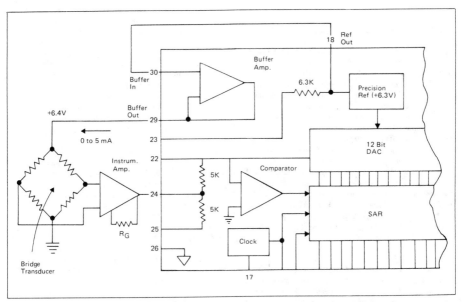

Fig 6 This circuit will provide accurate and stable measurements for computer usage. Because A/D converter's internal buffer amplifier is not used, the amplifier can drive the transducer bridge from the converter's reference.

the converter is powered and running allows you to achieve a linearity specification of ±½ least significant bit.

Universal Operating Features

Certain features appear in hybrid D/A converters that make them industry standards. These features became an important 'design goal after their appearance in some of the modular converters on the market a few years ago.

Pin-programmable input ranges. Hybrid A/D converters provide six usable input ranges: 0 to +5V, 0 to +10V, 0 to +20V, ±2.5V, ±5V and ±10V. You can obtain the first three of these ranges by various connections of the two 5KΩ input resistors; in addition, if pin 22 is connected to pin 23, an offset current derived from the internal reference is applied to the comparator input, offsetting the converter's range by exactly half-scale to give bipolar (positive/negative input) operation.

Internal buffer amplifier. This operational amplifier is connected as a unity gain follower and has an input impedance of typically 10^8 to $10^9 \Omega$. Externally pin-connecting the amplifier ahead of the input resistors increases the converter's input impedance from the normal range (2.5KΩ to 10KΩ depending on how the range-setting resistors are connected) to over $10^8 \Omega$.

This high input impedance does not come without strings attached — the 0 to +20V input range cannot be used since the amplifier's maximum input and output voltage ranges are ±10V. Also, the conversion time of the A/D converter is increased by the settling time of the buffer amplifier. A little thought about the operation of the successive approximation converter reveals that the output of the buffer ampli-

fier must have settled to within ±½ least significant bit of final value before the A/D conversion cycle can be initiated. In some applications the settling time may not alter the conversion rate since the input amplifier can be settling to a new value during the time that the output of the A/D converter is being transferred out.

Short cycling capability. You can terminate the conversion cycle at less than 12 bits via external pin connection, resulting in a faster conversion time with less resolution. Speeding up the conversion time is also helped by speeding up the clock rate through an external connection. This method works because lower resolution requires less settling time at the output of the D/A converter.

Fig 4 shows how to effect short cycling. The short cycle terminal (pin 14) of the SAR is externally connected to the N+1 output bit for an N-bit conversion. The figure shows the connection for a 10-bit conversion. For a full resolution 12-bit conversion the short cycle pin is connected to the +5 volt logic supply.

To speed up the clock rate, connect the clock rate input (pin 17) to an adjustable positive voltage. This voltage should be +5V for 10-bit conversion and +15V for 8-bit conversion. These changes result in reductions in conversion time of 25% for 10 bits and 50% for 8 bits (compared to 12-bit conversion time).

Choice of output codes. You can choose complementary binary, complementary offset binary or complementary two's complement. Use of unipolar operation requires the first code; for bipolar operation, you can select either complementary offset binary or complementary two's complement codes by using either the most significant bit output or the complemented most significant bit output from the converter.

Precision reference voltage output (pin 18). This output permits referencing external circuitry to the internal voltage reference in order to give identical tracking of the A/D converter and external circuits with both time and temperature. This results in stable ratiometric operation of the measurement, but the reference output must be buffered by a high impedance amplifier and hence cannot drive other circuits directly. 10 microamps can be drawn from the reference itself. One way you can buffer the reference uses the internal buffer amplifier, if your application does not require the amplifier at the A/D converter input.

Clocked serial output (pin 32). This serial output occurs during the conversion cycle and is synchronized with the clock (pin 19). The serial output format is most significant bit first, nonreturn to zero with either complementary binary or complementary offset binary coding. The serial output can aid in digital data transmission over long distances and in pulse code telemetry. Together with the clock output, the serial output can help align the converters since the codes are readily observed on an oscilloscope.

Applications

Fig 5 shows an application that requires multiplexing of slowly changing signals without sample-hold. The circuit shown will multiplex up to 16 channels. Since the multiplexer may have a channel resistance between 250Ω and 2KΩ, the multiplexer must see a very high impedance at its output. The converter's buffer amplifier can provide this high impedance load.

If you use a hybrid A/D converter with an 8 microsecond conversion time and allow multiplexer buffer amplifier

settling time of 5 microseconds, you can realize a throughput as high as 77 KHz. The system will be accurate to ±1 least significant bit for up to 5 Hz input signal frequency.

Fig 6 shows a typical measurement application where the measured value must be fed to a digital computer. The differential output of a transducer bridge is amplified by the instrumentation amplifier before being fed to the A/D converter input. Since the instrumentation amplifier buffers the bridge output with its high input impedance, you don't need the internal amplifier for input buffering. The amplifier can then drive the transducer bridge from the converter's internal reference. The buffer amplifier typically draws 125 nA bias current from the reference and provides up to 5 mA output current to the bridge.

This circuit arrangement achieves the most stable measurement results over time and temperature. In the circuit, as the internal reference changes, the magnitude of the input signal changes. The converter operates ratiometrically, providing error cancellation for reference changes.

Figure 7 shows the circuit connection for a sampling 10-bit A/D converter. A 12-bit hybrid A/D with 8 µsec conversion time is short cycled to 10-bit operation. This is done by connecting the short cycle terminal, pin 14, to pin 2, the bit 11 output. Pins 3 through 12 then serve as data outputs with complementary offset binary coding. The input to the A/D converter is connected for ±5V bipolar operation.

Ahead of pin 24 is a sample-hold circuit (which is a monolithic device) that samples the analog input and provides high impedance buffering. This sample-hold requires a 1000 pF holding capacitor, and with this value acquires a 10 volt input change in 4 µsec. The sample control pulse is therefore set to 4 µsec width.

After the sample control pulse returns to zero, putting

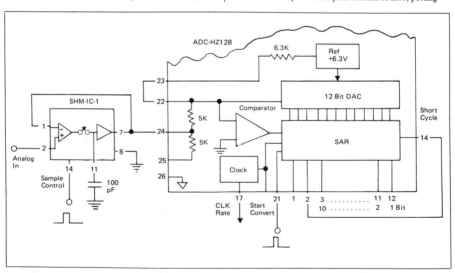

Figure 7 shows the circuit connection for a sampling 10 bit A/D converter. A 12 bit hybrid A/D with 8 µsec conversion time is short cycled to 10 bit operation. This is done by connecting the short cycle terminal, pin 14, to pin 2, the bit 11 output. Pins 3 through 12 then serve as data outputs with complementary offset binary coding. The input to the A/D converter is connected for ±5V bipolar operation.

GLOSSARY
OF TERMS

Absolute Accuracy: The output error, as a percent of full scale, referenced to the NBS standard volt.

Charge Balancing A/D Converter: A type of A/D Converter that uses a closed loop integrator with a switched current at its input to exactly balance the current produced by the input signal.

Conversion Time: The time from when a conversion is initiated until the output digital data, representing the analog input value, is ready.

Differential Linearity: The maximum deviation of the analog transition between any two adjacent codes in an A/D converter from the ideal value. This quantity is generally expressed as a fraction of a least significant bit.

Dual Slope A/D Converter: A type of A/D converter that operates by the indirect method of converting a voltage input to a time period, using an integrator, and then measuring the time period by a clock and counter.

Error Budget: A detailed list of all sources of error in a system or circuit to determine overall accuracy.

Gain Error (or Scale Factor Error): The difference in slope between the actual transfer function and the ideal transfer function, generally given in percent.

Linearity (or Integral Linearity): The maximum deviation of the A/D converter's transfer function from an ideal straight line between its end points. It is generally given in percent of full scale or fraction of a least significant bit.

Missing Code: The phenomenon of skipping one or more of the sequence of output codes over the total analog input range.

Offset Error: The amount by which the A/D converter transfer function fails to pass through the origin, generally given in millivolts or percent of full scale.

Parallel A/D Converter (or Flash Converter): A type of A/D converter that uses a bank of 2^n-1 comparators and a decoder circuit to perform ultra-fast conversions.

Quad Current Switch (QCS): A monolithic circuit which employs four matched, switched current sources and a reference current source to achieve 4 bit D/A conversion.

Quantizing Error (or Quantization Uncertainty): The inherent uncertainty associated with digitizing an analog signal by a finite number of digital output states. The ideal A/D converter has a maximum quantizing error of $\pm 1/2$ least significant bit.

Reference: A circuit providing an accurate, stable voltage used as the standard for comparison in an A/D converter.

Relative Accuracy: The output error of an A/D converter as a percent of its full scale value.

Resolution: The smallest analog input change an A/D converter can distinguish. This is a function of the number of output states, 2^n, where n is the number of bits and is generally expressed in number of bits or in percent.

Successive Approximation Register (SAR): A digital circuit that controls the operation of a successive approximation A/D converter and accumulates the output digital word in its register.

Settling Time: In a D/A converter or an amplifier, the time elapsed from the application of a full scale input step to when the output has entered into and remained within a specified error band around its final value.

Short Cycling: Termination of the conversion sequence of an A/D converter to less than the total number of clock periods required for a full resolution conversion.

Status Output: An output logic state indicating when the A/D converter is busy and when output data is ready.

Successive Approximation A/D Converter: A popular type of A/D converter in which conversion is accomplished by a sequence of n comparisons where n is the number of resolution bits.

Temperature Coefficient: The stability with temperature of the scale factor of the A/D converter, generally expressed in parts per million per degree Celsius.

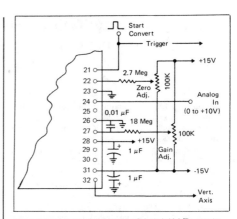

Figure 8 illustrates simple calibration of the hybrid A/D converter. Two external 100K Ωpotentiometers adjust zero and full scale for the converter.

the sample-hold circuit into the hold mode, a 100 nsec start convert pulse is applied to the A/D converter after a 1 µsec delay. The 1 µsec delay allows the sample-hold output to settle from its turn-off transient so that this does not cause a conversion error. The 10-bit A/D conversion then takes place and is completed in just 6 µsec. The clock rate is increased by 20% by connecting the clock rate, pin 17, to ±5V. This, in addition to short cycling, reduces the conversion time from 8 µsec at 12 bits to 6 µsec for 10 bits.

The time required for sampling, delay, and conversion is therefore about 11 µsec, giving a maximum throughput rate of 90 KHz. Such a circuit is commonly used in fast data acquisition systems.

The sample-hold circuit reduces the aperture, or measurement uncertainty, time of the circuit. With the A/D converter alone the measurement time is 6 µsec, but with the sample-hold this time is reduced to about 5 nsec. This sampling A/D converter can thus accurately sample signals as fast as 70 kHz.

Figure 8 illustrates simple calibration of the hybrid A/D converter. Two external 100KΩ potentiometers adjust zero and full scale for the converter. A pulsed start convert pulse is applied to the start convert input and also externally triggers an oscilloscope. The converter output code is simply monitored by displaying the serial output together with the clock output on the vertical axis of the scope. There are 13 clock pulses and 12 intervals that show up as HI's or LO's on the scope.

Assuming 0 to ±10V input range, the input pin 24 should first be connected to a precision voltage source set to +1.2 mV (zero + 1/2 LSB). The zero adjust potentiometer is adjusted to give an output code that just flickers between 1111.....1110 and 1111.....1111. Next, set the precision voltage source to +9.9963V (+FS - 1 1/2 LSB) and adjust the gain potentiometer to give an output code that just flickers between 0000.....0000 and 0000.....0001.

The converter is now precisely aligned and gives a quantization error of ±1/2 LSB maximum. ⅅⅅ

Video analog-to-digital conversion

calls for virtuoso performances. And the plot
really thickens when you have to produce high resolution.

Accurately digitizing analog signals containing high frequencies, demands ultrahigh-speed, or video, a/d converters. Such a converter is essential to diverse uses like radar-signature or transient analysis, high-speed digital-data transmission, video densitometry, and digital television. In television alone, a speedy converter can help enhance images, correct time-base errors, convert standards, synchronize or store frames, reduce noise, and record TV.

Most video a/d converters work in the 1-to-20 MHz range. But at these speeds, resolution can be a problem. Fortunately, 8 bits and fewer most often suffice in ultrafast a/d applications.

Higher resolutions are hard (and expensive) to come by, particularly at 10 to 20 MHz. In this ultrahigh-speed range, 4 bits is about the practical limit for a single-stage converter. However, you can cascade a/d stages for more than 4 bits.

Below 5 MHz, you can retain the "one bit at a time" concept of the familiar successive-approximation converter, while reducing the time delays inherent in converting each bit. The "propagation" (or variable-reference-cascade) converter of Fig. 1 does just this.

Comparators star in propagation a/d's

The critical parts of the circuit are the comparators, which must be very fast, and the switches, which must be not only very fast but also capable of withstanding the reference voltage. A propagation a/d converter uses one comparator per bit. Furthermore, each bit is converted in sequence, beginning with the most significant. With a −5 V reference, the circuit of Fig. 1 handles inputs from 0 to +10 V.

Comparator A_1 makes its decision at a +5 V input: when the analog-input voltage exceeds +5 V, the output is true. The threshold of comparator A_2 is set for an input of either +2.5 or +7.5 V, depending on the output of comparator A_1. If the analog input voltage exceeds +7.5 V, comparator A_2 also goes true. If, however, the analog input voltage is between +5 and +7.5 V, the output becomes ZERO; an input

Table 1. Comparator thresholds for a 4-bit propagation-type a/d converter

Scale	Comparator Number			
	1	2	3	4
FS−1 LSB			+8.750	+9.375
				+8.125
3/4 FS		+7.500		
			+6.250	+6.875
				+5.625
1/2 FS	+5.000			
			+3.750	+4.375
				+3.125
1/4 FS		+2.500		
			+1.250	+1.875
1 LSB				+0.625

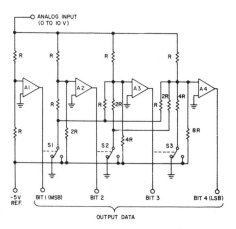

1. **A propagation-type a/d converter** uses one comparator per bit, with each bit converted in sequence. At best, this type of a/d runs at 5 MHz for up to four bits.

Eugene Zuch, Product Manager, Datel Systems, 1020 Turnpike St., Canton, MA 02021.

between +2.5 and +5 V produces a ONE. And for less than 2.5-V input, the output becomes ZERO.

As you can see, then, the output of comparator A_1 sets the threshold of comparator A_2 via electronic switch S_1. S_1 switches one end of the resistive divider at comparator A_2 to ground when the output of comparator A_1 is ZERO, and to the -5 V reference when it is ONE. Therefore, the threshold of the second comparator is set for either of two analog-input-voltage levels: +2.5 or +7.5 V.

This process continues for comparators A_3 and A_4. Each succeeding threshold is set by the result of all previous comparator decisions. Thus, comparator A_3 has four possible threshold levels, +1.25, +3.75, +6.25, or +8.75 V. Similarly, comparator A_4 has eight possible threshold levels (for a summary of each comparator's threshold levels, see Table 1).

Obviously, a propagation-type converter becomes more complex as its resolution increases beyond 4 bits. Higher resolution requires not only more resistors—to set the new threshold levels—but also higher-value resistors. The resistor values go up in a 1, 2, 4, 8,...binary sequence. So as the number of bits increases, the resistors soon take on values so large as to affect the conversion time for the less-significant bits. The fault lies with slow settling of the currents switched through the resistors. The time constants, caused by switch plus stray capacitances and the high-value resistors, cause the delays.

Still, you can achieve 50-ns per bit conversions with a propagation-type converter. After a new input is applied to the converter, the resulting digital output word propagates rapidly down the converter-output lines, as each comparator and switch change states. Instead of simply allowing the circuit to propagate naturally, you can also operate it in a clocked mode by using sampling (gated) comparators, rather than the usual ungated kind.

But 5-MHz and higher conversion rates, together with the complexity required for higher than 4-bit resolution, severely limit the video uses of propagation-type analog-to-digital converters.

Quantizer plays the lead

Fortunately, a much faster technique is available. Parallel conversion (also called flash, or simultaneous)

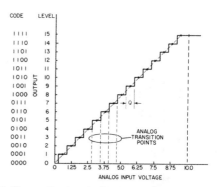

2. **The quantizer transfer function** for a 4-bit parallel-type converter shows how the analog input is broken into 16 different levels. Each word of digitally coded output signals represents a range, Q, of input voltage.

is more popular because it is faster than propagation. A parallel-type a/d converter is simply a quantizer circuit followed by a decoder circuit. As a matter of fact these two functions are fundamental to all a/d converters. The difference is that these functions are clearly separate in a parallel a/d.

The quantizer section of a parallel converter is defined by its transfer function, which is shown for a 4-bit quantizer, in Fig. 2. The quantizer breaks up the continuous-analog input (horizontal axis) into discrete-output levels (vertical axis).

In Fig. 2, the output is divided into 16 different states, or 2^n levels, where n is the number of bits. Along the horizontal axis of the transfer function are 2^n-1 or 15 analog-transition points which represent the voltage levels that define the edges between adjacent output states or codes.

There is no one-to-one correspondence between input and output for the quantizer, which assigns one output code word to a small range, or band, of analog-input values. The size of this band is the quantum, Q, and is equal to the full-scale-analog range divided by the number of output states:

$$Q = \frac{FSR}{2^n}$$

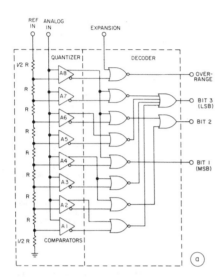

3. **The circuit for a parallel 3-bit a/d converter** (a) has just two basic sections: the quantizer and the decoder. The transition points in the quantizer are set by biasing each comparator, through a resistive divider and reference. The complete 3-bit analog-to-digital converter comes packaged as a thin-film hybrid (b).

In Fig. 2, where the full-scale-input range is 10 V,

$$Q = \frac{10}{2^4}$$

$$= \frac{10}{16}$$

$$= 0.625 \text{ V}.$$

Fig. 2 snows levels of 0 through 15 at the output. When binary-code words are assigned to these output states, as shown in the leftmost column, the transfer function becomes that of a complete a/d converter rather than just a quantizer alone.

Table 2. Parallel 3-bit a/d coding

Scale (fraction of full scale)	7-Line equally weighted code with overrange	Binary code
+9/8	11111111	1000
	01111111	0111
+3/4	00111111	0110
	00011111	0101
+1/2	00001111	0100
	00000111	0011
+1/4	00000011	0010
	00000001	0001
0	00000000	0000

The binary codes are assigned by a circuit that decodes the quantizer-output logic. Though you can select any code, the code shown, natural binary, is most used. Notice that the analog center of each code word—the exact analog value—is depicted by a dot on the transfer-function graph.

The transfer function in Fig. 2 depicts an ideal quantizer or a/d converter. A real device, of course, has errors in offset, scale-factor (gain) and linearity.

Fig. 3 shows a circuit implementation of a 3-bit parallel a/d converter. Usually, the quantizer portion of such a circuit consists of a bank of $2^n - 1$ high-speed comparators. But, in Fig. 3, 2^n or 8, comparators are used, because this circuit also provides an overrange output that can be used for expansion.

The bank of comparators has 2^n analog-transition points. These are directly set by biasing one side of the comparator inputs from a reference with a series string of equal-value resistors, R. The Q for this circuit depends on the value of R, the reference voltage, and the total resistance:

$$Q = (V_{REF}R)/R_{TOTAL.}$$

The bottom and top resistors in the string have values of R/2, which correspond to the values of the first and last analog-transition points. These transitions are at Q/2 and FS −(Q/2), respectively.

Without the overrange output, the last analog transition point would be at FS − (3Q/2). The value of the top resistor would then be 3R/2.

Enter the decoder

The parallel converter's decoder section is a rather straightforward logic circuit. It translates the logic outputs from the comparators into the most commonly used code, natural binary.

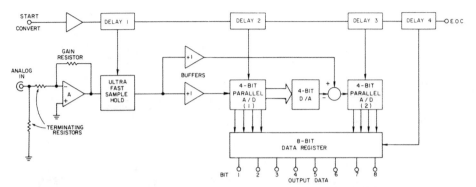

4. Two-stage parallel a/d converters can develop 8-bit resolutions at 20 MHz. Though conversion 1 begins at the Start-Convert pulse and ends 65 nanoseconds later, subsequent conversions take only 50 nanoseconds.

Table 2 shows the coding for quantizer and decoder outputs. In this quantizer-output code, the seven comparator-output lines (eight, counting the over-range comparator) are equally weighted. This equally weighted code is simple and unambiguous, but inefficient—only one output line changes at a time from all-ZERO to all-ONE outputs. Except for not being cyclical, the quantizer code is like the Johnson code used in shift counters. Like the quantizer code, Johnson code proceeds from all-ZEROs to all-ONEs, but then cycles back to all ZEROs.

In the decoder, simple NOR and OR gates perform the logic according to the following equations:

Bit 1 = A_4
Bit 2 = A_6 + $A_2 \cdot \overline{A_4}$
Bit 3 = A_7 + $(A_5 \cdot \overline{A_6})$ + $(A_3 \cdot \overline{A_4})$ + $(A_1 \cdot \overline{A_2})$,

where the A_n's are the numbered-comparator outputs in Fig. 3, Bit 1 is the MSB and Bit 3 is the LSB. The AND function in the equations is replaced by a NOR in the actual circuit. The OR function can be implemented by tying together the appropriate outputs of wire-ORed ECL logic.

With ultrafast analog comparators, parallel conversion offers the ultimate conversion speed. Since the comparators all change state simultaneously, the quantizer output is available after just one propagation time. Of course, the decoder adds more delay, but high-speed Schottky-TTL or ECL circuits can minimize the decoding time.

In 3-bit form with an additional comparator, for overrange, the parallel converter in Fig. 3 can be expanded for higher resolution. You can connect two converters, combine into one flash converter to get often-needed 4-bit resolution. Likewise you can connect four such circuits for 5-bit resolution—and so forth. In this way, these circuits can be used as "building blocks" for ultrafast a/d converters. Conversion rates of 50 MHz, for 3, 4, or 5-bit a/d's, are possible using the commercial hybrid version of these expandable parallel converters.

Comparator plays a complex role

The most critical component in a parallel a/d converter—as in a propagation converter—is the comparator. It not only determines the speed of the converter but also the accuracy. Ultrafast sampling comparators like the 685, 686 and the dual 687 are excellent for this function.

A sampling comparator has two Latch-Enable inputs that switch it into either a Compare or Latched mode. In the latter, the comparator's digital output is locked until the next comparison is made.

Whether or not you use a sampling comparator, you must consider the propagation delay for small overdrive. This is important because the analog full-scale-signal range is generally small for ultrafast a/d converters—commonly between 1 and 4 V. The comparator must change state rapidly for a Q/2 analog-input change. For a 4-bit converter with a 1-V input range, this represents an overdrive of 31 mV; for an 8-bit converter with the same input range, the overdrive is just 2 mV.

The analog-input characteristics of a comparator are important because they affect conversion accuracy. Input-offset voltage and input-bias current are usually the most significant of these parameters. The offset voltage directly affects the accuracy of the quantizer's analog-transition points; the input-bias current also affects the accuracy through the effective input resistance of the comparator.

Since an ultrafast comparator generally has bias currents as high as 10 μA, its inputs must look into low resistances. Fortunately, for small-signal ranges like 1 to 4 V, each resistance in the series network can be kept low. In an actual 3-bit parallel hybrid

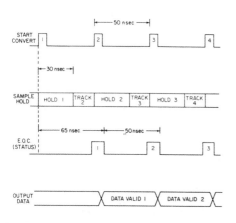

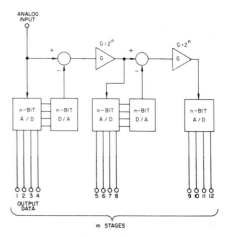

5. **Timing for the 8-bit two-stage a/d converter** allows for two modes in the sample-and-hold circuit—Hold and Track. These occur between successive Start-Converts. The second and succeeding conversions take 50 ns.

6. **A generalized n-bit, m-stage a/d converter** develops an output with n × m bits of resolution. In each stage, except the first, the analog result of the subtraction is amplified by a circuit whose gain is 2^n.

converter, laser-trimmed, thin-film-resistor networks make the transition points stable and accurate.

One comparator parameter that greatly affects speed is input capacitance. For example, the analog-input line to a 4-bit a/d with overrange feeds 15 parallel-comparator inputs. It must be driven from a low-impedance source to retain high speed. Therefore, either a high-speed input-buffer amplifier or a sample-and-hold circuit drives the input.

Parallel a/d conversion suffers from one significant drawback; more resolution than four bits requires many comparators. The number (N_c) increases exponentially with n, the number of bits:

$$N_c = 2^n - 1$$

An 8-bit converter, for example, requires 255 comparators. That many comparators vastly complicates bias-current and input-capacitance problems—to say nothing of the high power dissipation they produce. Another problem, of course, is how to position so many comparators while minimizing lead lengths.

Coming onstage—the two-stage a/d

As a result, the practical limit of parallel a/d converters is usually 4 bits. Higher-resolution designs use a two-stage parallel technique that is really a combination of the parallel and propagation techniques. It cascades two 4-bit conversions.

This two-stage method is illustrated in Fig. 4, which shows the block diagram of a complete 8-bit, 20-MHz converter, including buffer amplifiers and a sample-and-hold. Starting at the input, amplifier A termi-

nates the analog input with the proper impedance and scales the signal for the sample-and-hold circuit. During its conversion to digital form, the ultrafast sample-and-hold acquires and holds the analog-input.

The sample-and-hold output goes into two unity-gain buffer amplifiers, one of which buffers the input to parallel 4-bit a/d converter 1. This a/d converts the input level, then stores the digital result in half of the output-data register. In addition, 15 undecoded comparator-output lines drive a 15-line, equally-weighted digital-to-analog converter. This d/a, in turn, generates an analog voltage that is subtracted from the other buffered-input signal.

The subtraction result, a residual signal, goes to the input of the second parallel 4-bit a/d, the output of which goes to the other half of the output-data register. The input signal is therefore sampled and converted to digital form in two 4-bit steps.

Four digital delays time the converter as shown in Fig. 5. A pulse at the Start-Convert input begins the timing sequence. The Start-Convert pulse puts the sample-and-hold into the Hold mode for 30 ns. During this time, the first 4-bit conversion is made and the second 4-bit converter quantizes the residual signal. While the second parallel 4-bit a/d conversion is decoded and transferred to the data register, the sample-and-hold goes into the Track mode to acquire the next value.

When the conversion is done and the 8-bit word is ready in the output register, the delay circuit generates and End of Conversion (or Status) pulse. In the timing diagram, numbers 1, 2, 3 and 4 indicate the relationship of the signals for the first, second, third

Slower a/d converters are alive and well

The two most popular techniques for a/d conversion are dual-slope (a) and successive-approximation (b). Together these methods probably account for over 98% of all analog-to-digital converters in use.

Dual-slope conversion, an indirect method, converts the analog-input voltage into a time period. Then a digital clock and counter measure the interval. For only serial-output data, a simple gate replaces the counter. The method is simple, accurate, and inexpensive, but suffers one major drawback: Conversion is usually slow—often taking milliseconds.

Successive approximation a/d converters, on the other hand, can be much faster. They can convert to 12 bits in 2 to 50 μs and to 8 bits in 400 ns to 20 μs. Also, every conversion is completed in a fixed number (n) of clock periods, where n is the resolution in bits.

Successive-approximation, a direct method, puts a d/a converter inside a feedback loop containing both analog and digital elements. The successive-approximation register controls the d/a converter, and the comparator and clock, in turn, control the register.

A conversion consists of turning on, in sequence, each bit of the d/a converter, starting with the most significant. During each clock period, the analog input and the d/a output are compared. The comparison determines whether to leave each bit on or turn it off.

So, after n clock periods, each bit has been turned on, a comparison has been made, each bit's logic state has been decided and the conversion is complete. Clock periods usually last from just fractions of a micro-second to several μs. Each clock period must allow time for comparator switching, changing successive-approximation-register states and d/a converter switching plus settling. Settling time for the d/a converter takes a large part of the clock period because the output must settle to within half the least-significant bit before the comparison starts.

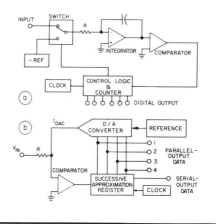

and fourth conversions. The delay from the leading edge of the Start-Convert pulse to the falling edge of the Status pulse is 65 ns—the delay for the first conversion. After the first conversion, new output data arrive every 50 ns—a rate of 20 MHz.

A two-stage parallel a/d converter is practically the only device used for ultrafast conversion at 8-bit resolution. Moreover, just about all new 8-bit converters have built-in sample-and-holds to shorten the effective aperture time of the conversion from the 50 ns of the converter in Fig. 4, to a fraction of an ns.

While the 8-bit a/d in Fig. 4 is functionally simple, it's actually difficult to develop. In fact, it usually takes longer to develop than today's other types of a/d's. More engineering time can go into just determining circuit and ground-plane layout than into any other part of the development.

Behind the scenes—a hybrid

At least one commercial 8-bit converter uses thin-film hybrid components as building blocks, which organize the critical-circuit functions into miniature packages. For example, each 4-bit a/d shown in Fig. 4 can be implemented with two hybrid 3-bit expand-able decoded a/d's. Also, the 15-line d/a converter, the sample-and-hold and the input-buffer amplifier can be readily hybridized. The remaining noncritical circuit elements can be made from standard monolithic devices and passive components.

The hybrid circuits' stable thin-film resistors can be laser-trimmed for optimum linearity. The entire circuit of Fig. 4 fits on a single circuit card, so laying out critical components is less formidable.

Propagation and parallel two-stage are specific examples of a more general conversion method by which m stages of n bits each, make an a/d converter with m × n bits of resolution (see Fig. 6). In each case, the residual analog signal from the subtraction is boosted for the next stage by an amplifier with gain of 2^n. This technique can produce a 12-bit a/d converter using three parallel 4-bit a/d stages.∎∎

Bibliography

Schmid, H., *Electronic Analog/Digital Conversions*, Van Nostrand Reinhold Co., New York, 1970.

Acknowledgement

The author wishes to acknowledge the contribution of James B. Knitter to this article in the form of helpful technical discussions with the author.

POWER D/A CONVERTERS USING THE IH8510

Dick Wilenken, Intersil Inc.

THE POWER D/A CONVERTER

Intersil has introduced a family of power amplifiers — the IH 8510 family. These power amplifiers have been specifically designed to drive D.C. servo motors, D.C. linear and rotary actuators, electronic orifice valves and X-Y printer motors. There are three versions presently offered — the IH8510 is specified at 1 amp continuous output with up to ±35V power supplies; the IH8520 is specified at 2 amps continuous output at up to ±35V; finally the IH8530 is a 3 amp version with the same power supply range.

The amplifiers are linear mode types and are basically a power version of the popular 741 differential op amp. The parts are available in 8-pin TO-3 packages. Using ±30V power supplies, the amplifiers are capable of delivering up to ±26V swings into a 10Ω load. The parts are biased Class AB, and have typical no-load quiescent current of 20mA. Frequency response, input offset voltage, input offset, and bias currents are the same as the 741 op amp. All three models can withstand indefinite shorts to ground on the output. When driving a D.C. motor, the amplifiers can also withstand the surges caused by motor lock-up and motor reversal (i.e., while running in one direction, the voltage is suddenly reversed).

The linear nature of these power amplifiers allows them to fit in very well with another Intersil product family — the D/A converter. Intersil has two low cost DAC's available — the 7520 series, and the 7105. When a DAC and a power amplifier are combined, one has a very useful building block for control functions, i.e., a digitally programmable power driver. This power DAC can interface directly with microprocessors, UARTS, computers, etc.

DESIGN DETAILS

A typical power DAC designed for 8 bit accuracy and 10 bit resolution is shown in Figure 1. The IH8510 power amplifier described in the introduction is driven by the Intersil 7520 monolithic D/A converter.

The 7520 contains the R/2R ladder network and the feedback resistor for proper scaling of the reference input voltage (±10V) and also the SPDT switches (CMOS) for each bit. Figure 2 shows a part of the system (first 4 bits). Note that a permanently biased "on" switch is in series with the 10KΩ feedback resistor. The $R_{DS(on)}$ of this "on" FET is 0.5 x $R_{DS(on)}$ of the Most Significant Bit (MSB) switch to maintain MSB accuracy (gain accuracy) at 25°C and over the temperature range. Since the FET switches are on the same I.C. chip, the temperature tracking is excellent. Actually, the 7520 specifies the temperature coefficient at 2ppm/°C maximum.

The circuit configuration is such that the SPDT switches in series with each 20KΩ resistor never see more than ±25mV; this minimizes DAC errors caused by $I_{D(off)}$ and $I_{D(on)}$ leakages. It also allows the DAC switch to handle ±10V references with only a single +15V power supply. The size of each DAC switch is scaled so that it does not distort the gain for each bit, i.e., the MSB switch $R_{DS(on)}$ is 25Ω; the next switch $R_{DS(on)}$ is 50Ω; the next is 100Ω, etc.

A summing amplifier is shown between the 7520 and the IH8510 in Figure 1. This apparently redundant amplifier is used to separate the gain block containing the 7520 on-chip resistors from the power amplifier gain stage whose gain is set only by external resistors. This approach minimizes drift since the resistor pairs will track properly.

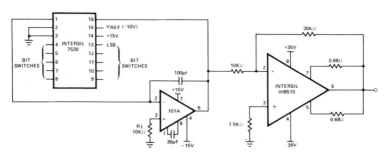

Figure 1:
The Basic Power DAC

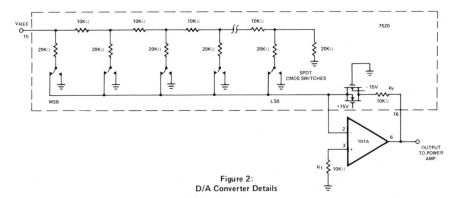

Figure 2:
D/A Converter Details

One of the decisions the user will have to make is the choice of summing amplifier. For 8 bit accuracy with 25 volt output swings, a ½ LSB is equivalent to approximately 50mV. The worst case errors introduced by the op-amp (i.e., the cummulative effects of I_B, and I_{OS}, and $\Delta V_{OS}/\Delta T$) should therefore be significantly less than 50mV.

In Figure 1 a 101A is shown. This amplifier meets the requirements outlined above. Over the military temperature range, the input bias current (average of the two input currents) is specified at 100nA maximum. The input offset current is given as 20nA maximum. Thus, in the worst case, one input bias current could be 110nA, the other one 90nA. Again, making the pessimistic simplification that R_1 = zero, that all the DAC switches are off, and that the higher of the two bias currents flows through the feedback resistor, the error due to input current equals 110 x R_f x 10^{-6}mV. Figure 3 shows this situation. The maximum value of R_f is not given in the 7520 data sheet, but in practice is around 15KΩ. The input current error (absolute worst case) therefore calculates out at 1.65mV. To this, one must add the effect of offset voltage drift. This amounts to a worst case of 1.5mV over the temperature range. The summation of these two errors is still an order of magnitude less than ½LSB in 8 bits, a comfortable safety margin. In fact, the 101A would be adequate for a 10 bit power DAC.

Performing the same calculations on a 741 over the military temperature range, the input current (worst case) error is

26mV, and the voltage drift (worst case) is 2.5mV. The latter number is an estimate since the 741 data sheet does not guarantee drift. It can be seen from these numbers that the 741 is marginal for this application. However a more detailed analysis, taking into account a non-zero value for R_1 (say 10KΩ), would show the 741 in a better light.

The initial offset voltage of the buffer amplifier adds to that of the IH8510, and is multiplied by three before appearing at the output. Depending on the application, it may be desirable to null out this offset. The nulling should be done at the buffer in the manner recommended for the amplifier being used.

In the majority of DAC applications, a full scale output adjustment is necessary. For example, set point controllers in servo systems are typically required to have an error no greater than 0.3% of full scale reading. This can be achieved by either adjusting the reference voltage up or down from a nominal 10.000V, or by using a potentiometer in the amplifier feedback network, as shown in Figure 4. The potentiometer should be a low temperature coefficient type.

A final important note on the 7520/101A interface concerns the connection between Pin 1 of the DAC and Pin 2 of the op amp. Remember this point is the summing junction of an amplifier with an AC gain of 50,000 or better, so stray capacitance should be minimized otherwise instabilities and

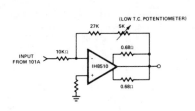

Figure 3:
Worst Case Error Due to Input Current

Figure 4:
Full Scale Gain Adjustment

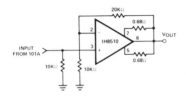

Figure 5:
Non-inverting Gain Connection

noise performance will result. Notice also that an in-
g gain stage follows the 101A output; this is to boost
ower DAC output to ±30V; thus a gain of −3 is used.
a non-inverting gain of +3 is desired, then the configuration
of Figure 5 should be used.

The 0.68Ω resistors from Pins 5 and 7 to Pin 6 are used to
set current limits for the power amp. These are safe area limiting structures which follow a definite V_{OUT}/I_{OUT} profile
This is shown in Figure 6.

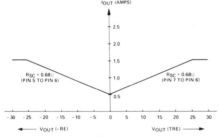

Figure 6:
Output Current Limiting

Notice that maximum output current is obtained when
V_{OUT} = +25V–30V, for either polarity of V_{OUT}; current
falls off as V_{OUT} decreases to limit the internal power dissipation. When driving 24V to 28V DC motors or actuators,
the power amp delivers full power. Since I_{OUT} is a maximum for this range, the internal power limiting does not
affect normal performance. For example, consider driving a
24V DC motor at 1.5 amps delivered current. The internal
power dissipation is (30V − 24V) x 1.5 amps = 9 watts.

Now the load is also taking 1.5 amps x 24V = 36 watts. The
amplifier efficiency = $\frac{36 \text{ watts}}{46 \text{ watts}}$ = 80%. Now, if the output
is mistakenly shorted to ground (through motor failure)
then $I_{OUT(max)}$ goes to 0.5 amps and the power dissipation
equals 30V x 0.5 amps = 15 watts. As long as the amplifier
is heat-sinked to dissipate this 15 watts, no damage will result
and proper performance will return when the fault is corrected. A significant advantage of the IH8510 family is that the
case is electrically isolated and is not tied to any pin. This
means that multiple IH8510's can be mounted on the same
heat sink.

The IH8510 family design is shown in Figure 7. It consists
of a 741 op amp driving a custom chip (called the IH8063).
The 8063 is a 60V circuit which boosts the voltage and current outputs of the 741 to drive internal power transistors.
It also contains plus and minus regulators to lower the ±30V
input voltages to ±15V for safe 741 operation.

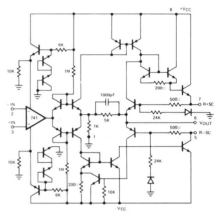

Figure 7:
IH8510 Schematic

COST OF THE POWER DAC SYSTEM

The complete, operational system is shown in Figure 4. At
the time of writing, the 7520 sells for $10 in small quantities,
and the 301A is in the 50¢ area. The IH8510 sells for $15
each in small quantities, so the system cost is as follows:

7520 DAC (Intersil)	$10.00
5KΩ 50ppm pot (full scale trim)	2.00
301A op amp (Intersil)	.50
100pF capacitors	.20
Miscellaneous resistors	1.10
0.68Ω 5 watt resistors	.50
IH8510 power amplifier (Intersil)	15.00
	$29.30

To obtain a D.C. reference for the DAC, one can buy a 10V
reference or use a circuit such as that shown in Figure 8.

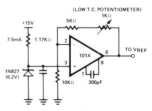

Figure 8:
Buffered DAC Reference

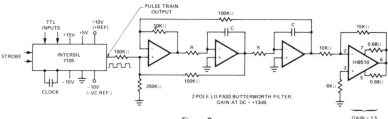

Figure 9:
Power DAC Design Using 7105 D/A

ANOTHER WAY TO BUILD
A POWERFUL D/A CONVERTER

Intersil will shortly introduce a D/A converter which operates on a new concept (no R/2R ladders or weighted resistors, etc.). Instead of dividing current or voltage into many small steps, the 7105 DAC divides time. The output configuration consists of a SPDT switch. A clock oscillator is provided, and data latches for the digital input. For a n-bit converter, in any 2^n consecutive clock pulses, the switch is thrown one way for a number of pulses corresponding to the input data and the other way for the remainder. Thus, if the switch is used to connect a reference voltage or current to an appropriate filter, the average output corresponds to the digital input as a ratio of the reference. The switching cycle is arranged so as to minimize the filtering required on the output; and hence optimize the settling time. By its very nature, this technique insures monotonicity and (except for two short sections near zero and full scale) excellent linearity. Other than the reference, no critical value components are needed, and the tolerance and temperature coefficients of the filter components affect only the settling time and ripple content. The main limitation of the converter is the relatively slow conversion rate. The technique does for D-to-A conversion what the dual-slope technique does for A/D conversion, that is it provides a slow but very accurate and stable conversion technique that avoids the use of high tolerance components.

A suitable interconnection between a 7105 D-to A converter and the 8510 power amplifier is shown in Figure 9. Note that two pole filtering is adequate for 8 through 12 bit converters, but three pole is required for optimum settling time on 14 and 16 bit devices.

APPLICATIONS

Motor Control

An important application for power D/A converters is in precision motor control systems (position controllers). Digitally controlled constant torque is best facilitated using the power DAC circuit shown in Figure 10. The desired torque is set by closing the appropriate DAC switches; this sets the DC output of the DAC. Torque is directly proportional to motor current, and the motor current is directly proportional to the voltage across R_S, i.e.,

$$\text{Torque} = KI_m = \frac{-KV_1}{R_S}$$

By setting the DAC input switches 2^0, 2^1, 2^2, etc., any desired torque can be obtained and a torque versus time profile can be established. Torque versus time profiles are important in controlling the acceleration and deceleration of motors and may be used to provide dynamic breaking for different load conditions. The digital control could be performed by a microprocessor or a programmable logic array such as Intersil's·IM5200 (Ref. 1).

Programmable Power Supply

Another big application for power DACs is the digitally controlled power supply. It is probably that the coarse and fine control adjustment knobs on power supplies will be replaced in the future by digit switches. With this, the user does not need to use a 3½ digit DVM just to set a power supply. An 8-bit power DAC allows the supply to be set instantly and provided remote control automatically. The practical problem one runs into here is the maximum load capacity the power DAC can drive without oscillating. Power supplies often use 0.1μF to 100μF decoupling capacitors to ground; this will cause most op amps to oscillate, including the 8510. The only answer for this application is to reduce the bandwith to gain C_L drive capability. Of course, the lower the bandwith, the bigger the value of C_L to keep the output impedance to a certain minimum value; thus there is a compromise involved here. This compromise is not unique to the 8510; the amplifiers in typical series pass regulators must also be designed to handle capacitance loads without misbehaving. Another possible solution is to isolate the amplifier output from the load by using a series inductor. Thus, when large decoupling capacitors to ground are used, the amplifier still sees at least the inductance as a load.

REFERENCE

1. Intersil Application Bulletin MB001, "Sequential Industrial Control Using the IM5200 FPLA" by John Nichols.

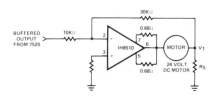

Figure 10:
Power DAC Driving DC Motor

The ICL7104
A Binary Output A/D
Converter for μProcessors

Peter Bradshaw, Intersil Inc.

1. INTRODUCTION

The ICL7104, combined with the ICL8052 or ICL8068, forms a member of Intersil's high performance A/D converter family. The 16-bit version, the ICL7104-16, performs the analog switching and digital function for a 16-bit binary A/D converter, with full three state output, UART handshake capability, and other outputs for a wide range of output interfacing. The ICL7104-14 and ICL7104-12 are 14 and 12-bit versions. The analog section, as with all Intersil's integrating converters, provides fully precise Auto-zero, Auto-polarity (including ± 0 null indication), single reference operation, very high input impedance, true input integration over a constant period for maximum EMI rejection, fully ratiometric operation, over-range indication, and a medium quality built-in reference. The chip pair also offers optional input buffer gain for high sensitivity applications, a built-in clock oscillator, and output signals for providing an external auto-zero capability in preconditioning circuitry, synchronizing external multiplexers, etc., etc. The basic schematic connections are shown in Figure 1.

The chip pair operates as a dual-slope integrating converter. The conversion takes place in three stages, each with the own configuration. In the first, or auto-zero phase (this is also the "idle" condition), the converter self-corrects for all the offset voltages in the buffer, integrator, and comparator. During the second, or input integrate phase, the converter integrates the input signal for a fixed time (2^{15} clock pulses for the -16 part, 2^{13} for -14, 2^{11} for -12). The converter the determines the (average) polarity of the input, and during the third, or deintegrate (alias reference integrate) phase integrates the reference voltage in the opposite polarity, until the circuit returns to the initial condition. This point is known as the zero-crossing, and terminates the conversion process. The time (number of clock pulses) required to reach zero-crossing is proportional to the ratio of the input signal to the reference. A more detailed discussion of the operation of the dual-slope converter, including the ICL8052-ICL7104 family, is given in Application Note A017 "The Integrating A/D Converter." Figure 2 shows the basic waveforms of the Integrator.

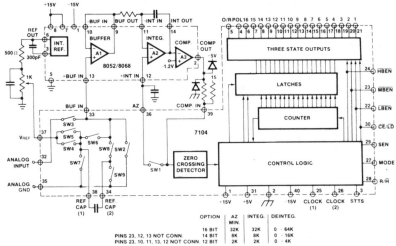

Figure 1: 8052A (8068A)/7104 16/14/12 Bit A/D Converter.

OPTION	AZ MIN.	INTEG.	DEINTEG.
16 BIT	32K	32K	0 · 64K
PINS 23, 12, 13 NOT CONN. 14 BIT	8K	8K	0 · 16K
PINS 23, 10, 11, 13, 12 NOT CONN. 12 BIT	2K	2K	0 · 4K

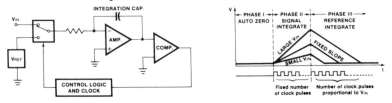

Figure 2: Simplified Dual-Slope Converter and the Three Phases of a Dual-Slope Conversion.

This application note will first cover the digital interface of the ICL8052(ICL8068)-ICL7104 chip pair to digital systems of various kinds, including microprocessors, using the three state output capabilities (covered in Section 2) and the handshake system built into the 7104 (Section 3). Finally, some (mainly) analog techniques to enhance the system performance in certain applications are covered in Section 4. An Appendix covers a normally undetectable but under some circumstances significant error generated in the auto-zero system.

2. DIGITAL INTERFACE
(Without Internal Handshake)

The output format of the ICL7104 is extremely versatile, and includes a full internal handshake capability, which is discussed in the next section. Here we will be concerned only with the "normal" three state output lines. To disable the handshake circuitry, the MODE pin (pin 27) should be tied low (to digital gnd).

In this mode, the most useful output-timing signal is the STaTuS (STTS) line (pin 3), which goes high at the beginning of the signal integrate phase. When zero crossing occurs (or overload detection), new data is latched on the next clock pulse, and 1/2 clock pulse later, the STTS line goes low. Thus, the new data is stable on this transition. The Run/Hold pin (R/H̄) (pin 28) is also useful for controlling conversions. A more detailed description of the operation of this pin is given in Section 4.B, but it will suffice to say here that if it is high, conversions will be performed continuously, while if it is low, the current conversion will be completed, but no others will start until it goes high again. There are 18 data output lines (16 and 14 on the 14-bit and 12-bit versions), including the polarity and over-range lines. These lines are grouped in sets of no more than 8 for three stated enable purposes, in the format shown in Figure 3, under the control of the byte and chip disable lines shown. To enable any byte, both the chip disable and the corresponding byte disable lines must be low. If all four (three for 7104-14 and -12) disable lines are tied low, all the data output lines will be asserted full time, thus giving a latched parallel output. For a three state parallel output, the three (two) byte disable lines should be tied low, and the chip disable line will act as a normal three state control line, as shown in Figure 4. This technique assumes the use of an 18 (16, 14) bit wide bus, fairly common among minicomputers and larger computers, but still rare among microprocessors (note that "extra" bits can sometimes be sensed as condition flags, etc.). For small words, the bit groups can be enabled individually or in pairs, by tying the chip disable line low, and using the byte disable lines either individually or in any combination as three state control lines, as shown in Figure 5. Several devices can be three stated to one bus by the technique suggested in Figure 6, comparable to row and column selection in memory arrays.

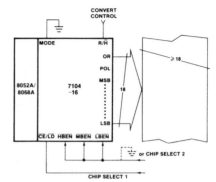

Figure 4: Full 18 Bit Three State Output

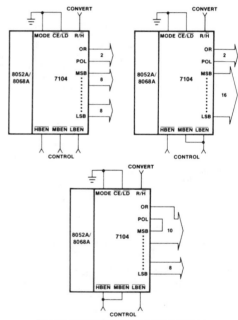

Figure 5: Various Combinations of Byte Disables

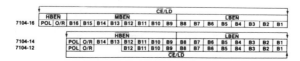

Figure 3: Three State Formats via Disable Pins

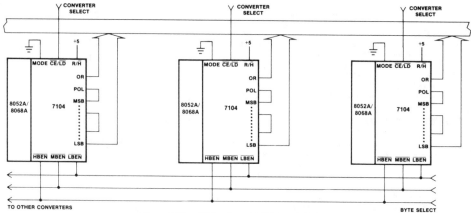

Figure 6: Three Stating Several 7104's to a Small Bus.

Some practical interface circuits utilizing the parallel and three state output capabilities of the ICL7104 are shown in Figures 7 through 13. Figure 7 shows a straightforward application to the Intel MCS-48, 80, and 85 systems via an 8255 PPI, using full-time parallel output. The I/O ports of an 8155 can be used in the same way. This interface can be used in a read-anytime mode, although there can be timing problems here, since a read performed as new data is being latched in the ICL7104 may lead to scrambled data. (Note that this will occur only very rarely, in proportion to the ratio

of setup-skew to conversion times). One way to overcome this problem is to read back the STTS line as well, and if it is high, read the data again after a delay exceeding 1/2 (converter) clock cycle. If STTS is now low, the second reading is correct, if it is still high, the first reading was correct (note that data never changes when STTS is low, and it goes low 1/2 clock cycle after data update occurs). Alternatively, the problem is completely avoided by using a read-after-update mode, as shown in Figure 8. Here the high to low transition of STTS triggers a "read data" operation

Figure 7: Full Time Parallel/Interface 8052(8068)-7104 to MCS-48, 80/85 Families

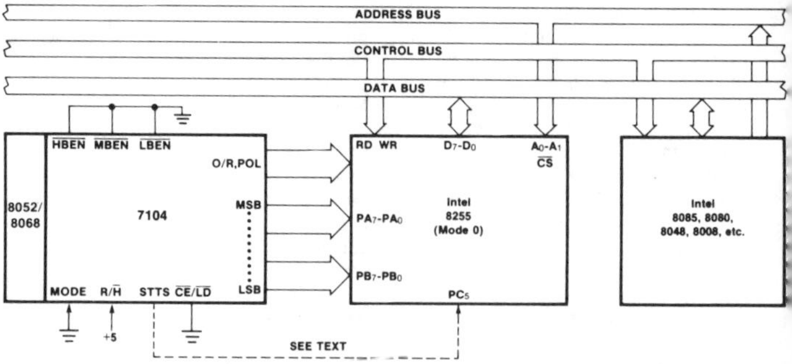

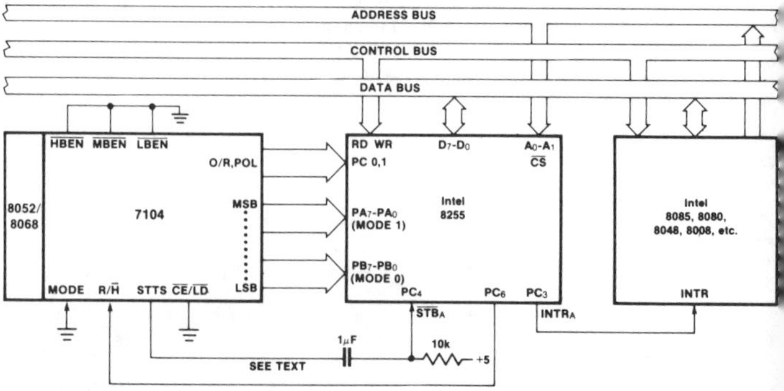

Figure 8: Full Time Parallel Interface 8052(8068)-7104 to MCS-48, 80/85 Families With Interrupt

through the MCS-8 Interrupt system. This application also shows the R/H̄ pin being used to initiate conversions under software control. If continuous conversions are desired, R/H̄ may be held high, and if the maximum possible conversion rate is desired, R/H̄ may be tied to clock out (see Section 4.B below).

A similar interface to the Motorola MC6800 system is shown in Figure 9. Since the maximum input-port count here is only 16, while the 16-bit ICL7104 has 18 outputs, control register A is used to input the two extra bits. The high to low transition of the STTS pin enables the two high bits, clocking the two interrupt flags in Control Register A if they are negative. A pullup resistor is needed on CA1, though CA2 has one internally. The same transition causes an interrupt via Control Register B's CB1 line. It is important to ensure that the software interrupt routine reads control register A before reading data port A, since the latter operation will clear the interrupt flags. Note that CB2 controls the R/H̄ pin through control register B, allowing software initiation of conversions in this system also. Naturally, the 14 and 12 bit versions of the ICL7104 avoid this problem since 16 or fewer bits need to be read back. Since the MOS Technology MCS650X microprocessors are bus-compatible with the MC6800's the same circuit can be used with them also.

Figure 10 shows an interface to the Intersil IM6100 microprocessor family through the IM6101 PIE device. Here the data is read back in a 10-bit and an 8-bit word, directly from the 7104 onto the 12-bit data bus. Again, the high to low transition of the STTS line triggers an interrupt. This leads to a software routine which controls the two read operations. As before, the R/H̄ pin is shown as being under software control, though the options mentioned above are equally acceptable, depending on system needs.

These Interrupt-fed systems essentially use an external handshake operation, under software control. An interesting variation, using the Simultaneous Direct Memory Access (SDMA) capability of the IM6100 family, is shown in Figure 11. The IM6102 MEDIC allows DMA during bus-idle processor cycles, so the transfer takes no extra time. The current address and extended current address registers of the IM6102 control the memory location to which the data will be sent, and the STTS output of the ICL7104 allows data transfer only when the converter is not updating information. The ECA register is used to drive the byte select lines (CA should be set to 7777, and WC to 2) and the User Pulse controls Chip disable CE/L̄D̄. A more fully loaded system can use address latches for CA. A DMA system can also be set up on the MCS-8 system using the DMA controller, 8257, and the three state outputs of the ICL7104.

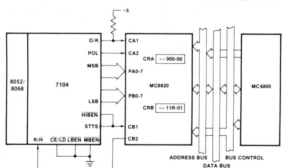

Figure 9: Parallel Interface from 7104 to MC 6800 Family (also MCS650X Family)

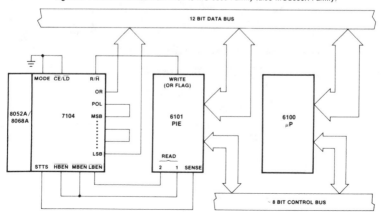

Figure 10: 8052(8068)/7104 Parallel Interface With 6100µP

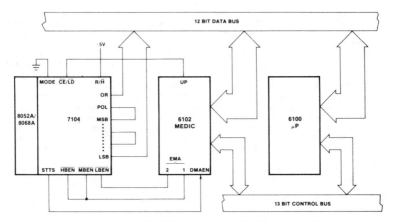

Figure 11: 8052(8068)/7104 Parallel Interface With 6100μP Using DMA

It is possible using the three state output capability, to connect the ICL7104 directly onto many microprocessor busses. Examples of this are shown in Figures 12 and 13. It is necessary to consider the system timing in this kind of application, and careful study should be made of the required set-up times from the microprocessor data sheets.

Note also the drive limitations on long busses. Generally this type of circuit is only favored if the memory peripheral address density is low, so that simple redundant address decoding can be used. Interrupt handling can require multiple external components also, and use of an interface device is normally advisable if this is needed.

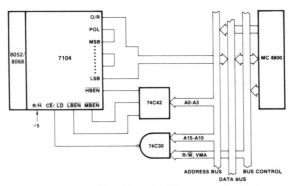

Figure 12: Direct 8052(8068)/7104 to MC6800 Microprocessor Interface

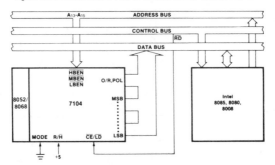

Figure 13: Direct Connection of 8052(8068)/7104 to MCS-80/85 System

3. HANDSHAKE MODE INTERFACE

Entry into the handshake mode will occur if either of two conditions are fulfilled; first, if new data is latched (i.e. a conversion is completed) while MODE pin (27) is high, in which case entry occurs at the end of the latch cycle; or secondly, if the MODE pin goes from low to high, when entry will occur immediately (if new data is being latched, entry is delayed to the end of the latch cycle). While in the handshake mode, data latching is inhibited, and the MODE pin is ignored. (Note that conversion cycles will continue in the normal manner). This allows versatile initiation of handshake operation without danger of false data generation; if the MODE pin is held high, every conversion (other than those completed during handshake operations) will start a new handshake operation, while if the MODE pin is pulsed high, handshake operations can be obtained "on demand."

During handshake operations, the various "disable" pins become output pins, generating signals used for the handshake operation. The Send ENable pin (SEN) (pin 29) is used as an indication of the ability of the external device to receive data. The condition of the line is sensed once every clock pulse, and if this is high (or first) byte is enabled on the next rising CL1 (pin 25) clock edge, the corresponding byte disable line goes low, and the Chip DisablE/LoaD line (pin 30) (CE/LD) goes low for one full clock pulse only, returning high.

On the next falling CL1 clock pulse edge, if SEN remains high, or after it goes high again, the byte output lines will be put in the high impedance state (or three-stated off). One half pulse later, the byte disable pin will be cleared high, and unless finished) the CE/LD and the next byte disable pin will go low. This will continue until all three (2 in the case of 12 and 14 bit devices) bytes have been sent. The bytes are individually put into the low impedance state i.e.: three-stated on during most of the time that their byte disable pin is

low. When receipt of the last byte has been acknowledged by a high SEN, the handshake mode will be cleared, re-enabling data latching from conversions, and recognizing the condition of the MODE pin again. The byte and chip disables will be three stated off, if the MODE pin is low, but held high by their (weak) pullups. These timing relationships are illustrated in Figure 14.

This configuration allows ready interface with a wide variety of external devices. For instance, external latches can be clocked on the rising edge of CE/LD, and the byte disables can be used to drive either load enables, or provide data identification flags, as shown in Figure 15. More usefully, the handshake mode can be used to interface with an 8-bit microprocessor of the MCS-8 group (eg. 8048, 8080, 8085, etc.) as shown in Figure 16. The handshake operation with the 8255 Programmable Peripheral Interface (PPI) is controlled by inverting its Input Buffer Full (IBF) flag to drive the Send ENable pin, and driving its strobe with the CE/LD line. The internal control register of the PPI should be set in mode 1 for the port used. If the 7104 is in handshake mode, and the 8255 IBF flag is low, the next word will be presented to the chosen port, and strobed. The strobe will cause IBF to rise, locking the three stated byte on. The PPI will cause a program interrupt in the MCS-8 system, which will result (after the appropriate program steps have been executed) in a "read" operation. The byte will be read, and the IBF reset low. This will cause the current byte disable to be dropped, and the next (if any) selected, strobed, etc., as before. The interface circuit as shown has the MODE pin tied to a control line on the PPI. If this bit is set always high (or mode is tied high separately), every conversion will be fed into the system (provided that the three interrupt sequences take less time than one conversion) as three 8-bit bytes; if this bit is normally left low, setting it high will cause a data transmission on demand. The interrupt routine can be used

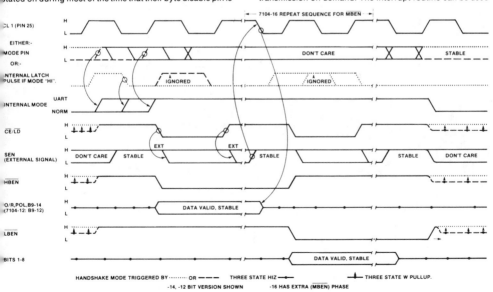

Figure 14: Timing Relationships in Handshake Mode

to reset the bit, if desired. Note also that the R/$\overline{\text{H}}$ pin is also shown tied to a control bit so that conversions can be performed either continuously or on demand under software control. Note that one port is not used here, and can service another peripheral device. The same arrangement can again be used with an 8155 I/O port and control lines.

Similar methods can be used with other microprocessors, such as the MC6800 or MCS650X family, as shown in Figure

17, and the Intel MCS4/40 family, as shown in Figure 18. These both operate almost identically to the method described above, except that in the former both R/$\overline{\text{H}}$ and MODE are shown tied high, to avoid using a full port for only two lines. Any 8-bit or wider microprocessor (or minicomputer), or narrower devices with 8-bit wide ports (most 4-bit devices have 8-bit wide ports available) can be interfaced in a handshake mode with a minimum of additional hardware, frequently none at all.

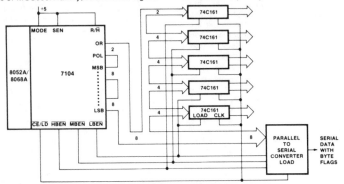

Figure 15: Use of Byte Disable Lines as Flags or for Loading

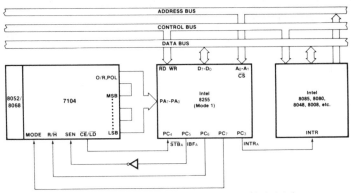

Figure 16: 8052A(8068A)-7104 to MCS-48, -80, or -85 Handshake Interface

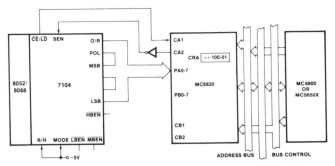

Figure 17: 8052(8068)/7104 to MC6800 or MCS650X Microprocessor With Handshake

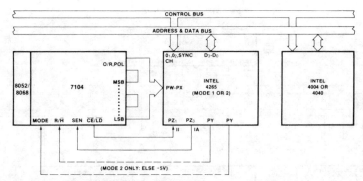

Figure 18: 8052A-7104 to MCS4/40 Microprocessor With Handshake

The handshake mode can also be used to interface with industry-standard UARTs, such as the Intersil IM6402/3 and the Western Digital TR1602. One method is shown in Figure 19. The arrangement here is such that if the UART receives any word serially down the Receiver Register Input line (RRI) the Data Received flag (DR) will be set. Since this is tied to the MODE pin, the current result will be loaded, full handshake style as before, into the transmitter buffer register, via the Transmitter Buffer Register Empty flag (TBRE) and the TBRLoad lines. The UART will thus transmit the full 18 (16, 14) bit result in 3 (2, 2) 8-bit words, together with the requisite start, stop and parity bits, serially down the Transmitter Register Output (TRO) line. The DR flag is reset via DRReset, here driven by a byte disable line. If we use DR to drive R/$\overline{\text{H}}$ instead, and use the received data word to drive a multiplexer, as shown in Figure 20, the multiplexer address sent to the UART will be selected, and a conversion initiated of the corresponding analog input. The result will be returned serially if the MODE pin is tied high. Thus a complete remote data logging station for up to 256 separate input lines can be controlled and readback through a three line interface. By adding a duplex or modem, telephone or radio link control is possible. (For a fuller discussion of this technique, see Application Note A025, Building A Remote Data Logging Station).

Alternatively, the data word could be used to select one of several A/D converters, as shown in Figure 21. The

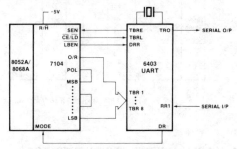

Figure 19: 8052(8068)/7104 Serial Inferface Using UART

unselected A/Ds all have three stated disable lines as well as data lines, so provided only one device is selected at a time, no conflicts will occur. (Note that byte disable lines are internally pulled-up when not active, so $\overline{\text{CE/LD}}$ has no effect on unselected converters). Naturally, care must be taken to avoid double selection errors in the data word, or an address decoder used. This technique could also be used to poll many stations on a single set of lines, provided that the TRO outputs are either three state or open collector/drain connections, since only that UART receiving an address that will trigger an attached converter will transmit anything.

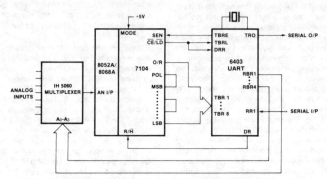

Figure 20: 8052(8068)/7104 Serial Interface Using UART and Analog Multiplexer

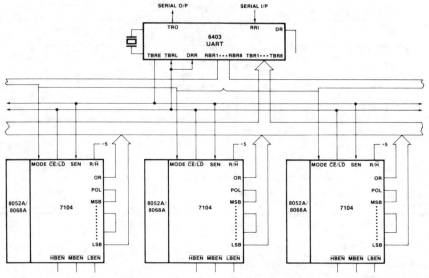

Figure 21: Multiplexing Converters Through the Mode Pin

4. MISCELLANEOUS TECHNIQUES FOR PERFORMANCE ENHANCEMENT

This section covers a few techniques, primarily analog, that can be used to enhance the performance of the ICL8052 (ICL8068)/ICL7104 chip pair for certain applications. Section 4.A. deals with buffer gain, for sensitivity increases of up to about 5 or 10 to 1, Section 4.B. with a special interconnection to allow the maximum rate of conversion with lower-valued inputs, and Section 4.C. external auto-zero for extending the benefits of auto-zero operation to preamplifiers, etc., to cover specialized signal processing or sensitivity enhancement by 10-100 to 1.

4. A. Buffer Gain

One of the significant contributions to the effective input noise voltage of a dual slope integrator is the so called auto-zero noise. At the end of the auto-zero interval, the instantaneous noise voltage on the auto-zero capacitor is stored, and subtracts from the input voltage while adding to the reference voltage during the next cycle. Although the open loop band width of the auto-zero loop is not wide, the gain from the input is very high, and the resulting closed loop band width to buffer noise is fairly wide. The result is that this noise voltage effectively is somewhat greater than the input noise voltage of the buffer itself during integration. By introducing some voltage gain into the buffer, the effect of the auto-zero noise (referred to the input) can be reduced to the level of the inherent buffer noise. This generally occurs with a buffer gain of between 3 and 10. Further increase in buffer gain merely increases the total offset to be handled by the auto-zero loop, and reduces the available buffer and integrator swings, without improving the noise performance of the system (see also the appendix). The circuit recommended for doing this with the ICL8068/ICL7104

is shown in Figure 22. With careful layout, the circuit shown can achieve effective input noise voltages on the order of 1-2μV, allowing full 16-bit use with full scale inputs of as low as 150mV. Note that at this level, thermoelectric EMFs between PC boards, IC pins, etc., due to local temperature changes can be very troublesome. Considerable care has been taken with the internal design of the ICL7104 and the ICL8068 to minimize the internal thermoelectric effects, but device dissipation should be minimized, and the effects of heat from adjacent (and not-so adjacent) components must be considered to achieve full performance at this sensitivity level.

4. B. Minimal Auto-Zero Time Operation

The R/$\overline{\text{H}}$ pin (pin 28) can be used in two basic modes. If it is held high, the ICL7104-16 will perform a complete conversion cycle in 131K clock counts (strictly 2^{17}), regardless of the result value (for the -14, 2^{15} counts, -12, 2^{13} counts).

If, however, the R/$\overline{\text{H}}$ pin (ever) goes low between the time of the zero-crossing and the end of a full $2^{16/14/12}$ count reference integrate phase, that phase is immediately terminated. If it is then held low, the 7104 will ensure a minimum auto-zero count (of $2^{15/13/11}$ counts) and then wait in auto-zero until the R/$\overline{\text{H}}$ pin goes high. On the other hand, if it goes high immediately subsequent to this minimal auto-zero count, the 7104 will start the next conversion after the least permissible time in auto-zero; i.e., at the maximum possible rate. The necessary "activity" on the R/$\overline{\text{H}}$ pin can be readily provided by tying it to the clock out pin (pin 26). Obviously under these conditions, the conversion cycle time depends on the result. Also note the scale factor and auto-zero effects covered in the Appendix.

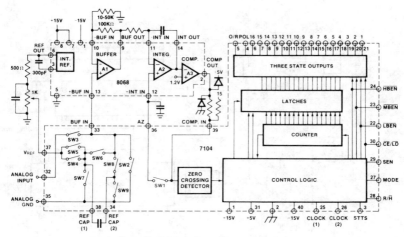

Figure 22: 8068/7104 Converter With Buffer Gain

4. C. External Auto-Zero

In many systems, signal conditioning is required in front of the converter for preamplification, filtering, etc., etc. With the exception of buffer gain, discussed in Section 4.A. above, it is generally not possible to include these conditioning circuits in the auto-zero loop. However, a sample-and-difference circuit keyed to the auto-zero phase can be used to eliminate offset and similar errors in preamplifiers, multiplexers, etc. A suitable circuit for a simple system is shown in Figure 23. The ICL8053 is used as a switch here primarily because of its extremely low charge injection (typically well below 10pC), even though it does limit the analog swing to ±4V. The use of an IH191 or IH5043 avoids this restriction, but increases the charge injection. The circuit of Figure 24 includes some balancing, but still injects typically 60pC (or 150pC for a DG191). Note that all these circuits have some sensitivity to stray capacitance at the converter input node. The amplifying or conditioning stages indicated in both these circuits must be capable of passing the chopping frequency with small enough delay, rise time, and overshoot to lead to insignificant error. Filtering should be done before or after the switching devices. Note also that although the input signal is still integrated over the normal time period, the input reference level is not. The time constant of the hold capacitor charging circuit should take noise and interference effects into consideration.

For a multiplexed input system, an arrangement similar to that of Figure 25 may be needed with individual preconditioning amplifiers, and Figure 26 with a common preconditioning amplifier. Note that in both of these cases, the capacitor may be charged to different voltages on each channel. By putting a capacitor in each line of Figure 25, the capacitor charging transients are eliminated, but the multiplexer capacitance becomes an important source of stray capacitance.

5. SUMMARY

The list of applications presented here is not intended to be, nor can it be, exhaustive, but is intended to suggest the wide range of possible applications of the ICL8052(ICL8068)/ICL7104 chip pair in A/D conversion in a digital environment. Many of the ideas suggested here may be used in combination; in particular, all the digital concepts discussed in Sections 2 and 3 can be used with any of the analog techniques outlined in Section 4, and many of the uses of the R/H̄ and MODE pins can be mixed.

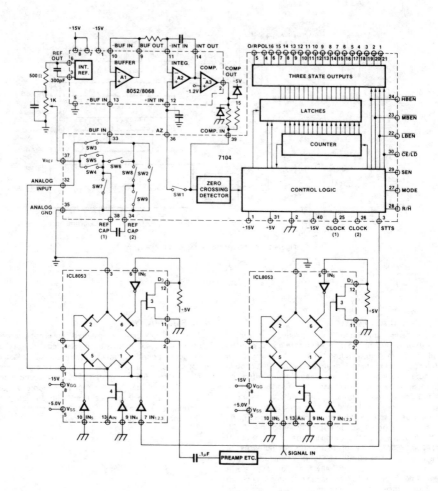

Figure 23: External Auto-Zero System Using 8053 Switches

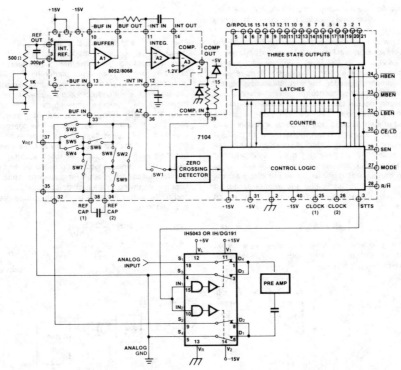

Figure 24: External Auto-Zero System for Large Signals Using IH5043 or Equivalent

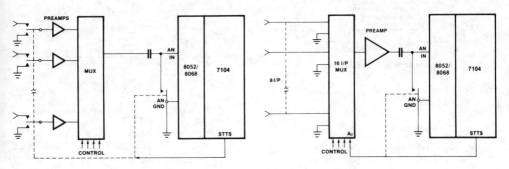

Figure 25: Multiplexed Auto-Zero System With Individual Preamps

Figure 26: Multiplexed Auto-Zero System With Common Preamp

APPENDIX A: The Auto-zero Loop Residual; A Relatively Complete Discussion for those with Strong Heads

The relevant circuit to be discussed is shown in Figure A1 and the major cycle waveforms in Figure A2. Let us first assume that the prior auto-zero cycle has been indefinitely long, or is otherwise ideal, so that the conversion starts with no residual error on the auto-zero capacitor. The integrate and deintegrate cycles will be classically perfect to the point at which a zero crossing actually occurs (at the output of the integrator). However, from this point two delays occur; first the comparator output is delayed (due to comparator delay) and secondly the zero crossing is not registered until the next appropriate clock edge. (For further discussion of this, see Application Note A017). At this point, the circuit is returned to the auto-zero connection (logic and switch delays may be absorbed in comparator delay as far as our discussion is concerned). The net result is that the integrator output voltage will have passed the zero-crossing point by an amount given by

$$V_{Ires} = \pm V_{IFS} \left(\frac{c_D + c_x}{c_{FS}} \right) \text{ where } 0 \leq c_x \leq 1 \quad \text{(A1)}$$

is the variable delay, where c_D is the fixed delay, c_{FS} is the full scale count in units of clock pulse periods, and V_{IFS} is the full scale integrator swing in volts.

The range of this residual voltage corresponds to the integrator swing per count, and is independent of input value, except for polarity. The immediate effect of closing the auto-zero loop may be seen by examining Figure A3. We may consider the comparator as acting as an op-amp under these conditions: the voltage across the auto-zero impedance is high, and the (nonlinear) impedance is low; on the other hand, the initial voltage across the integrating resistor is zero. Thus the auto-zero capacitor will be charged rapidly to exactly cancel the residual voltage, as shown in Figure A4. The output of the integrator is now at the correct position, but the two inputs are not. The residual voltage will decay away with a time constant controlled by the integrating resistor and capacitor, while the auto-zero capacitor is easily kept in step owing to the high comparator gain. Thus at the end of the auto-zero time, $t_{AZ} = c_{AZ} t_{cp}$, the residual will be reduced to:

$$V_{AZres} = V_{Ires} \exp\left(\frac{-c_{AZ} t_{cp}}{R_{INT} C_{INT}} \right)$$

$$= V_{IFS} \left(c_x + c_D \right) \frac{1}{c_{FS}} \exp\left(\frac{-c_{AZ} t_{cp}}{R_{INT} C_{INT}} \right) \quad \text{(A2)}$$

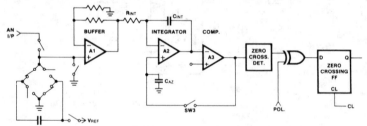

Figure A1: The Analog System

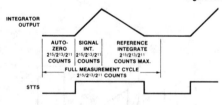

Figure A2: Major Cycle Waveforms

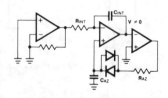

Figure A3: Analog System During Auto-Zero

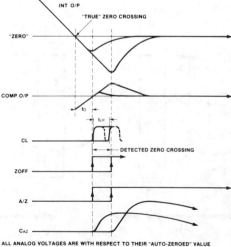

ALL ANALOG VOLTAGES ARE WITH RESPECT TO THEIR "AUTO-ZEROED" VALUE

Figure A4: Waveforms at Beginning of Auto-Zero Interval

Now $R_{INT}C_{INT}$ is controlled by the buffer swing, V_{BFS}, the integrator swing, V_{IFS}, and the integration time $t_{INT} = C_{INT} t_{cp}$, so that

$$V_{BFS}/R_{INT} \cdot t_{INT} = C_{INT} V_{IFS}, \text{ or } R_{INT} C_{INT} = C_{INT} \frac{V_{BFS}}{V_{IFS}} t_{cp}$$

and $V_{AZres} = V_{Ires} \left(\exp - \frac{C_{AZ}V_{IFS}}{C_{INT}V_{BFS}} \right)$ **(A3)**

This residual voltage on the auto-zero capacitor effectively increases the magnitude of the input voltage as seen on the output of the buffer. Thus, converting this voltage to count-equivalents,

$$C_{AZres} = \frac{V_{AZres}}{V_{BFS}} \cdot C_{FS} = \frac{V_{IFS}}{V_{BFS}} \left(c_x + c_D \right) \exp \left(-\frac{C_{AZ}}{C_{INT}} \cdot \frac{V_{IFS}}{V_{BFS}} \right)$$

(A4)

Since this voltage also subtracts from the reference, its effect at the input is magnified in the ratio

$$C_{INres} = C_{AZres} \left(\frac{C_{INT} + C_{DE}}{C_{INT}} \right) \text{ so that}$$

$$C_{INres} = \left(1 + \frac{C_{DE}}{C_{INT}} \right) \left(\frac{V_{IFS}}{V_{BFS}} \right) \left(c_x + c_D \right) \exp \left(-\frac{C_{AZ}}{C_{INT}} \cdot \frac{V_{IFS}}{V_{BFS}} \right)$$

Note that c_{DE} is equal to the displayed result.   **(A5)**

Two things should be noted here. First, this residual acts to increase the input voltage magnitude, and secondly, a small increase in input voltage tends to decrease the magnitude of the residual (until the result count changes). These effects lead to "stickyness" in the readings; suppose, in a noise-free system, that the input voltage is at a level where the residual is a minimum; the detected zero crossing follows the true one as closely as possible. A minute increase in input voltage will cause the zero crossing to be detected one pulse later, and the residual to jump to it's maximum value. The effect of this is a small increase in the apparent input voltage; thus if we now remove the minute increase, the residual voltage effect will maintain the new higher reading; in fact we will have to reduce the input voltage by an amount commensurate with the effective residual voltage to force the reading to drop back again to the lower value. In more detail, we should consider the equilibrium conditions on the auto-zero capacitor. Clearly, the voltage added at the end of reference integrate must just balance that which decays away during the auto-zero interval. So far the relationships we have developed have assumed a zero residual before the conversion, but clearly in the equilibrium condition the residual given by equation (A4) remains, and at the end of conversion, the new amount, given by equation (A1), is added to this, so we start the "auto-zero decay" interval with

$$C_{Ires} = C_{AZres} + \frac{V_{IFS}}{V_{BFS}} \left(c_x + c_D \right)$$ **(A6)**

By combining equations (A4) and (A6) we find, for the equilibrium condition,

$$C_{AZres} = \pm \frac{V_{IFS}}{V_{BFS}} \left(c_x + c_D \right) \left[\exp \left\{ + \frac{C_{AZ}V_{IFS}}{C_{INT}V_{BFS}} \right\} -1 \right]^{-1}$$

Once again, the effect of this at the input is multiplied by the ratio of total input integrate times, so that, under equilibrium conditions,

$$C_{INres} = \pm \frac{V_{IFS}}{V_{BFS}} \left(1 + \frac{C_{DE}}{C_{INT}} \right) \left(c_x + c_D \right) \left[\exp \left\{ \frac{C_{AZ} V_{IFS}}{C_{INT}V_{BFS}} \right\} -1 \right]^{-1}$$

(A7)

Those expert at skipping to the end of the difficult bit will recognize that as the final equation, in terms of complexity. So let us now see what it means. Clearly, the error term is greater, the larger $\frac{C_{DE}}{C_{INT}}$, and the smaller $\frac{C_{AZ}}{C_{INT}}$. For the ICL7104 combinations, (and also the ICL7103, and the data sheet systems for the ICL8053 pairs), these are both worst case near full scale input, where $\frac{C_{DE}}{C_{INT}} \approx 2$ and $\frac{C_{AZ}}{C_{INT}} \approx 1$. (Note that the minimum auto-zero time technique of section 4B will make $\frac{C_{AZ}}{C_{INT}} = 1$ for all input values). Substituting these, we find the worst case

$$C_{INres} \approx \pm \frac{V_{IFS}}{V_{BFS}} \left(3 \right) \left(c_x + c_D \right) \left[\exp \left(\frac{V_{IFS}}{V_{BFS}} \right) -1 \right]^{-1}$$ **(A8)**

Recall the c_D is fixed; and c_x must be between 0 and 1. The expression is now a function purely of the ratio of integrator and buffer full scale swings; the relationship is plotted in Figure A5, and shows the desirability of keeping the integrator swing higher than the buffer swing. Note also that the comparator delay (c_D in equation (A8)) is also effectively enhanced. This has the effect of shrinking the zero somewhat more than normally occurs. Since this term changes sign with polarity, the converter will have a tendency to keep the current sign at zero input.

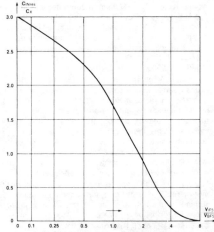

Figure A5: Auto-Zero Loop Residual vs. Integrator/Buffer Swing Ratio

The effects of noise should be mentioned here. The worst case value of residual shown in Figure A5 assumes a very gradual approach to equilibrium, and any noise spike causing the reading to flash to the next value will destroy all this carefully established residual value! Thus for any system with noise of ~ 1/3 count or more, the effect is greatly reduced, and even 1/10 count of noise will restrict the actual hysteresis value found in practice. The detailed analysis of the auto-zero residual problem in the presence of appreciable noise is left as an exercise for the masochist.

SELECTING A/D CONVERTERS

Dave Fullagar, Intersil Inc.

One of the popular pastimes of the nineteen sixties was to predict the explosive growth of digital data processing, fed by the newly-developed semiconductor MSI circuits, and the subsequent demise of analog circuitry. The first part of this prediction has certainly come true - the advent of the microprocessor has caused, and will continue to cause, a revolution in digital processing which was unthinkable 10 years ago. But far from causing the demise of analog systems, the reverse has occurred. Nearly all the data being processed (with the notable exception of financial data) consists of physical parameters of an analog nature - pressure, temperature, velocity, light intensity and acceleration to name but a few. In every instance this analog information must be converted into its digital equivalent, using some form of A/D converter. Converter products are thus assuming a key role in the realization of data acquisition systems.

Increased use of microprocessors has also caused dramatic cost reductions in the digital components of a typical system. The $8000 mini-computer of a few years ago is being replaced by a $475 dedicated microprocessor board. This trend is also being reflected in the analog components. No longer is it possible to justify buying a $400 data acquisition module when a dedicated system, adequate for the task under consideration, can be put together for $50.

Thus many engineers, who in the past have had limited exposure to analog circuitry, are having to come to grips with the characteristics of A/D converters, sample & holds, multiplexers and operational amplifiers. Contrary to the propaganda put out by many of the specialty module houses, there is nothing mysterious about these components or the way they interface with one another. Now that many of them are available as one or two chip MSI circuits, a block diagram may be turned into a working piece of hardware with relative ease.

The purpose of this note is to compare and contrast the more popular A/D designs, and provide the reader with sufficient information to select the most appropriate converter for his or her needs.

THE IMPORTANT PARAMETERS

Let's begin by taking a look at some actual systems, since this will illustrate the diversity of performance required of A-to-D converters.

Case 1: A seismic recording truck is situated over a potential natural gas site. Some 32 recording devices are laid out over the surrounding area. An explosive charge is detonated and in a matter of seconds it is all over. During that time it is necessary to scan each recorder every 100 microseconds. Speed is clearly the most important requirement. In this instance, 12 bit accuracy is not required; and, since the truck contains many thousands of dollars of electronics, cost is not a critical parameter. The A/D will be a high speed successive approximation design.

Case 2: A semiconductor engineer is measuring the 'thermal profile' of a furnace. It is necessary to make measurements accurate to a few tenths of a degree Centigrade, which is equivalent to a few microvolts of thermocouple output. Sampling rates of a few readings per second are adequate and costs should be kept low. The integrating ('dual slope', 'triphasic', 'quad slope', depending on which manufacturer you go to) A/D is the only type capable of the required precision/cost combination. It has the added advantage of maintaining accuracy in a noisy environment.

Case 3: A businessman is talking to his sales office in Rome. Assuming the phone company is not on strike, his voice will be sampled at a 10KHz rate, or thereabouts, in order not to lose information in the audio frequency range up to 5KHz. This requires a medium accuracy (8 bit) A/D with a cycle time of 100 microseconds or less. In this application the integrating type is not fast enough, so it is necessary to use a slow (for this approach) successive approximation design.

These examples serve to introduce both the two most popular conversion techniques (successive approximation and integrating) and the three key parameters of a converter, i.e. speed, accuracy and cost. In fact the first choice in selecting an A/D is between successive approximation and integrating, since greater than 95% of all converters fall into one of these two categories.

If we look at the whole gamut of available converters, with conversion speeds ranging from 100 ms to less than 1 μs, we see that these two design approaches divide the speed spectrum into two groups with almost no overlap. (Table 1) However, before making a selection solely on the basis of speed, it is important to have an understanding of how the converters work, and how the data sheet specifications relate to the circuit operation.

TABLE 1

Type of converter	Relative speed	Conversion time			
		8 bits	10 bits	12 bits	16 bits
integrating	slow	20 ms	30 ms	40 ms	250 ms
	medium	1 ms	5 ms	20 ms	—
	fast	0.3 ms	1 ms	5 ms	—
successive approximation	general purpose	30 μs	40 μs	50 μs	—
	high performance	10 μs	15 μs	20 μs	400 μs
	fast	5 μs	10 μs	12 μs	—
	high speed	2 μs	4 μs	6 μs	—
	ultra-fast	0.8 μs	1 μs	2 μs	—

THE INTEGRATING CONVERTER

Summary of Characteristics

As the name implies, the output of an integrating converter represents the integral or average value of an input voltage over a fixed period of time. A sample-and-hold circuit, therefore, is not required to freeze the input during the measurement period, and noise rejection is excellent. Equally important, the linearity error of integrating converters is small since they use time to quantize the answer - it is relatively easy to hold short-term clock jitter to better than 1 in 10^6.

The most popular integrating converter uses the dual-slope principle, a detailed description of which is given in Ref. 1.

Its advantages and disadvantages may be summarized as follows:

> **Advantages:**
> Inherent accuracy
> Non-critical components
> Excellent noise rejection
> No sample & hold required
> Low cost
> No missing codes

> **Disadvantages:**
> Low speed (typically 3 to 100 readings/sec)

In a practical circuit, the primary errors (other than reference drift) are caused by the non-ideal characteristics of analog switches and capacitors. In the former, leakage and charge injection are the main culprits; in the latter, dielectric absorption is a source of error. All these factors are discussed at length in Ref. 1.

A well-designed dual slope circuit such as Intersil's 8052A/7103A is capable of 4½ digit performance (± 1 in $\pm 20,000$) with no critical tweaks or close tolerance components other than a stable reference.

Timing Considerations

In a typical circuit, such as the 8052A/7103A referred to above, the conversion takes place in three phases as shown in Fig 1. Note that the input is actually integrated or averaged over a period of 10,000 clock pulses (or 83.3 ms with a 120 KHz clock) within a conversion cycle of 40,000 clock pulses in toto. Also note that the actual business of looking at the input signal does not begin for 10,000 clock pulses, since the circuit first goes into an auto-zero mode. For a 3½ digit product, such as the 7101 or 7103, the measurement period is 1000 clock pulses (or 8.33 ms with a 120 KHz clock).

These timing characteristics give the dual slope circuit both its strengths and its weaknesses. By making the signal integrate period an integral number of line frequency periods, excellent 60Hz noise rejection can be obtained. And of course integrating the input signal for several milliseconds smoothes out the effect of high frequency noise.

But in many applications such as transient analysis or sampling high frequency waveforms, averaging the input over several milliseconds is totally unacceptable. It is of course feasible to use a sample & hold at the input, but the majority of systems that demand a short measurement window also require high speed conversions.

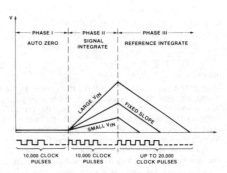

Figure 1: 4½ Digit A/D Converter Timing Diagram (8052A/7103A)

THE SUCCESSIVE APPROXIMATION CONVERTER

How it works.

The heart of the successive approximation A/D is a digital-to-analog converter (DAC) in a feedback loop with a comparator and some clever logic referred to as a 'successive approximation register' (SAR). Fig 2 shows a typical system. The DAC output is compared with the analog input, progressing from the most significant bit (MSB) to the least significant bit (LSB) one bit at a time. The bit in question is set to one. If the DAC output is less than the input, the bit in question is left at one. If the DAC output is greater than the input, the bit is set to zero. The register then moves on to the next bit. At the completion of the conversion, those bits left in the one state cause a current to flow at the output of the DAC which should match I_{IN} within $\pm$ ½ LSB. Performing an 'n' bit conversion requires only 'n' trials, making the technique capable of high-speed conversion.

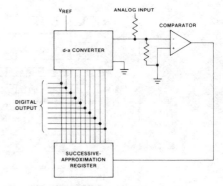

Figure 2: Successive Approximation A/D Converter

The advantages and disadvantages of successive approximation converters may be summarized as follows:

> **Advantages:**
> Hi Speed
> (Typically 100,000 conversions/sec)

Disadvantages:

Several critical components

Can have missing codes

Requires sample and hold

Difficult to auto-zero

High cost

Error Sources

The error source in the successive approximation converter are more numerous than in the integrating type, with contributions from both the DAC and the comparator. The DAC generally relies on a resistor ladder and current or voltage switches to achieve quantization. Maintaining the correct impedance ratios over the operating temperature range is much more difficult than maintaining clock pulse uniformity in an integrating converter.

The data sheet for a hypothetical A/D might contain the following accuracy related specifications:

Resolution	: 10 Bits
Quantization Uncertainty	: ± ½ LSB
Relative Accuracy	: ± ½ LSB
Differential Non Linearity	: ± ½ LSB
Gain Error	: Adjustable to zero at 25°C
Gain Temp. Coeff.	: ± 10 ppm of Full Scale Reading /°C
Offset Error	: Adjustable to zero at 25°C
Offset Temp. Coeff.	: ± 20 ppm of Full Scale Reading /°C

Now, referring to the definition of terms on page 6, what does this tell us about the product? First of all, being told that the *quantization uncertainty* is ± ½ LSB is like being told that binary numbers are comprised of ones and zeros - it's part of the system. The *relative accuracy* of ± ½ LSB, guaranteed over the temperature range, tells us that after removing gain and offset errors, the transfer function

never deviates by more than ± ½ LSB from where it should be. That's a good spec., but note that gain and offset errors have been adjusted prior to making the measurement. Over a finite temperature range, the temperature coefficients of gain and offset must be taken into account.

The *differential non-linearity* of ± ½ LSB maximum is also guaranteed over temperature: this ensures that there are no missing codes.

The *gain temperature coefficient* is 10 ppm of FSR per °C, or 0.001% per °C. Now 1 LSB in a 10 bit system is 1 part in 1024, or approximately 0.1%. So a 50°C temperature change from the temperature at which the gain was adjusted (i.e. from +25°C to +75°C) could give rise to ± ½ LSB error. This error is separate from, and in the limit could add to, the relative accuracy spec.

The *offset temperature coefficient* of 20 ppm per °C give rise to ± 1 LSB error (over a +25°C to +75°C range) by the same reasoning applied to the gain tempco. The reference contributes an error in direct proportion to its percentage change over the operating temperature range.

We can summarize the effect of the major error sources:

Relative Accuracy	± ½ LSB or ± .05%
Gain Temp. Coefficient	± ½ LSB or ± .05%
Offset Temp. Coefficient	± 1 LSB or ± 0.1%

A straight forward RMS summation shows that the A/D is 10 bits ± 1¼ LSB over a 0°C to +75°C temperature range. However it is over-optimistic to RMS errors with such a small number of variables, and yet we do know that the error cannot exceed ± 2 LSB. A realistic estimate might place the accuracy at 10 bits ± 1½ LSB.

Timing Considerations

The 2502/2503/2504 successive approximation register is now used in the majority of high speed A/D converters and the timing diagram shown in Fig. 3 is taken from the

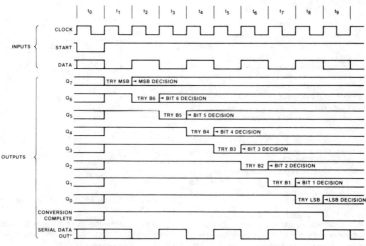

*FOR PURPOSES OF ILLUSTRATION. SERIAL DATA OUT WAVEFORM SHOWN FOR 01010101.

Figure 3: Typical Timing Diagram for Successive Approximation Converter

2502 data sheet. However all successive approximation converters have essentially similar timing characteristics. Holding the start input Low for at least a clock period initiates the conversion. The MSB is set low and all the other bits high for the first trial. Each trial takes one clock period, proceeding from the MSB to the LSB. Note that, in contrast to the integrating converter, a serial output arises naturally from this conversion technique.

Although the successive approximation A/D is capable of very high conversion speeds, there is an important limitation on the slew rate of the input signal. Unlike integrating designs, no averaging of the input signal takes place. To maintain accuracy to 10 bits, for example, the input should not change by more than $\pm\frac{1}{2}$ LSB during the conversion period. Fig 4(a) shows maximum allowable dV/dt as a function of sampling (or aperture) time for various conversion resolutions. Now for a sinusoidal waveform represented by $E\sin\omega t$, the maximum rate of change of voltage $\Delta e/\Delta t$ is $2\pi f E$. The amplitude of one $\frac{1}{2}$ LSB is $E/2^n$, since the pk-pk amplitude is $2E$. So the change in input amplitude Δe is given by:

$$\Delta e = E/2^n = 2\pi f E \Delta T, \text{where } \Delta T = \text{conversion time}$$

$$f \max = \frac{1}{2\pi\Delta T2^n}$$

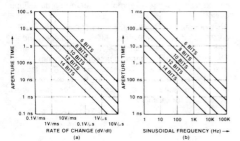

Figure 4: Maximum input signal rate change (a) and sinewave frequency (b) as a function of sampling or aperture time for $\pm\frac{1}{2}$ LSB accuracy in 'n' bits.

This is the highest frequency that can be applied to the converter input without using a sample and hold. For n = 10 bits, $\Delta T = 10$ μs, f max= 15.5 Hz. Frequencies this low often come as a surprise to first time users of so-called high speed A/D converters, and explain why the majority of non-integrating converters are preceded by a sample & hold. Fig. 4(b) plots equation (1) for a range of ΔT values. Note that when a sample & hold is used, ΔT is the aperture time of the S & H. With the help of a $5 sample & hold such as Intersil's IH5110 (worst case aperture time = 200 ns), f max in the above example becomes 780 Hz.

Consideration must also be given to the input stage time constant of both the sample & hold, if there is one, and the converter. The number of time constants taken to charge a capacitor within a given percentage of full scale is shown in Fig 5. For example, consider a product with a 10 pF input capacitance driven by a signal source impedance of 100KΩ. For 12 bit accuracy, at least 9 time constants, or 9 μs, should be allowed for charging.

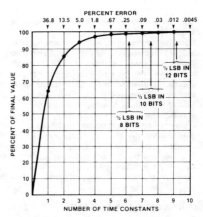

Figure 5: Voltage across a capacitor (as % of final value) as a function of time (# of time constants)

CONVERTER CHECKLIST

In selecting a converter for a specific application, it will be helpful to go through the following checklist, matching required performance against data sheet guarantees:

a) How many bits?

b) What is total error budget over the temperature range?

c) What is full scale reading and magnitude of LSB? Make sure that the 95% noise is substantially less than the magnitude of the LSB. If no noise specifications are given, assume that the omission is intentional!

d) What input characteristics are required? With most successive approximation converters, the input resistance is low ($\simeq 5$KΩ) since one is looking into the comparator summing junction. In a well designed dual slope circuit, there should be a high input resistance buffer ($R_{in} \simeq 10^{12}$ Ω) included within the auto-zero loop. However in some designs (Teledyne 8700, Analog Devices AD7550) the input looks directly into the integrating resistor (1 MΩ).

e) What aperture time (or measurement window) is required? If an averaged value of the input signal (over some milliseconds) is acceptable, use an integrating converter. Refer to Fig. 4 for systems where an averaged value of the input is not acceptable. Remember most successive approximation systems rely on a sample & hold to 'freeze' the input while the conversion is taking place. Thus the sample & hold characteristics should be matched to the input signal slew rate, and the A/D converter characteristics matched to the required conversion rate.

f) What measurement frequency is required? This will determine the maximum allowable conversion time (including auto-zero time for integrating types).

g) Is microprocessor compatibility important? Some A/D's interface easily with microprocessors; others do not. Ref. 2 explores the microprocessor interface in considerable depth.

h) Does the converter form part of a multiplexed data acquisition system?

Note that some integrating converters (Motorola MC14433) assess polarity based on the input voltage during the previous conversion cycle. Such designs are clearly unsuitable for multiplexed inputs where the signal polarity bears no relationship to the previously measured value. They can also give trouble with inputs hovering around zero.

i) Is 60Hz rejection important?

If the line frequency rejection capabilities of the integrating converter are important, make sure that the duration of the measurement (input integrate) period is a fixed number of clock pulses. In some designs, the input integration time is programmed by the auto-zero information, making rejection of specific frequencies impossible.

MULTIPLEXED DATA SYSTEMS

The foregoing discussion has summarized the characteristics of A/D converters as stand-alone components. However, one of the most important applications for A/Ds is as part of a multiplexed data acquisition system. Traditionally, systems of this type have used analog signal transmission between the transducer and a central multiplexer/converter console. (Fig 6a) To sample 100 data points 25 times per second requires a 100 input analog multiplexer and an A/D capable of 2500 conversions per second. A successive approximation converter would be the obvious choice.

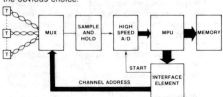

Figure 6(a): Data Acquisition using one central A/D.

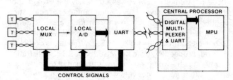

Figure 6(b): Data Acquisition using several local A/Ds

Another approach, which becomes attractive with the availability of low cost IC converters, is to use localized A/D conversion with digital transmission back to a central console. In the limit one could use a converter per transducer, but it is often more economical to have a local conversion station servicing several transducers (Fig 6b). Several advantages result from this approach. Firstly, digital transmission is more satisfactory in a noisy environment, and lends itself to optical isolation techniques better than analog transmission. Secondly, using local conversion stations significantly reduces the number of interconnects back to the central processor. When one considers that the instrumentation for a typical power plant uses 4.5 million feet of cable, this can result in real cost savings. Finally, by sharing the conversion workload among several A/Ds, it is frequently possible to switch from a successive approximation to a dual slope design.

An example of a local conversion station featuring an 8052/7103 dual slope A/D, a CMOS multiplexer, and an UART for serial data transmission is discussed in Ref 2. The local conversion station concept can be taken a stage further by the addition of a microprocessor. This may be used to reduce the data prior to transmission to the central computer, and/or to look for dangerous conditions, for example.

DEFINITION OF TERMS

Quantization Error. This is the fundamental error associated with dividing a continuous (analog) signal into a finite number of digital bits. A 10 bit converter, for example, can only identify the input voltage to 1 part in 2^{10}, and there is an unavoidable output uncertainty of $\pm \frac{1}{2}$ LSB (Least Significant Bit). See Fig. 7.

Linearity. The maximum deviation from a straight line drawn between the end points of the converter transfer function. Linearity is usually expressed as a fraction of LSB size. The linearity of a good converter is $\pm \frac{1}{2}$ LSB. See Fig. 8.

Differential Non-Linearity. This describes the variation in the analog value between adjacent pairs of digital numbers, over the full range of the digital output. If each transition is equal to 1 LSB, the differential non-linearity is clearly zero. If the transition is 1 LSB $\pm \frac{1}{2}$ LSB, then there is a differential linearity error of $\pm \frac{1}{2}$ LSB, but no possibility of missing codes. If the transition is 1 LSB $\pm$ 1 LSB, then there is the possibility of missing codes. This means that the output may jump from, say 011 .... 111 to 100 .... 001, missing out 100 .... 000. See Fig. 9.

Relative Accuracy. The input to output error as a fraction of full scale, with gain and offset errors adjusted to zero. Relative accuracy is a function of linearity, and is usually specified at less than $\pm \frac{1}{2}$ LSB.

Gain Error. The difference in slope between the actual transfer function and the ideal transfer function, expressed as a percentage. This error is generally adjustable to zero by adjusting the input resistor in a current-comparing successive approximation A/D. See Fig. 10.

Gain Temperature Coefficient. The deviation from zero gain error on a 'zeroed' part which occurs as the temperature moves away from 25°C. See Fig. 10.

Offset Error. The mean value of input voltage required to set zero code out. This error can generally be trimmed to zero at any given temperature, or is automatically zeroed in the case of a good integrating design.

Offset Temperature Coefficient. The change in offset error as a function of temperature.

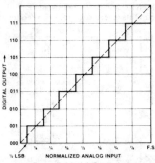

Figure 7: Ideal A/D conversion

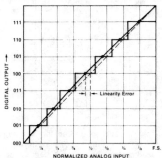

Figure 8: Linearity Error

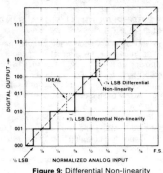

Figure 9: Differential Non-linearity

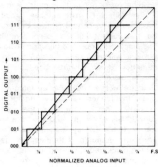

Figure 10: Gain Error

DO'S AND DONT'S OF APPLYING A/D CONVERTERS

Peter Bradshaw and **Skip Osgood**, Intersil Inc.

In many applications, the limitation in the performance of any system lies in how the individual components are used. The Analog-to-Digital Converter (A/D) can also be considered as a component and, therefore, proper design procedures are necessary in order to obtain the optimum accuracy. Intersil IC A/D converters are inherently extremely accurate devices. To obtain the optimum performance from them, care should be taken in the hook-up and external components used. Test equipment used in system evaluation should be substantially more accurate and stable than the system needs to be. The following sections illustrate DO's and DON'Ts to obtain the best results from any system.

1. DON'T INTRODUCE GROUND LOOP ERRORS

Plan your grounding carefully. Probably the most common source of error in any Analog-Digital system is improper grounding. Let's look at Fig 1. All the grounds are tied together, so everything should be alright, right? WRONG! Almost everything is wrong with this connection.

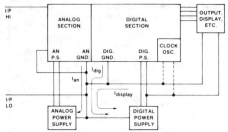

FIGURE 1 Don't hook it up like this!

The power supply currents for the analog and digital sections, together with the output or display currents, all flow through a lead common to the input. Let us analyze some of the errors we have introduced. The average currents flowing in the resistance of the common lead will generate a D.C. offset voltage. Even the autozero circuit of an integrating A/D converter cannot remove this error. But, in addition, this current will have several varying components. The clock oscillator, and the various digital circuits driven from it, will show supply current variation at the clock frequency, and usually at submultiple also. For a successive approximation converter, these will cause an additional effective offset. For an integrating converter, at least the higher frequency components should average out. In some converters, the analog supply currents will also vary with the clock (or a submultiple) frequency. If the display is multiplexed, that current will vary with the multiplex frequency, usually some fraction of the clock frequency. For an integrating converter, both digital and analog section currents will

change as the converter goes from one phase of conversion to another. (Currents of this type injected into an autozero loop are particularly obstinate). Another serious source of variation is the change in digital and display section currents with the result value. This frequently shows up as an oscillating result, and/or missing results; one value being displayed displaces the effective input to a new value, which is converted and displayed, leading to a different displacement, a new value and so on. This sequence usually closes after two or three values, which are displayed in sequence.

A more subtle source of errors in this circuit comes from the clock oscillator frequency. For an integrating converter, variations in clock frequency during a single conversion cycle due to varying digital supply voltage or supply currents, or ground loops to a timing capacitor, will lead to incorrect results.

Fig 2 shows a much better arrangement. The digital and analog grounds are connected by a line carrying only the interface currents between sections, and the input section is also tied back by a low-current line. The display-current loop will not affect the analog section and the clock section is isolated by a decoupling capacitor. Note that external reference return currents and any other analog system currents must also be returned carefully to analog ground.

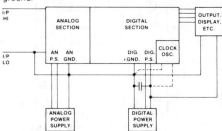

FIGURE 2 Do hook it up like this.

2. DON'T COUPLE DIGITAL SIGNALS INTO ANALOG LINES

Although Intersil's A/D converter circuits have been designed to minimize the internal coupling of digital signals into analog lines, the external capacitive coupling is controlled by the user. For the best results, it is advisable to keep analog and digital sections separated on PC boards. A few examples of the results of capacitive coupling follow.

On dual slope converters, the "busy" line swings from one state to the other at the end and beginning of the autozero cycle. Capacitive coupling from this line to the autozero or integrating capacitors will induce an effective input offset voltage. A similar effect occurs with the

"Measure/Zero" line on charge-balancing converters and for a successive approximation converter with coupling between "End of Conversion" and a sample-and-hold capacitor. For a multiplexed display device, coupling between the multiplex or "digit" lines and these capacitors can lead to non-linearity of the converter. And coupling from any digital line into a high-impedance input line can lead to errors in any system.

3. DO USE ADEQUATE QUALITY COMPONENTS

For successive approximation converters, the resistors used must have excellent time and temperature stability to maintain accuracy. Any adjustment potentiometers, etc. must be of compatible quality (note that in some trimpots, the slider position moves with temperature!)

For dual slope converters, the component selection is less critical. Long term drifts in the integrating resistor and the capacitors are not important. However, any resistive divider used on the reference, especially if it is adjustable, must be of sufficient stability not to degrade system accuracy. Dielectric absorption in the integrating capacitor is important (see reference 1) and the integrating resistor must have a negligible voltage coefficient to ensure linearity. Noisy components will lead to noisy performance, whether in the integrator, autozero or clock circuits.

4. DO USE A GOOD REFERENCE

Good references are like good wines; nobody is quite sure how to make them but generally the older the technology used, the better the result, and the proof lies in the tasting (or testing). Thus, it is hard to beat the old temperature compensated zener with the current flow adjusted to the optimum for each diode. If you aren't into Zinfandel Superior Premier Cru (1972), the Intersil 8052 has a fairly good reference built in. In either case, the division down from what you get to the required reference voltage requires care also (see above). And it is a fundamental fact that no converter can be better than its reference voltage.

5. DO WATCH OUT FOR THERMAL EFFECTS

All integrated circuits have thermal time constants of a few milliseconds to dissipation changes in the die. These can cause changes in such parameters as offset voltages and V_{be} matching. For example, the power dissipation in an 8018 quad current switch depends on the digital value. Although the die is carefully designed to minimize the effects of this, the resultant temperature changes will affect the matching between current switch values to a small degree. Inappropriate choice of supply voltages and current levels can enhance these differences, leading to errors. Similarly, the power dissipated in a dual-slope converter circuit depends on the comparator polarity and hence varies during the conversion cycle. Offset voltage variations due to this cannot be autozero'd out, and so can lead to errors. Again a poor choice of comparator loading or swing will enhance this (normally) minor effect. The power dissipation in an output display could be coupled into the sensitive analog sections of a converter, leading to similar problems. And thermal gradients between IC packages and PC boards can lead to thermo-electric voltage errors in very sensitive systems.

6. DO USE THE MAXIMUM INPUT SCALE

To minimize all other sources of error, it is advisable to use the highest possible full scale input voltage. This is particularly important with successive approximation converters, where offset voltage errors can quickly get above 1LSB, but even for integrating-type converters, noise and the various other errors discussed above will increase in importance for lower-than-maximum full scale ranges. Pre-converter gain is usually preferable for small original signals. All Intersil's integrating converters have a digital output line that can be used to extend autozero to preconditioning circuits (being careful not to couple the digital signal into the analog system, of course).

Also, DO CHECK THESE AREAS

Tie digital inputs down (or up) if you are not using them. This will avoid stray input spikes from affecting operation. Bypass all supplies with a large and a small capacitor close to the package. Limit input currents into any I.C. pin to values within the maximum rating of the device (or a few mA if not specified) to avoid damaging the device. Ensure that power supplies do not reverse polarity or spike to high values when turned on or off. Remember that many digital gates take higher-than-normal supply currents for inputs between defined logic levels. And remember also that gates can look like amplifiers under these circumstances. An example is shown in Fig 3, where stray and internal input-to-output capacitance is multiplied by the gain of the gate just at the threshold causing a large effective load capacitance on the 8052 comparator (see reference 1 for the effects of this.) A non-inverting gate here could lead to oscillations.

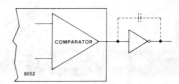

FIGURE 3

External Adjustment Procedure

Most of the A/D converters now offered by Intersil do not require an offset adjustment. They have internal autozero circuits which typically give less than 10 μV of offset. Therefore, the only optional adjustment required to obtain optimum accuracy in a given application is the full scale or gain reading.

With the A/D converter in a continuous mode of conversion, the following procedure is recommended: The full scale adjustment is made by setting the input voltage to precisely ½ LSB less than full scale or ½ LSB down from nominal full scale. (Note that the nominal full scale is actually never reached but is always one LSB short). Adjust the full scale control until the converter output just barely switches from full output to one count less than full output.

Graphs give aperture time required for a-d conversion

by Eugene L. Zuch
Datel Systems Inc., Canton, Mass.

The time required for an analog-to-digital converter to make a conversion is known as "aperture time," and depends on both the resolution and the particular conversion method employed. For commercially available a-d converters that use the successive approximation

method, the aperture time may be 40 microseconds for a relatively low-cost 12-bit converter, or as little as 4 μs for a more expensive high-speed 12-bit converter. In many cases a sample-hold circuit is used ahead of an a-d converter to effectively reduce the aperture times; the sample-hold can take a very fast sample of the analog signal and then hold the value while the a-d operation is performed. (The time interval during which the signal-hold circuit turns off is then the aperture time, and determines the conversion accuracy. The time for actual a-d conversion can be longer.)

It is important for the designer to know what aperture time is required to keep the system error to a tolerable value in terms of the resolution of his a-d coverter. The

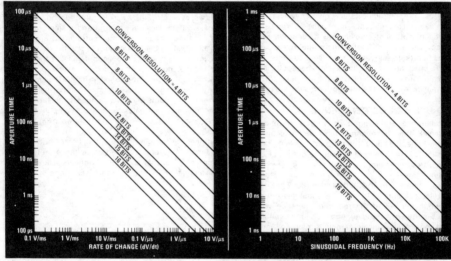

1. Sampling time. Aperture time for 1-bit accuracy at various resolutions in a-d conversion are shown here. Graph (a) gives aperture time as a function of signal rate of change for signals that are 10 volts full scale or 10 volts peak to peak. Graph (b) gives aperture time as a function of frequency for sinusoidal signals. Aperture times for larger allowed error can be found by reading on line for lower resolution, e.g., a 2-bit error and 8-bit resolution requires the same time as a 1-bit error and 7-bit resolution. Equations for these graphs are found in text.

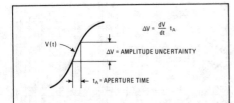

2. Error. Possibility of error in a-d conversion depends upon aperture time. The greater t_A is, the greater the uncertainty in value of an analog voltage that has been converted to digital level.

maximum aperture time that allows 1-bit accuracy in conversion of an analog signal to 4 bits, 6 bits, . . . or 16 bits is given here in two useful graphs. The graph in Fig. 1(a) shows this aperture time as a function of signal rate of change, for signals that are 10 volts full scale or peak to peak. Fig. 1(b) gives the aperture time as a function of the frequency of a sinusoidal signal.

The two graphs are derived with reference to Fig. 2, which shows a time-varying signal and the amplitude uncertainty ΔV associated with an aperture time t_A

$$t_A = \Delta V/(dV/dt)$$

If the fractional error ε is the ratio of ΔV to full-scale voltage V_{FS},

$$t_A = (\varepsilon \, V_{FS})/(dV/dt)$$

If ΔV is held to 1 bit, and V_{FS} is resolved into n bits, then $\varepsilon = 1/(2^n)$, and

$$t_A = V_{FS}/2^n(dV/dt)$$

This is the equation for the family of lines in Fig. 1(a), with $V_{FS} = 10$ volts and n = 4, 6, . . . 16.

For a sinusoidal signal, which has a maximum rate of change at its zero crossing,

$$\Delta V = t_A \, [d/dt(\tfrac{1}{2})(V \sin \omega t)]_{t=0} = \omega V t_A/2$$

where V is peak-to-peak signal value. This gives

$$t_A = (2\Delta V)/(\omega V) = \varepsilon/\pi f = 1/(2^n \pi f)$$

for a 1-bit error and n-bit resolution. This is the equation for the family of lines in Fig. 1(b).

If the allowed error is to be 2 bits instead of 1 bit, then $\varepsilon = 2/(2^n)$, so aperture times are doubled. An error of 3 bits gives $\varepsilon = 4/(2^n)$, and so on; thus a 1-bit increase in error is equivalent to a 1-bit decrease in resolution on the graphs.

As an example of the usefulness of these graphs, assume that a 1-kilohertz sinusoidal signal is to be digitized to a resolution of 10 bits. What aperture time must be used to give less than 1 bit of error? The answer, readily found from Fig. 1(b), is 320 nanoseconds. For ½ bit error the aperture time would have to be 160 ns. This is surprising, because a 1-kHz signal is really not very fast, and a 10-bit/320-ns converter is not to be found commercially available as a module. Therefore, a sample-hold circuit would be required ahead of a slower a-d converter. □

NOTE: Pages 108 and 109 show large, detailed versions of Figure 1.

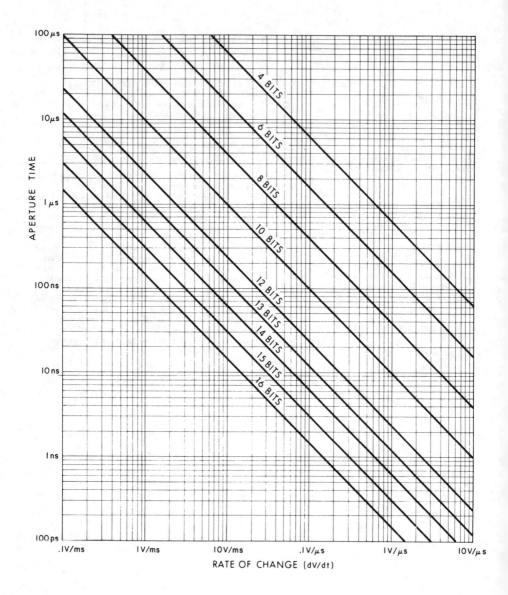

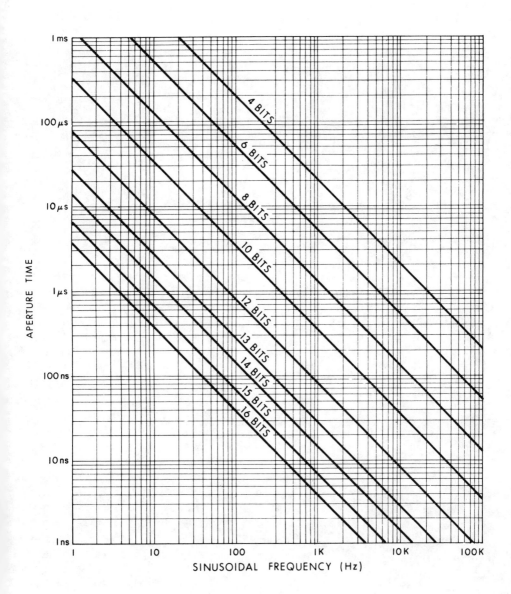

3. Data Conversion Systems

Linking the analog world to digital computers

The link is made with devices such as analog-to-digital and digital-to-analog converters. Learn how they're used and what they can do for control systems.

Eugene L. Zuch,
Datel Systems, Inc., Canton, Mass.

Data conversion devices link the real world of analog physical parameters with the artificial world of digital computers. They are used in many industries in a wide variety of applications, including data telemetry, automatic process control, test and measurement, computer display, digital panel meters and multimeters, and voice communications, as well as in remote data recording and video signal processing. The devices include not only analog-to-digital (A/D) converters and digital-to-analog (D/A) converters, but also a number of auxiliary components—analog multiplexers, sample-holds and various amplifiers and filters.

To get acquainted with data conversion, let's first look at where the various data conversion components fit in a control

system and then what type of data converter will meet system requirements of speed, cost, or accuracy.

In a typical automatic chemical process control system (Fig. 1), the chemicals in a vat must be mixed according to a prescribed temperature-pressure-time relationship stored in the computer's memory. The state of the process is sensed by two transducers connected to the vat: a temperature transducer, such as a thermocouple, and a pressure transducer.

The transducer outputs are low-level signals, which must be amplified before further processing can be done. Each amplifier output is filtered to remove noise from the signal and prevent errors in the sampling process. A multiplexer then alternately samples the temperature and the pressure. Since

---

Data Conversion Glossary

Bit is a binary digit consisting of a "1" or "0".
Resolution is the smallest change that can be distinguished by a converter (in bits or percent).

Resolution (bits)	Accuracy
4	6%
6	1.5%
8	0.4%
10	0.1%
12	0.02%
14	0.006%

Nonlinearity is the maximum deviation of a converter response from an ideal straight line (expressed in bits or percent).

Monotonicity is when the converter output always increases for increasing input.

Quantizing Error is the basic uncertainty associated with digitizing any analog signal value.

Conversion Rate is the number of complete conversions per second executed by an A/D or D/A converter.

Relative Accuracy is the input to output error of a data converter as a percent of full scale.

Absolute Accuracy is the input to output error, as a percent of full scale, referred to the NBS standard volt.

there are just two channels in this example, a simple multiplexer acts like a single pole double throw switch. Both the temperature and the pressure are slowly changing variables so it is not necessary to monitor them continuously.

The multiplexer output goes to a sample-hold circuit, which stores the analog value between samples, and holds the value long enough for the A/D converter to convert it to digital data. The digital output of the A/D converter enters the computer via a bidirectional data bus line. An additional circuit controls the timing of the various operations of the system.

The computer receives the input temperature and pressure data and compares it to the desired value stored in memory. It then computes correction data which it feeds out to the D/A converters over the data bus. The converters drive the actuators, which control the system directly. This closes the feedback loop.

What types of conversion

When looking at converters you undoubtedly run into the terms dual slope, successive approximation and parallel, to cite the most common ones. When you ask your vendor what these terms mean to you and your system, you more than likely get a long winded technical dissertation! What you probably want to know is what are the basic operating differences. If you want more details after reading this article, handbooks with this type of information are available from many manufacturers, including us.

Many conversion techniques have been used over the years, each striving for a higher degree of accuracy, faster speeds or an inexpensive price tag. Those that have survived and are in common use today include: parallel input D/A, successive approximation A/D, dual slope A/D, parallel A/D and charge balancing A/D. Briefly, here's what they are and where they fit.

Parallel input D/A

When the term D/A converter (or DAC) is used today, it automatically implies a parallel input D/A. The control outputs in Fig. 1 would use this type.

The alternative to the parallel DAC is the serial DAC in which the output analog value is developed sequentially, one bit at a time.

The parallel DAC has become popular for two reasons: it's fast and it's compatible with most digital data today, which is in parallel rather than serial form. Output settling time for one of today's D/A converters can vary from 20 nanoseconds (ns) for an ultra-fast current output to several microseconds (µs) for a voltage output. Accuracy depends on the trimming of the resistors used in the internal network, how well they track each other with temperature, and the type of electronic switch used (CMOS, bipolar or current source switch).

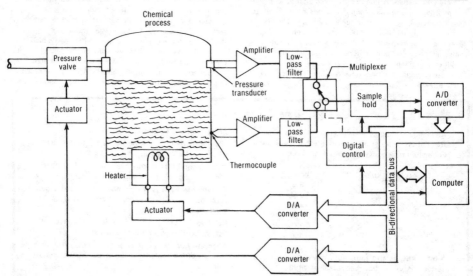

Fig. 1: Data conversion in a process control system. From the transducers and thermocouples, the analog data passes through a filter to a multiplexer. Either signal is amplified, digitized and fed to the computer. The computer calculates the error and sends back correction signals, which a D/A converter changes to analog signals that are fed to the control actuator.

Successive approximation A/D converter

The most widely used A/D converter, especially for control systems, is the successive approximation type. It's accurate and has a conversion time fast enough to handle a large number of channels. This type would be used in the example in Fig. 1.

In addition to its use in data acquisition and control systems, the successive approximation converter is also used for high speed measurement systems and pulse code modulation (PCM) systems. For control systems where there may be several hundred different parameters to measure, its fast conversion time makes it ideal. Most 12-bit A/D converters of this type have conversion times from 2 μs up to 50 μs. The accuracy is generally good, although it depends on careful circuit design.

Dual slope A/D converter

A slower, although more accurate converter, is the dual slope type. This technique is second in popularity to the successive approximation type.

The relative simplicity of the dual slope converter gives it a high degree of accuracy over both time and temperature changes.

As we said before, dual slope A/D converters are, however, relatively slow—conversion can take anywhere from a few milliseconds (ms) up to several hundred milliseconds, depending on the particular converter design. For this reason, they are used where accuracy, not speed, is important—slow data acquisition and measurement systems, digital multimeters and digital panel meters.

Parallel A/D converter

Ultra high speed conversion may require the parallel A/D technique, also known as the "flash" or "simultaneous" method. But resolution beyond 4 bits is not practical, so this method is not as frequently used as the preceding two.

If a fast 8-bit conversion is needed, a two-step technique is used with two four-bit converters. Although low in resolution, the parallel method is very fast—converting 8 bits in as little as 50 ns. This makes parallel A/D conversion ideal for video signal processing and radar digitizing applications, but not for most types of control.

Charge balancing A/D converter

Low-cost V/F (voltage to frequency) converters and some A/D converters are using the increasingly popular charge balancing technique. As with the dual slope method, its conversion time is relatively slow and its accuracy depends on a very linear internal operational integrator circuit.

Like the dual slope method, the charge balancing technique is relatively noise free. V/F converters, in particular, have many uses. They are practical, for example, when converting an analog voltage into a train of pulses, which can

Data converters come in a variety of packages. Shown is a small hybrid 12-bit A/D converter.

then be transmitted with high noise immunity, to another location and then counted. As with the dual slope method, this method is more practical for slower applications, such as digital panel meters.

Modules, hybrids and monolithics

Data conversion devices come in a wide assortment of packages. The highest performance A/D or D/A converters are packaged as discrete modules. The multiplexer, sample hold, amplifier and the computer interfacing are external to the module. These would be interconnected, as needed, on printed circuit boards or available as complete modules. Newer hybrid microelectronic converters come in small 24- or 32-pin packages (usually less than 1.1 by 1.7 inches) and provide high performance conversion as well.

Monolithic integrated circuit converters are small and inexpensive, although they usually require external amplifiers, capacitors or resistors. Three types of monolithic converters are available: parallel D/A, dual slope A/D and charge balancing A/D.

Packaging of A/D converters may be interesting to watch as the packages shrink, but the most important selection criteria for control users is speed, accuracy or, in some cases, cost. If users want to convert digital to analog data, there's hardly a choice—the parallel D/A converter is the answer. For both speed and accuracy, the successive approximation A/D is the logical choice. Users who want very high resolution, but don't care much about speed, should look at dual slope A/D converters. Extra high speeds require parallel A/D converters. And if low-cost is a consideration, then a charge balancing type of V/F or F/V converter should be considered. ■

Single hybrid package houses 12-bit data-acquisition system

Handling either 8 differential or 16 single-ended inputs,
device acquires data at 50 kHz or faster from many sources

by Wayne E. Marshall, *Datel Systems Inc., Canton, Mass.*

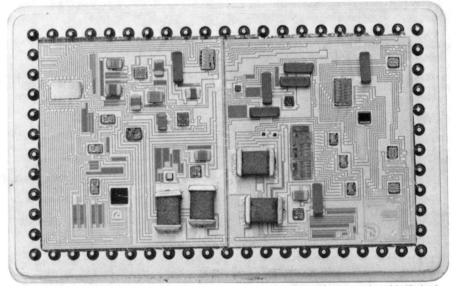

□ The shift from minicomputers to microcomputers in data processing has been paralleled by the shift from boards and modules to microcircuits in data conversion. By now, complete microprocessor-compatible data-acquisition systems are available as single plug-in hybrid or monolithic components. Eight-bit performance has been the limit, though, with the hybrid devices being much faster though less economical than the monolithic converters. For 12-bit performance, users have had to turn back to bulky modules or else interconnect two or more hybrid circuits.

Getting down to one package

But a new 12-bit hybrid data-acquisition system is offering users the convenience and cost savings of a single integrated-circuit-compatible package, together with the high performance and reliability of a hybrid circuit. Besides multichannel capability, the device includes address decoding logic, an adjustable-gain instrumentation amplifier, a sample-and-hold circuit, a 12-bit successive-approximation analog-to-digital converter, control logic, and three-state output buffers for interfacing with a microprocessor data bus. It is manufactured in two versions, the HDAS-8 handling eight differential inputs and the HDAS-16 handling 16 single-ended inputs.

Housed in a hermetic 62-pin ceramic package, the device meets all the requirements of MIL-STD-883A, class B. To shrink its overall size, as well as optimize the internal layout and make external access easy, the pins are arranged around all four sides of the package, instead of in two parallel rows. The use of ceramic instead of metal keeps cost and especially weight down.

With such a complex hybrid, internal power consumption, of course, must be minimized. An equivalent modular unit uses about 4.5 watts, which in the hybrid's 62-pin ceramic package would push the temperature at the chip-mounting surface 50°C above ambient. Since

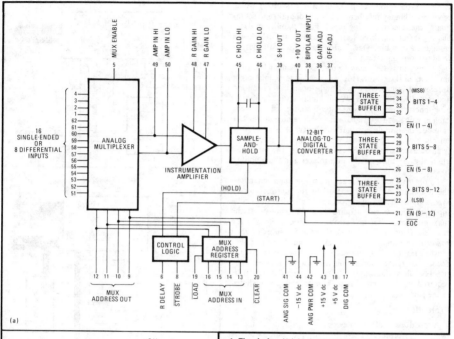

(a)

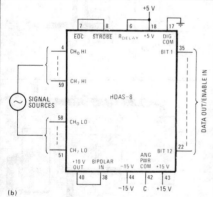

(b)

1. The device. Hybrid data-acquisition system (a) delivers 12-bit data for 8 differential or 16 single-ended input channels. A few simple connections (b), and the hybrid will automatically address the input channels sequentially for a system throughput rate of 50 kHz.

Finally, in a move that reduces device complexity as well as temperature rise, as many of the internal thin-film resistors as possible are placed directly on the ceramic substrate, and not on separate chips of glass, silicon, or ceramic. With either technique, there will always be a resistor-to-conductor interface. But making a resistor part of the substrate eliminates the two wire-bond interfaces at its terminations, making wire-bond weakness a less likely cause of failure.

How the device operates

The circuit configuration (Fig. 1a) for the device is a fairly common one for a data-acquisition system. At the front end is an analog multiplexer having either 8 differential or 16 single-ended channels, which may be addressed randomly or scanned sequentially. Following the multiplexer is an instrumentation amplifier that extracts the input signal from common-mode noise. The gain of this amplifier is adjustable (through an external resistor) from 1 to 1,000, so that the maximum expected range of the input signal becomes ±10 volts at the amplifier output for optimum dynamic range.

A precision sample-and-hold circuit then buffers the selected signal, holding its level constant during the actual conversion. The output of the sample-and-hold

the unit must be able to operate at 125°C ambient, and silicon semiconductors deteriorate at junction temperatures above 150°C, the internal temperature rise must be limited to 25°C. Considerations of power therefore override those of space so that, wherever possible, the device employs bulky tantalum chip capacitors and low-power transconductance-mode amplifiers, while the digital control circuitry uses low-power Schottky transistor-transistor logic only.

serves as the input to a 12-bit a-d converter, which produces a binary number that is the digital representation of the selected analog input. For flexibility in data-bus organization, three-state logic elements, which are configured in 4-bit bytes, buffer the digital data output from the a-d converter.

The hybrid is very easy to use, as is evident from the simplicity of the circuit (Fig. 1b) needed to acquire eight differential inputs. A few straightforward connections, and the HDAS-8 delivers 12-bit binary data at a rate of 50 kilohertz from eight sequentially addressed channels, each having a ±10-v signal range. Since no gain resistor is used, the amplifier's gain is unity. A single strap selects bipolar operation (+10 v), and another strap from R delay to the +5-v supply selects the internally allotted delay time for the multiplexer and the amplifier to settle.

To obtain continuous scanning of the input channels, the user need do nothing at all to the address control inputs. With its end-of-conversion flag tied to the strobe input, the device will acquire data continuously at the maximum rate. For self-strobe operation, though, the rise time (from 10% to 90%) of the +5-v supply (when power is first applied or interrupted and then reapplied) must be less than 10 microseconds, or else a latchup may occur. For reliable operation, the user should examine the $\overline{EOC}$ flag and apply a $\overline{STROBE}$ signal when it is required. Even supply-bypass components are included in the package.

Protection

A good part of the device's ruggedness is due to overvoltage protection circuitry for the multiplexer. A 1-kilohm resistor on each channel input limits the current flowing through protection diodes and, in combination with stray nodal capacitance, limits the rise time of large spikes so that the diode can clip them before they do any damage. Even without using any external components, protection is assured to 20 v beyond the ±15-v supply voltages.

Adding a series resistance to each input can increase protection up to a diode current limit of ±10 milliamperes. But large values of input resistance are not altogether desirable. Besides raising the input noise, they increase the settling time of the instrumentation amplifier for changing input signals, as well as the multiplexer's recovery time from switching transients.

Expanding the channel capacity of the hybrid requires just one external component, connected as shown in Fig. 2a. This hookup converts the HDAS-16 from a 16-channel single-ended unit into a 16-channel differential part. In fact, channels may be added almost without limit at very little cost, as Fig. 2b illustrates. Here, with the addition of just 15 multiplexers and one logic device (a one-of-16 decoder), the HDAS-16 acquires 256 channels of low-level analog signals. In this application, the unit compares the outputs from 256 temperature-sensing

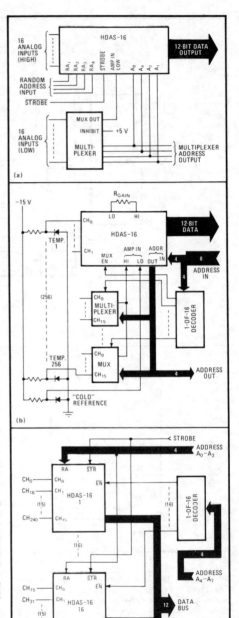

2. Easy channel expansion. One external component converts the HDAS-16 into a 16-channel differential part (a). Adding 15 multiplexers and a single logic decoder accommodates 256 input channels (b). For throughput faster than 50 kHz, more hybrids are needed (c).

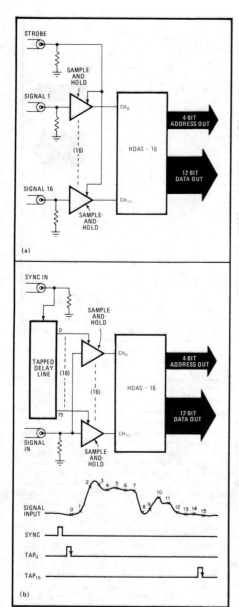

3. Handling high-frequency inputs. To acquire signals beyond the mid-audio range requires a sample-and-hold circuit for each channel (a). For a nonrepetitive high-frequency signal, a delay line and a string of sample-and-holds slice the input into 16 pieces (b).

diodes with the output of a single reference diode.

Indeed, the hybrid is built to be expanded—it can handle up to 65,536 channels with the addition of only 17 logic circuits. The unit's multiplexer-enable line is what makes this possible. Left alone, it is high, and the internal multiplexer is enabled. But when pulled low, it disables the internal multiplexer and frees the amplifier input lines for external multiplexer control.

Although the circuit of Fig. 2b is an economical way to handle 256 channels at a 50-kHz rate, that throughput may not be fast enough for some applications. A faster throughput of 800 kHz is easily achieved by interleaving 16 hybrids into 256 channels (Fig. 2c). This circuit is actually just as simple as the slower one, for it still requires only one external decoder device. Because the hybrid uses three-state data outputs, all 16 units can be tied to one data bus and enabled one at a time during the delay period preceding the next conversion while the data from the last conversion is still valid.

Both the HDAS-8 and the HDAS-16 are ideally suited to acquiring data quickly from many sources, with two provisos: the sources should all have similar maximum signal levels, and the highest frequency components of the signal sources must be in the low audio range. When the signal sources have dissimilar ranges, the dynamic range of some signals will be less than optimum because the gain of the differential amplifier will be set to accommodate the largest signal range. This limitation is normally overcome by using prescaling amplifiers, which also serve as convenient low-impedance signal line drivers and as filter points to reduce unwanted power-line signals and the like.

Acquiring high-frequency signals

When the signal sources are to contain high-frequency components that the data-acquisition system must recognize and acquire accurately, a very fast track-and-hold circuit or, better yet, a true sample-and-hold should intercept the signal and hold it for a precisely controlled time. Once the signal has been processed by the multiplexer, the amplifier, and so on, its bandwidth and phase delay are no longer precisely known. Figure 3a shows one way to do real-time analysis of input signals having frequencies up to 25 kHz. With this circuit, to retain precise information as to the time of sample, 16 sample-and-holds simultaneously sample the input signals, and the data-acquisition system digitizes the held analog value on each input channel.

Beyond 25 kHz, the inability of the hybrid to generate two data points per cycle of the input signal violates the Nyquist criteria of signal sampling. When repetitive events need not be analyzed in real time—for example, when synchronized sampling heads provide sample snatches with varying delays—the frequency limit extends to the bandwidth of the sample-and-hold circuits. But for real-time analysis of nonrepetitive signals, another approach is needed.

Radar pulses are a common example of nonrecurring pulses that contain critical target data that must be analyzed in exceedingly fine detail in real time. To handle them, the HDAS-16 data-acquisition system requires just a tapped delay line and a string of fast

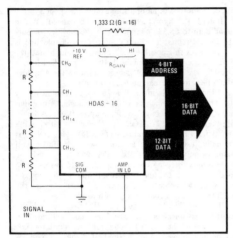

4. Putting amplifier gain to work. It is even possible to turn the HDAS-16 into a 16-bit a-d converter by applying the input signal to the internal amplifier's inverting input. Here, the amplifier-input-low line is being viewed as a high-impedance, transient-free signal input.

sample-and-holds, as noted in Fig. 3b. In effect, the sample-and-holds slice the radar pulse into 16 easy-to-digest pieces, while the delay line causes each sample-and-hold to retain the analog information at incremental times following the synchronization pulse. Meanwhile, the hybrid can address and digitize each input slice at a comparatively leisurely pace, producing a 12-bit binary word for each of the 16 slices at a word rate of 50 kHz. Clearly, there is a limit to the number of sample-and-hold circuits that may be addressed and digitized before hold-capacitor droop problems destroy analog signal accuracy. This limit may be circumvented by adding more hybrids to the circuit, at any rate until system cost reaches that of a real-time video converter.

To increase resolution up to 16 bits

Besides being useful as a video a-d converter, the HDAS-16 may be operated as a 16-bit a-d converter. Unlike the HDAS-8, in which the two multiplexer outputs are both committed to the amplifier's inputs, the HDAS-16 has only one multiplexer output so committed. It is tied internally to the amplifier's noninverting (high) input, leaving the inverting (low) amplifier input for the user to connect, for example, to the signal source common. (In any event, the user must of necessity return eventually the signal source common to the hybrid's signal or power common.)

Another way of looking at the HDAS-16's amplifier-input-low line is as a high-impedance transient-free signal input, as illustrated in Fig. 4. Wired in this way, the HDAS-16 operates as a 16-bit a-d converter. Fifteen resistors, precisely matched and equal in value, divide the internal 10-v reference into 16 equally spaced voltages, so as to bias the input channels into 16 contiguous windows. The amplifier will only amplify the difference

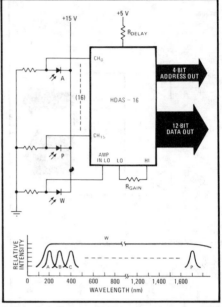

5. High gain. In this fast spectrophotometer application for monitoring industrial waste, the hybrid's high-gain capability and adjustable settling time are exploited. Careful tailoring of delay time versus gain provides best system resolution in terms of data rate needs.

between the input signal and the selected channel voltage. (With R gain at 1,333 ohms, amplifier gain is 16.)

Only one channel address will be associated with an in-range 12-bit data word, and all other channels will yield all zeros or all ones. When the address of the selected channel is used as the top 4 bits and the resulting conversion data as the bottom 12 bits, the HDAS-16 generates a 16-bit complementary binary data word. For input signals in the audio-frequency range, the channel address will change by no more than one count from one conversion to the next, so that no more than two conversions are ever necessary to obtain valid data. This means that the HDAS-16 will typically deliver 16 bits in 20 microseconds, or 40 μs maximum.

When high gain is needed

Some applications require both high gain and multichannel capability. However, when the gain exceeds 20, the hybrid's amplifier needs more than the internally allotted 9 μs for settling to within 12-bit accuracy. Even though the signal inputs may change slowly, the amplifier sees the multiplexer output as a fast-changing step function, with changes occurring whenever the multiplexer address changes.

The amplifier, then, must have enough time to settle fully in response to these abrupt changes before a conversion takes place. Suppose, for example, the appli-

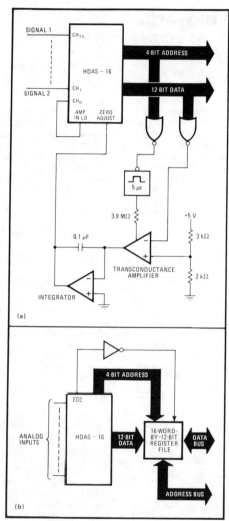

(a)

(b)

6. Odds and ends. Charge-pump loop (a) cancels troublesome offset errors for all time and temperature. A twin circuit could be used to cancel gain errors also. Register file (b) creates memory location for HDAS-16, so data access is independent of the hybrid's status.

cation calls for a fast spectrophotometer for monitoring industrial waste or a similar cost-sensitive task. Figure 5 shows one solution utilizing the hybrid's high-gain capability and its user-adjustable settling delay time. Here, the outputs of 16 photodiodes, each of which has a different narrow-band filter, are compared to the output of an unfiltered white-light reference diode. Since the

photon-induced diode voltage is small, amplifier gain must be large for a reasonable dynamic range. Instead of strapping the hybrid's R delay pin directly to the +5-v supply, as is usually done, the user may add a series resistor to increase the delay time between an address change and the start of a conversion. By carefully tailoring the delay time to the gain, the user can optimize system resolution versus data-rate needs. Even at a gain of 1,000, throughput rate will be at least 3.3 kHz, with root-mean-square system noise held to less than ½ least significant bit.

Dealing with accuracy errors

Many users of data-conversion devices are puzzled by the seeming inconsistency of specifications for relative accuracy and absolute accuracy. But distinguishing between the two is not all that difficult. In brief, relative accuracy is a measure of a device's differential linearity and monotonicity, while absolute accuracy reflects the unit's gain and offset stability. Furthermore, relative accuracy requires that similar components do the same thing with time and temperature, whereas absolute accuracy requires that a component does not change with time and temperature—a requirement that flies in the face of reality.

As it advances, process technology will continue to reduce accuracy errors, but it will always come closer to optimizing relative than absolute accuracy. Certain circuit techniques, however, permit doing away with absolute-accuracy errors altogether. For example, the simple one shown in Fig. 6a cancels offset errors, and a twin circuit could be used to cancel gain errors as well. This technique uses a charge-pump loop to hold absolute errors below measurable levels for all time and all temperatures. When data (offset voltage) appears on channel zero, the transconductance amplifier receives a bias-set pulse for 5 μs. If the data is zero, this amplifier sinks (or sources in the case of non-zero data) a current pulse to the integrator that minutely adjusts the hybrid's zero. At null, there is an imperceptible ±1-pulse hunt traded off against capture time.

In a microprocessor-based system the time needed to digitize analog data can become very long with respect to the processor's cycle time, particularly if the data-conversion device is a reasonably priced unit. This time difference causes all sorts of software problems that require complex interrupt schemes to solve. But, in fact, the delay is totally unrelated to the need for fully updated signal data, and the data-conversion device is usually quite capable of generating digital data at a fast enough rate to satisfy most signal-analysis requirements.

One simple way to work around the delay is to insert a multiple-port register file between the data-conversion device and the digital processor, as shown in Fig. 6b. Essentially, the register file creates a memory location for a continuously scanning HDAS-16. Data access is fast, free, and independent of the hybrid's status. Thus, the hybrid generates new data words at 50 kHz and updates a 16-word file at a rate of over 3 kHz. Meanwhile, the digital processor can request and retrieve data at normal memory-access speeds without disturbing or waiting for the data-acquisition system.   □

Put video a/d converters to work.

These small, inexpensive show-stoppers can digitize the analog signals required for a variety of applications.

Video-speed, 8-bit, a/d converters—particularly those that use two, 4-bit, hybrid, flash stages[1]—are now small enough and inexpensive enough to work in a variety of applications, including digital television, transient recording, radar-signature analysis and distortion analyzers.

Probably the most extensive use of ultra-high-speed a/d converters will be broadcast TV, where digital picture processing has started a revolution that is perhaps even profounder than the transition from tubes to semiconductors.

Though the potential advantages of digital television were obvious for some time, its potentiality didn't become reality until compact, ultra-high-speed, reasonably priced, a/d converters and high-density LSI memory chips appeared.

Basically, digital television-picture processing requires three major steps:

1. Digitizing the analog signal from the camera (or other video source) using very fast a/d converters.

Eugene Zuch, Product Manager, Datel Systems, 1020 Turnpike St., Canton, MA 02021.

2. Processing the converted data digitally.

3. Reconverting the processed picture data into analog form for transmission via d/a converters.

Right now, digital TV extends only to processing video signals in studios. Digital data aren't transmitted to home receivers—yet. But the digitized video signals do have the following advantages:

■ They're immune to noise.

■ They can be stored in digital form and read out at selectable rates.

■ They can be simply converted to different TV standards.

■ They can be delayed, compressed and stretched.

Video a/d stars in digital TV

From the performance viewpoint, a digital-TV system's a/d converter is the most important block. The converter limits the system's two crucial characteristics—resolution and sampling rate. Fortunately, 8-bit resolution faithfully reproduces a TV picture. At video speed, higher resolution gets prohibitively expensive. An 8-bit converter quantizes the luminance, or video-signal amplitude, into 2^8, or 256, discrete

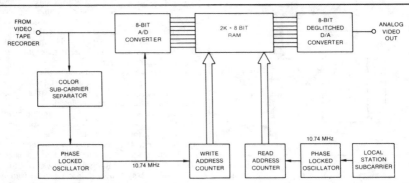

1. **Digital time-base correction** systems synchronize data converted by this video-speed, 8-bit a/d converter to the local-station color subcarrier. The RAM stores up to three lines of digitized video data.

levels. These 0.4% amplitude steps produce a grey scale that appears continuous.

Today's high-speed a/d converters sample at the rates required by digital TV. The well-known Nyquist criterion of the sampling theorem spells out the required theoretical sampling rate (to recover a band-limited signal without distortion, it must be sampled at least twice as fast as its highest-frequency component). In the U.S., the National Television System Committee (NTSC) standard is in force. The TV signal has a 4.2-MHz bandwidth, which requires a minimum 8.4-MHz sampling rate.

In practice the sampling frequency is higher than the required minimum, and usually an integral multiple (three or four) of the 3.58-MHz color subcarrier. Thus, the most common sampling rates are 10.74 and 14.32 million per second.

There is another standard to consider: the wider-bandwidth, European, phase-alternating line (PAL) standard. The video bandwidth is 5.5 MHz and the color-subcarrier frequency is 4.43 MHz. Sampling three and four times the color-subcarrier rate means 13.29 and 17.72-MHz conversion rates, respectively. To compare data for both U.S. and European systems,

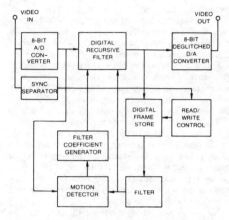

3. **Digital noise reducers** store the converted frame data for element-by-element processing in a recursive filter. To avoid smearing moving pictures, frames whose elements show too much motion aren't filtered.

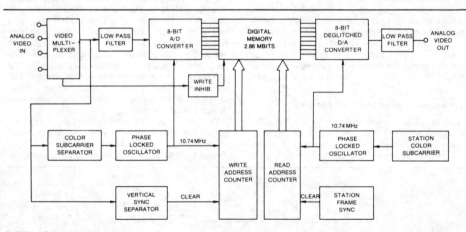

2. **Digital frame synchronizers** retime TV frames to the local station's color subcarrier and vertical sync.

see the information in the table.

One of the first TV problems solved by digital technology was signal jitter, or time-base error, which is a common problem at the output of video-tape recorders synchronized to a power-line frequency. TV broadcasting requires that recorders be synchronized to local-station color subcarriers.

Fig. 1 illustrates the basic operation of a digital time-base corrector system that synchronizes a videotape recorder's output to the local TV station's subcarrier. This system combines a fast, semiconductor, digital memory with an ultrafast a/d.

The memory is the key to resynchronization. The system reads out the stored converted video by means of its read-address counter, which is controlled by clock pulses from the station's color subcarrier. A phase-locked oscillator derives the 10.74-MHz read pulses from the subcarrier. The data from memory updates an ultrafast, deglitched d/a converter that reconstructs the video signal.

No matter how much the input signal jitters, the output, after comparison and storage, is jitter-free because it is closely synchronized to the station's color subcarrier. But the time base itself must then be stable to within ±5 nanoseconds.

Time-base-corrector memories generally store up to three video lines—with an associated delay of 189 μs for the three lines. Three-line storage requires the memory capacity for 2048 samples of 8 bits each. So, a 2-k × 8-bit RAM is sufficient. Of course, the average rate of data into the memory can't exceed the average of data out, or the memory can run out of capacity.

Fast a/d and a memory: a TV twosome

Like the time-base corrector, another important TV-processing system, a digital frame synchronizer, combines a video a/d converter and a memory. The frame synchronizer integrates nonsynchronous TV signals from remote sources, into a broadcast, which enables a station to switch video sources without breaking up its picture. Moreover, all the station's video sources, both local and remote, are put into simultaneous raster and color phase.

Typical remote sources are portable news cameras, satellite links, and videotape recorders. Portable-camera signals are either relayed to the studio or recorded first on videotape. Satellite signals go to the network rather than to local studios.

Because it corrects both instantaneous time-base errors and source delays, a digital-frame synchronizer is more complex than a time-base corrector. To synchronize incoming and station-generated frames, the equipment is, in effect, a variable delay line.

Though it synchronizes frames similarly to the way time bases are corrected, a frame synchronizer requires more memory. Whereas a time-base corrector stores up to three lines of video, frame synchronizers store a full frame of 525 lines (33-ms delay). Because there are 455/2 cycles of color subcarrier in each raster line, the memory capacity must be at least 2.87 Mbits (227.5 subcarrier cycles per line × 525 lines × three samples per cycle, × eight bits per sample).

Fig. 2 shows a digital frame synchronizer in block diagram. This system first filters a video-source signal through a low-pass network, then sends it to the a/d converter. Separate circuits extract the color subcarrier and vertical sync from the incoming composite video. The color subcarrier controls a 10.74-MHz phase-locked oscillator, which in turn triggers the a/d and controls the memory write-address counter. The vertical-sync pulse clears the write-address counter at the end of every frame. Thirty entire frames pass in and out of the memory, every second.

The frames of composite digitized video are read out of the memory independently of their writing, since the station color-subcarrier and vertical-sync signals control the read-address counter. The station

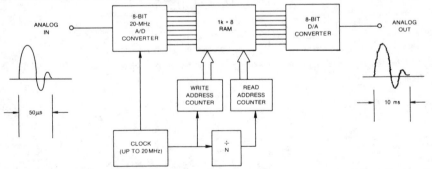

4. **Recording transients** requires two times scales—fast for input sampling, slow for output display. Once the digitized data are read into the RAM, readout can be at any rate convenient for display.

U.S. and European TV standards

	Lines	Band-Width	Color Sub-Carrier	Sampling Rate 3X Subcarrier	4X Subcarrier
NTSC	525	4.2 MHz	3.58 MHz	10.74 MHz	14.32 MHz
PAL	625	5.5 MHz	4.43 MHz	13.29 MHz	17.72 MHz

color subcarrier phase-locks the 10.74-MHz oscillator, which both controls the read-address counter and synchronously updates the d/a input. The station vertical-sync pulse clears the read-address counter after every frame is completed.

The write-inhibit circuit in Fig. 2 prevents picture disturbance when the frame-synchronizer switches among nonsynchronous sources. To prevent changing video sources in the middle of a field when the input is switched, this circuit inhibits writing until the frame pulse of the new video source arrives.

All noise isn't sound

As in all communications systems, noise reduction has always been an objective in TV. Unlike their expensive analog predecessors, which reduce TV noise by only a few dB, digital noise-reduction systems like the one in Fig. 3 can mow down picture noise by 9 to 15 dB, and at a resonable cost.

This system is based on a one-frame, first-order, recursive filter. (A recursive filter's output depends on both its previous output and its input.) Depending on the filter coefficient, K, you can get almost any level of filtering you may need.

The noise-reduction technique rests on a simple concept—after a number of frames, the output is the average of all previous inputs, so noise averages out. However, there is a problem inherent in this system. Averaging delays the output to the point where the effect is objectionable on moving images. So, only still pictures can be averaged.

The motion-detection scheme is ingenious. It compares the luminance of each element of one picture with its counterpart in the previous frame. Changed luminance indicates motion and lowers K, and filtering and lag along with it. With little or no motion, K stays high and the frame is heavily filtered. As a result, noise disappears from relatively still pictures but remains in frames showing motion.

Fig. 3 shows a TV-noise reducer that stores an entire frame digitally. An ultrafast a/d digitizes the input-video signal, which then goes to a recursive digital filter. A deglitched d/a converts the recursive-filter output back to analog form. The digital frame store holds all picture elements from the previous frame.

After filtering, the frame store feeds both the recursive filter and the motion detector. The motion detector determines the recursive filter, K, by means of the filter-coefficient generator.

In addition to time-base correction, frame synchronization and noise reduction, digital-TV equipment using a/d converters can store still pictures and convert standards. The technique is called, not surprisingly, still-store. TV news programs usually store still pictures via slide projection or card display. Digital still-store replaces both with a disc-based all-electronic system that uses an a/d converter.

The a/d converts stills into digital form, then a disc-pack memory, with up to a 200-Mbyte capacity, stores the data. The stored pictures can then be recalled in fractions of a second. What's more, disc-based, digital still-store can deliver still pictures in whatever sequence you program it to.

Standards converters produce the signals required by the NTSC's 525-line, 60-Hz system from the PAL's 625-line, 50-Hz system, and vice-versa. Analog TV-standards converters have been expensive, complex and bulky. Digital standards converters, while smaller and less costly, are also rather complex.

There's more than TV

Of course, video a/d converters can do more than digitize TV signals. You can combine an ultra-high-speed a/d and a fast digital memory to record fast transients like those in shock and explosion testing, pulsed nuclear-magnetic resonance, high-speed chemical reactions and power-line disturbances. Fig. 4 shows such a transient recorder in block diagram. Here, the 8-bit, 20-MHz a/d samples a transient at up to a 20-MHz rate. The fast, 1-k × 8 random-access memory stores 1024 sequential a/d-output samples of 8 bits each. The converter and memory simply stay synchronized: The same signal clocks both the write-address counter and the a/d converter.

After the memory stores 1024 samples of digital data, representing the analog transient, the system switches modes from write to read. But reading is much slower than data entry, because the read-address clocking is derived by dividing the 20-MHz clock frequency by a constant, N. Unlike the one-shot

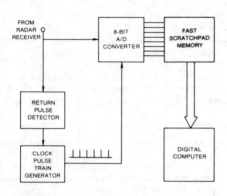

5. **Radar-signature-analysis systems** use powerful computers to process information contained in the return pulse's frequency content, amplitude and wave shape. You need a fast converter but not much memory.

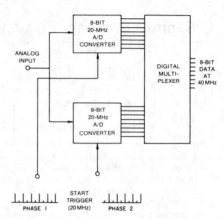

7. **"Ping-pong" operation** of two fast a/d converters from a two-phase clock doubles the data-output rate.

way data are written into the RAM, reading is repetitive because the address counter recirculates to zero after address 1024.

The RAM output goes to a fast, 8-bit d/a converter, which reconstructs the analog signal sample by sample. With a high N, you can read data slowly; by letting the clock run on, you can read over and over. The repetitive output signal is suitable for oscilloscope display. For an analog strip-chart recorder, data can be read only once, but even more slowly (higher N).

For a simple example of transient recording, look

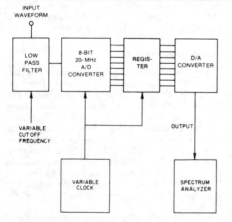

6. **Distortion analyzers** follow the video a/d converter with only a single register for storage.

at the 50-μs transient in Fig. 4. Here, the circuit samples this wave 1024 times (approximately once every 50 ns). Reading recurrently with a 100-kHz clock (20 MHz divided by 200) repeats the transient every 10 milliseconds. This period is compatible with slow time-base oscilloscope display.

Of course, by using fewer than the full 1024 samples, you can record transients that are even faster than 50 microseconds. For instance, you can capture 5-μs transients by using only 100 samples.

To set the reconstructed analog output to an appropriate time base for display or recording, simply change the clock-frequency divisor.

You can even reverse the relative speeds of the input and output clocking. For a slowly varying input, you can also sample slowly and store the converted samples, then read these faster than they were sampled. In this way you speed up the time scale—in effect, compressing the input signal in time. Naturally, the speed requirements reverse for the converters in such a signal compressor. The d/a must be a faster device than the a/d.

The spotlight's on radar

Another way to use ultra-high-speed a/d converters is in processing radar signals. A complete radar reflection often tells more than just time of arrival; additional information can be extracted from the shape, structure and frequency content of the received pulse, the object's radar signature. However, radar-signature analysis is often so complex that it must be done by a large-scale digital computer.

Fig. 5 shows the basics of a system that captures radar-signature data for computer analysis. Like the transient recorder, this system also combines an ultrafast, 8-bit a/d converter with a fast digital memory—in this case, a scratchpad memory.

When the radar-return pulse reaches the return-pulse detector, the detector triggers the clock-pulse-train generator. During the received pulse, each clock pulse triggers the a/d; the memory stores the resulting 8-bit samples. After the return pulse, the memory is read into the computer for processing.

Yet another good home for video-speed a/d converters is in variable-frequency, sampled-data distortion analyzers. For complex waves, you'll have such a hard time analytically optimizing the sampling rate for minimum distortion that often your only practical approach is empirical. The system in Fig. 6 lets you set very high sampling rates via its ultrafast, 8-bit a/d converter. For each sampling rate you can read the resulting distortion from the spectrum analyzer.

You must, of course, use a low-pass filter ahead of the converter to band-limit the input signal. Since the filter is variable, you can adjust the cutoff frequency as you vary the sampling rate (clock frequency).

After each a/d conversion, the digital output goes to a register. The register, in turn, updates the d/a converter that reconstructs the analog signal, which is then analyzed for distortion.

To use this set-up, apply the input wave and test the harmonic-distortion level at the output. Vary the clock and filter-cutoff frequencies until you get minimum distortion. Usually, the critical measurements will be at the upper range of clock frequencies.

Faster and faster

Sometimes even 20-MHz conversion rates aren't enough. For example, efficient data transmission could call for 40-MHz byte rates. Fortunately, you can often double the effective conversion rate at a reasonable cost with the "ping-pong" connection (Fig. 7).

With only two moderate-cost, 8-bit, 20-MHz devices, this scheme can convert every 25 ns—a 40-MHz rate. The technique involves alternately triggering each converter at its maximum 20-MHz rate. Then you switch the final-output channel between the two 8-bit converter outputs via a digital multiplexer.

Accuracy can be a problem, though. For opposite-direction linearity errors of both converters, the nonlinearity of the combination can be as much as twice that of each converter. By aligning both converters' zero and full-scale carefully, you can keep the combination's total nonlinearity to ±1 LSB, for units with ±1/2 LSB max nonlinearity.■■

References

1. Zuch, E., "Video Analog-to-digital Conversion," *Electronic Design*, April 12, 1978, pp. 66-71.

Acknowledgment

The author is grateful to his colleague, James B. Knitter, for many helpful discussions on this topic.

GEORGE F. BRYANT / Datel Systems Inc.

Microcomputers In An Analog World

Here are some new analog applications that depend on the union of low-cost microcomputers with analog I/O conversion products.

Some form of analog I/O is required by an estimated 37 percent of all computer applications. Since more of these applications are being accomplished with microcomputers, there is a growing need to interface microcomputers and analog signals. Fortunately there are a variety of single board analog I/O products available. This article will explore analog I/O options and show some of the vastly different applications in which system designers have used them for measurement and control.

The application determines the type and number of analog signals involved. In some process control and monitoring systems, hundreds of control points may be continuously measured. In these, the data acquisition system is more likely to be a rack mounted system, separate from the computer. The microcomputer systems, that we are considering here, handle fewer analog signals. They are smaller in scope because of the limited throughput of their computers. Since there are fewer analog channels, the analog circuitry can be located on the same P.C. board as the I/O interface logic. This results in a single-board, plug-in unit, that is treated as a standard I/O peripheral and sold by several manufacturers in various versions. They are: A-D with 8-64 channel input; multiplexer expander units for additional analog channels; D-A with 4-8 channel output; analog-out expander boards for multi-channel use; and combination A-D/D-A units with 8-32 analog input and 1-4 analog output channels. Numerous optional features are available on these microcomputer bus-compatible I/O cards (see box).

Because of the rich choice of options, the microcomputer system designer has considerable leeway in his choice of single board analog I/O peripherals to

GEORGE F. BRYANT is Manager of Systems Engineering at Datel Systems Inc. in Canton, MA. A BSEE graduate of Northeastern University, he was previously President of Integrated Control Systems, Inc. and Chief Systems Engineer for Control Logic Inc.

TYPICAL ANALOG I/O OPTIONS

- Single ended or differential analog inputs.
- Current loop (i.e. 4-20 mA) inputs.
- High level analog inputs (0 to +5V, 0 to +10V, ±5V, ±10).
- Low level (10-100mV full scale) analog inputs requiring instrumentation amplifiers with gains of 100-1000.
- Amplifier with software programmable gains of 1, 2, 4, and 8.
- Operation under program control, program interrupt or DMA.
- With or without DC to DC converter to generate ±15V.
- Simultaneous sample and hold circuits on analog input channels.
- Different full scale voltage ranges on analog outputs.
- Current loop (4-20mA) on analog output channels.

---

accomplish a wide variety of applications. Datel analog I/O peripherals, for example, were used in a range of applications including energy, process control, weather research, medicine, and communications.

MONITORING NUCLEAR REACTOR START-UP

Putting a reactor on-line at a nuclear power station requires a precise procedure with detailed information on the operating condition of many devices. This information must be available at all steps of the start-up procedure.

Temperature, pressure, and water flow had to be measured at 150 different points. Transducer outputs were connected to a signal conditioning unit which generated analog voltages in the 0 to ±10V range to a measurement system that operated in two modes.

In slow scan mode, each sensor is measured four times per hour to sense long term trends. Fast scan mode looks at important primary sensors during start-up or when taking the reactor off-line.

DMA operation was used to poll all units quickly and then release the machine to perform other control functions. Analog I/O boards provided DMA capability and multiplexer boards allowed expansion to 150 channels.

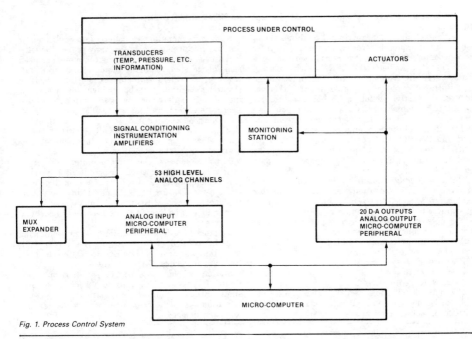

Fig. 1. Process Control System

This system was used as a monitoring station for operator information only, not as a control system. It is now being evaluated as a monitoring system to be used during power station operation. It would identify equipment for repair or replacement during scheduled maintenance periods.

For example, if the system was monitoring a group of pumps, and detected excessive wobble on one pump shaft, maintenance personnel could be alerted to replace or repair the pump during the next scheduled maintenance period. The use of microcomputers permits monitoring stations to be dedicated to specific groups of equipment and distributed around the power station.

RETURNING CONTROL TO THE PROCESS SITE

In a process control application, a materials manufacturer had to measure 53 channels of temperature, pressure, line speed, and other types of process data. Low level analog signals from the sensors were signal conditioned by external instrumentation amplifiers to present high level analog signals to the data acquisition analog input peripheral unit. Additional high level analog channels were entered through an analog channel expander board. Low level signal input ranges were up to 50mV full scale and each had a bandwidth of less than 20 Hz (Fig. 1).

In operation, the analog channels are selected and digitized under control of the microcomputer. The microcomputer performs computation and processing operations on the digitized analog data and switch position inputs. The microcomputer generates 20 analog signals via D-A converters located on the analog output peripheral boards. These analog outputs drive actuators in the manufacturing process to complete the real time, computer aided, process control loops. Additionally, the computer sends data to a local monitoring station. Process status is displayed in bar graphs on a color CRT and digital meters which show several process variables.

By using local micro-controllers at different stages of the process, on-site personnel can diagnose errors, correct problems, or fine tune the system by manual overide. Also, expensive cabling is reduced, cost is lowered, and misinterpretation of operation by operators at a remote computer site is prevented.

PHYSICAL STRUCTURE OF CLOUDS

This research effort is being conducted under the auspices of the NASA Goddard Space Flight Center.

Maps of parameters indicative of cloud physical structure are of value in studies of the earth's climate. The parameters to be measured are cloud amount, optical thickness, altitude, temperature, thermodynamic phase and particle number density. Global distributions of these parameters will be assembled according to season and local time and in this format will serve as input data to climate models based on radiative energy balance. This data base will also be of use in meterological studies of shorter time scale such as severe storm and cloud physical studies.

The cloud climatology experiment combines active and passive remote observation techniques to infer cloud parameters. The passive section consists of a Cloud Physics Radiometer (CPR) which is an 8 channel scanning radiometer with 7 channels in the near infrared and one channel in the thermal infrared. The active section consists of a cloud Lidar System (CLS) which is a two wavelength polarized scanning laser radar. To prove the sensor technique and the utility of the data, engineering models of the CPR and the CLS will be flown on a NASA high altitude aircraft. Results from these flights will be used to design a Space Shuttle (Spacelab) sensor system.

The microcomputer controls all operating sections of the system. A microcomputer was used in this application because of physical size, as the entire system was to be installed on an aircraft.

The data acquisition microcomputer peripheral monitors the following parameters:

All system power supply voltages.
Temperature in all system boxes.
Pressure in all system boxes.
Laser water flow.
Laser water temperature.

The data distribution (D-A's) microcomputer peripheral is employed as a μP controlled test fixture with quick look CRT terminals.

PATIENT MONITORING

Applying computers to collect data and monitor patients has been going on for many years. Previously, in most cases, the monitoring computer has been remotely located, requiring the data to be transmitted over considerable distances. Portable bedside monitoring stations have become feasible by employing microcomputers and analog I/O peripherals. Such applications require analog conversion products, since most monitoring instruments provide information in analog form. Additionally, the number of parameters being monitored on each patient requires multi-channel data acquisition.

The emergence of the microcomputer has significantly reduced the cost of the monitoring systems. Also, by employing a microcomputer at each bedside station, the measurements taken can differ, catering to the exact needs of the patient. Monitoring station terminals can be located at the bedside or nearby at the nurses' station.

Detailed here is a two-station patient monitoring system installed at St. Vincent's Hospital in New York that was developed by Edward De Wath at the Institute of Medical Sciences (Fig. 2).

Station #1 monitors post-operative cardiac patients. It is a portable bedside station capable of simultaneously monitoring two patients.

Station #2 monitors patients with acute respiratory insufficiencies.

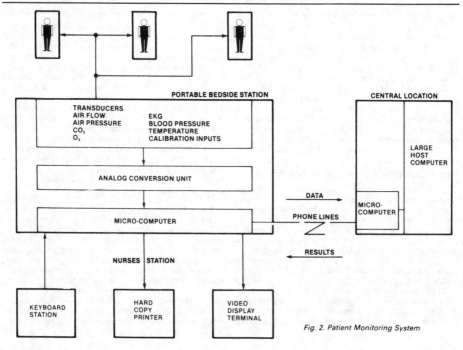

Fig. 2. Patient Monitoring System

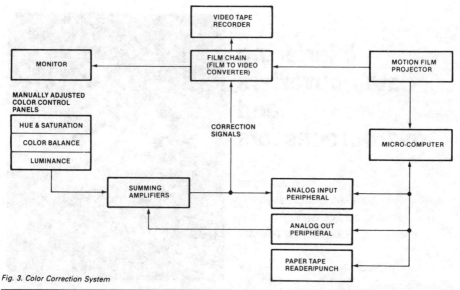

Fig. 3. Color Correction System

As many as 16 parameters are measured at the bedside station. Gas flow and pressure transducers as well as gas analyzers are used as measuring devices. The system is supported by calibration devices for flow, pressure, and gas analyzing. A tank of known mixture of oxygen and carbon dioxide are used as calibration standards for the gas analyzers. A source of known positive pressure is used as a standard for the gas pressure transducer. A pump of known positive displacement is used as the calibration standard for the gas flow transducer.

All calibration procedures typically last 30 seconds and are operator initiated via a keyboard and then microcomputer controlled. Long term drifts are manually compensated for on a monthly basis.

The outputs of the sensors are digitized by the microcomputer's analog input peripheral and the data is transmitted via phone lines from the bedside to another microcomputer at a central control location. The second microcomputer interfaces to a large host computer specifically programmed for patient monitoring applications. The host computer is programmed to derive over thirty physiological functions from the transducer data it receives. These include blood pressure, heart rate, respiratory rate, resistance and compliance of the lungs, maximum inspiratory pressure, oxygen intake, carbon dioxide exhaled, positive end expiratory pressure, and measurement of tidal volume per breath.

This resulting computed information is transmitted via phone lines back to the bedside microcomputer station. There, it is available at the nurses' station either on a video display terminal or via a hard copy printer. A keyboard is located at the station to allow the clinical staff to select which parameters of each patient are to be monitored.

FILM TO VIDEO TAPE

A system for electronic color correction of video signals, produced going from motion picture film to video tape, corrects scene by scene for hue and saturation of colors. It matches the spectral response in motion picture colors to the spectral distribution of the components in the film-to-video-converter or film chain (Fig 3).

The system corrects color at slow film speed prior to the actual reproducing of the film at normal speed. For sharpness and contrast reasons, it is not desirable to reproduce on video tape while running the film at a slow speed. The corrected color data is stored separately for use later in producing video tape.

The film is run on the projector on a frame by frame, scene by scene basis. Initially, a standard correction value is selected to provide a picture pleasing to the eye. Incremental corrections (from the color control panel) are added or subtracted on a scene by scene basis to compensate for different lighting, color patterns, cameras, etc.

These corrected values are digitized by the A-D peripheral and stored in the CPU in sync with the frame reference received from the projector. The film can be rerun, stopping on selected frames, until the desired color effect is obtained.

The film is rerun a final time and recorded on video tape. The corrected color signals are sent out from the CPU to the D-A converters to generate the correction signals to the film chain unit. ∎

Interfacing data converters and microprocessors

In intelligent
data-acquisition systems,
microprocessors must stay
as busy as possible

by David Fullagar, Peter Bradshaw, Lee Evans,
and Bill O'Neill, *Intersil Inc., Cupertino, Calif.*

☐ By latching onto the power and versatility of micro-processors, data-acquisition systems are vaulting into more extensive and demanding new applications. But the success of these "intelligent" data systems depends on the ability of the designer to mate the microprocessor to the other key system component, the analog-to-digital converter.

For a long time, converters have evolved independently of microprocessors, and there is often a communications gap between the two when they must work together as a team. Although this interface problem is usually not difficult to solve, many subtle details can make the difference between an efficient system and a wasteful one.

Oddly enough, the interface itself is not affected by the type of converter chosen—this decision depends largely on the particular application (see "Selecting the right converter," p. 84). Instead, the interface is primarily influenced by whether the digital data is transmitted in serial or parallel format and by the assistance options provided by the converter and the microprocessor being used.

Choosing between serial and parallel data

Clearly, the question of data format must be resolved before any progress can be made on the interface hardware at either the converter or microprocessor end. This choice is usually straightforward, and it depends principally on the distance separating the converter and the microprocessor.

Basically, the two methods of interfacing may be characterized as close-in parallel and remote serial. If high sampling rates are required, the converter should be located near the microprocessor, and the interface between the two should certainly be parallel. On the other hand, when data is gathered several hundred yards from the microprocessor, a twisted-pair serial connection makes better sense than a parallel one.

At the a-d end of the system, there is not much difference between successive-approximation and integrating converters in terms of the ease with which they produce either parallel or serial data. For the most part, both types are designed to put out parallel data with no additional components, and both can produce serial data with a little help.

In contrast, the task of interfacing at the microprocessor end appears formidable at first sight, because even the popular chips differ greatly. In some, such as the Intel 8008 and Intersil's IM6100, both addresses and data are timeshared on the same bus lines, and control signals differentiate between them. In others, like Motorola's MC6800 and the MOS Technology 650X series, addresses and data flow on different lines simultaneously, though sometimes they require strobing to indicate when each is valid.

These mixed situations come about because of crowding between bits and pins. The 6800 provides 40 pins for 8 bits, whereas the 8008 has only 18 pins for 8 bits. Although some efforts toward bus standardization are under way, significant progress is unlikely soon, if ever, in view of the already wide acceptance of substantially different products.

Even so, there are ways around the situation. For serial data, there is a ready-made standard just waiting

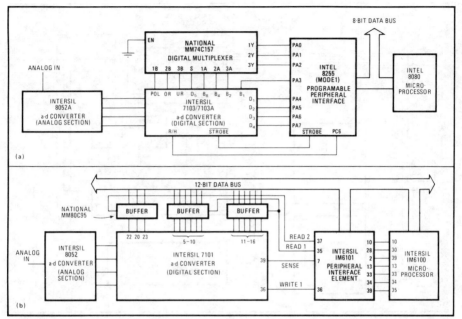

1. Parallel interface. All microprocessor families contain a programable interface device that can mate the converter and the microprocessor when the data format is parallel. Some of these devices (a) handle data directly, while others (b) have read and write lines.

to be hooked up. And for parallel data, a *de facto* standard is available from the same people who created the problem in the first place—the microprocessor manufacturers.

All microprocessors are members of chip families, and somewhere in each family is a device called a programable peripheral interface, programable interface element, programable interface adapter, or something similar—it may even be called "universal." This programable interface device handles address latching and decoding, relevant instruction recognition, interrupt processing, and bus access. It also has registers to control the polarity of incoming and outgoing signals, input/output status of outside lines, interrupt enabling and sensing, external flag lines, and the like.

De facto standard for parallel interfacing

When viewed from the outside, these devices look so similar that they constitute a *de facto* standard for parallel interfacing. Many, such as the Motorola MC6820 programable interface adapter and the Intel 8255 programable peripheral interface, give or take data directly on 4, 8, 12, 16, or even 24 pins. Figure 1a shows an a-d converter connected to one of these. Others, like the Intersil IM6101 programable interface element, do not handle the data directly themselves but have write-enable and read-latch lines to put triple-state data onto and latch data off the bus. Figure 1b shows the same converter interfaced in such a system.

In both situations, the converter can be set to run continuously or commanded to start. When a conversion has been completed, the microprocessor is interrupted to read back the data, if enabled to do so. Therefore, any a-d converter that provides a signal transition identifying the presence of new data and having standard triple-state output-disable controls in 8-bit bytes can interface with one of these programable devices without the need for additional components, as long as the logic levels are compatible. Similarly, any digital-to-analog converter with input latches in 8-bit groups can also interface directly with one of these chips.

In the past, a-d converters with serial outputs have been difficult to interface. The serial output was usually synchronous with some conversion clock and either had no synchronizing signals or had them on separate lines requiring gating for recognition. However, both these problems were solved by a device called a universal asynchronous receiver/transmitter (UART), which has become a standard pin-compatible part available from several suppliers.

UARTs handle serial interface

Any reasonable microprocessor family will interface with a UART or have a member of the family that looks like one from the outside—and two of these devices can talk to each other over pairs of wires. Although the UART grew out of teletypewriter-signal specifications, it can operate at much higher speeds and still provide synchro-

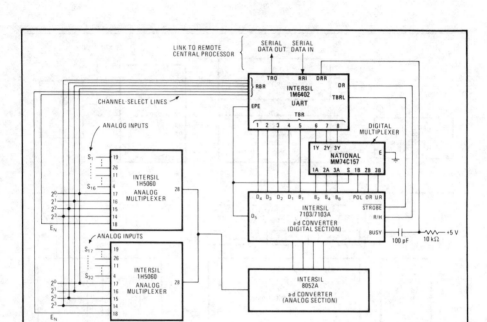

(a)

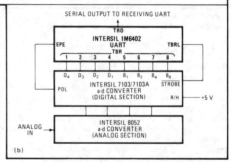

(b)

nization, a controlled data rate, parity generation, and clocking, as well as a full complement of handshaking signals for the microprocessor. With two-way communications and a phone-line tie-in through acoustic couplers, any UART-compatible a-d or d-a converter may talk to a friendly microprocessor, no matter how far away it is, over telephone lines.

Unfortunately, however, most converters cannot talk to a UART unless supplemented by lots of external components. One exception is the Intersil 8052/7103 integrating a-d, which happens to have the right signals available for interfacing with a UART via only one external digital multiplexer and a single RC differentiator, as indicated in Fig. 2a. Even these components may be omitted if the system can tolerate continuous conversion and lack of overrange information, and polarity can be sent on the parity system, as in Fig. 2b.

Considering multiword applications

The number of bits that can be handled with the serial or parallel interface may not coincide with the requirements of the converter, which usually has words of 8, 10, 12, 14, or 16 bits. Depending on the microprocessor, a parallel interface can handle words of 4, 8, 12, or 16 bits, but the UART can cope with only 5, 6, 7, or 8 bits at a time.

When the interface is wider than the converter, the extra bits may be ignored, but the more common situation of a wider converter requires that several microprocessor data words be transferred to complete one converter word. In such multiword applications, some

2. Serial interface. A universal asynchronous receiver/transmitter easily handles serial interfaces, although extra components are needed at the converter end (a). Even these can be eliminated (b) by running the a-d continuously and sending polarity on parity system.

sequencing and recognition requirements must be met by both the converter and the microprocessor, and a way must be provided to avoid use of only partially updated information. In many systems, a programable interface device can simplify this operation somewhat.

Logic levels must be compatible

Most digital devices are directly compatible with each other with respect to logic level. Typically, converters have bipolar outputs (usually for mating with transistor-transistor logic) or either p-channel MOS or complementary-MOS outputs, which generally are TTL-compatible at

Selecting the right converter

There are many different ways to convert analog data to digital form, but the two most popular approaches are successive-approximation and integrating techniques, which dominate more than 95% of all applications. The three most important factors in selecting the appropriate analog-to-digital converter are speed, accuracy, and cost.

If speed were the only consideration, the choice would be simple because there's almost no overlap between integrating and successive-approximation types, as shown in the table. Integrating converters provide excellent accuracy at low cost, but they require from 1 to 30 milliseconds to make a 10-bit conversion. Successive-approximation converters are a lot faster. Some can complete a 12-bit conversion in only 2 microseconds, but their cost is directly related to their accuracy.

How integrating types work. All integrating a-d converters have two characteristics in common. As the name implies, their output represents the integral or average of an input voltage over a fixed period of time. A sample-and-hold circuit, therefore, is not required to freeze the input during the measurement period. Equally important, because they use time or frequency to quantize a signal, the linearity error is small.

Among the numerous versions of integrating converters, such as charge-balancing and triple-ramp devices, the most widely used is the so-called dual-slope technique, shown in a simplified diagram (a).

With a dual-slope device, the conversion takes place in three distinct phases. During the first phase, or auto-zero portion of the cycle, the errors (such as offset voltage) of the analog components are automatically nulled out. The converter's input is grounded, closing the feedback loop and causing the error information to be stored by the capacitor.

During the second phase, the input signal is integrated for a fixed number of clock pulses, yielding an integrator output voltage that is directly proportional to the input. At the beginning of the third phase, the input of the converter is switched from the signal voltage to the reference voltage. Because of the polarity of the reference, the integrator output discharges back toward zero. The number of clock pulses counted between the beginning of this phase and the time when the integrator output passes through zero is a digital measure of the magnitude of the input voltage.

In theory, the linearity of such a conversion is limited only by the equality of the individual clock-pulse periods within a given cycle. This short-term frequency jitter can easily be held to 1 part in 10^6. Successive-approximation

converters, on the other hand, rely on matching resistor ratios for quantization and are hard-pressed to keep nonlinearities to less than 1 part in 10^3 — and to achieve 1 part in 10^4 requires trimming individual resistors in the binary ladder network.

Error sources are few. The dual-slope technique is immune to long-term changes in such components as the integrator capacitor and the comparator. In a very real sense, the designer is presented with a nearly perfect system, and his principal job is to avoid introducing error sources through ground loops or the use of noisy components, for example.

Although the integrating converter is conceptually straightforward, designing a good one is by no means a trivial task. Several sources of error must be taken into account. They include capacitor droop caused by switch-leakage current, the change in capacitor voltage when the switch turns off, the nonlinearity and high-frequency limitations of the analog components, the dielectric absorption of the capacitor, and the charge lost by the capacitor to stray capacitance.

All in all, though, these error contributions are small, compared to those of the successive-approximation technique. In general, integrating converters provide the accuracy needed for making precision measurements. With a good monolithic part, for instance, the offsets are less than the peak-to-peak noise, typically as little as 10 microvolts. Also, rollover error, which is encountered when changing from a positive measurement to an identical negative measurement, should be held within 50 μV, or the equivalent of half a count.

Successive approximation offers speed. When conversion times of 1 ms to 1 μs are required, successive-approximation devices are without competition. They are

FASTEST SPEEDS FOR a-d CONVERTERS						
Type of converter	Relative speed	Conversion time			
		8 bits	10 bits	12 bits	16 bits
integrating	slow	20 ms	30 ms	40 ms	250 ms
	medium	1 ms	5 ms	20 ms	-
	fast	0.3 ms	1 ms	5 ms	-
successive approximation	general purpose	30 μs	40 μs	50 μs	
	high performance	10 μs	15 μs	20 μs	400 μs
	fast	5 μs	10 μs	12 μs	-
	high speed	2 μs	4 μs	6 μs	-
	ultra fast	0.8 μs	1 μs	2 μs	-

some supply voltages. Similarly, microprocessors come with bipolar or various MOS outputs, which are also usually TTL-compatible at some supply voltages.

Problems arise in only two situations — when different logic-supply voltages are desired in different parts of the system and when long bus lines must be driven. The former could apply, for instance, when interfacing a C-MOS microprocessor and random-access memory operating at 10 volts (for maximum speed) with a bipolar programable successive-approximation register operating at 5 V.

However, integrated circuits are available for dealing with problems like these. Among them are Intersil's recently announced IM6404, which is a hex latch/driver capable of performing level translations from either C-MOS/MOS to TTL or from TTL to C-MOS/MOS, and Intel's 8216, a 4-bit bidirectional bus driver/receiver that can transmit data over long bus lines.

Another possible problem is the signal polarity, but this can be easily handled by the software via a COMPLEMENT DATA instruction. Also, the "high true" polarity convention for binary-coded-decimal data is most frequently used in data-acquisition systems that have a large number of inputs multiplexed through a single converter. Admittedly, successive-approximation converters are more expensive than integrating types of similar accuracy, but, because of their much faster data-throughput rate, they are usually less expensive on a per-channel basis.

Typically, a successive-approximation converter (b) consists of a digital-to-analog converter in a feedback loop with a comparator and some clever logic, which is usually referred to as a successive-approximation register. The output from the d-a is compared with the analog input, progressing from the most-significant bit to the least-significant bit (LSB), one bit at a time.

The bit being processed is set to logic 1. If the d-a output is less than the input voltage, the bit in process is left at logic 1. But, if the d-a output is greater than the input voltage, the bit is set to logic 0, and the register moves onto the next bit. Since the decision to turn each

(a)

(b)

bit on or off is made before the next bit is tried, the digital output data can be presented in either serial or parallel format, after all decisions have been made.

Accuracy can be expensive. Probably the greatest disadvantage of a successive-approximation converter is its numerous sources of error—conceptually, it is simply not as elegant as an integrating converter. The primary error-contributing components are the d-a converter and, to a lesser extent, the comparator and the voltage reference.

All in all, nearly 10 different error contributions affect the fidelity of the conversion. They include quantization uncertainty, nonlinearities of the transfer function, output-leakage current, offset errors, and temperature drift.

Because many of the error sources are interrelated, a worst-case error analysis must be done to determine just how accurate the conversion will be. After all major error contributions are taken into account, any well-designed part should provide an accuracy of within ± ½ LSB over its full operating temperature range.

Making converter tradeoffs. In selecting the most appropriate a-d converter for a given application, the decision is seldom clear-cut. Because cost is always the bottom line, the designer is forced to shop around within a budget—trading off speed against accuracy and size requirements.

Integrating converters provide the tightest accuracy for the money; however, they are comparatively slow. On the other hand, successive-approximation converters are inherently fast, but because of their numerous error sources, tight accuracy at high throughput rates can be expensive. If the data-acquisition system contains a microprocessor, the selection process takes on yet another dimension—the necessity to make the most efficient use of computer time.

For example, the conversion time of successive-approximation converters and the instruction-execution time of MOS microprocessor chips are on the order of a few microseconds. So putting the chip's central processor unit into a wait loop while the converter does its work doesn't waste much computing time. This combination is probably the best when many channels of analog data must be processed, but individual channels require minimal data manipulation.

In contrast, integrating converters are a wise choice when only a few channels of analog information are being gathered, but a large number of computations must be carried out for each channel. While the microprocessor is executing its instructions, the converter can take its time to digitize the next channel.

virtually a universally accepted industry standard.

Furthermore, the computing power of microprocessors permits ready conversion between two's complement and sign-magnitude notation. That leaves only control-signal polarity to worry about; however, all of the interface chips are programable enough to cope with almost any eventuality. Also, if the one selected has a triple-state enable that is low-active (strictly a disable line in positive logic), connections can be made directly from pin to pin without the need for intermediate inverters.

Another important consideration is the software to

handle the interface. Besides shaping hardware requirements, the operating mode of the converter affects software.

In general, d-a converters are easier to work with than a-d converters. A data word or a series of data words arrives, is assembled, and proceeds through the d-a. Some provision may be needed to avoid conversion of data that is partly new and partly old in multiword applications, and some users are expressing interest in read-back capability.

However, most d-a converters look much like the

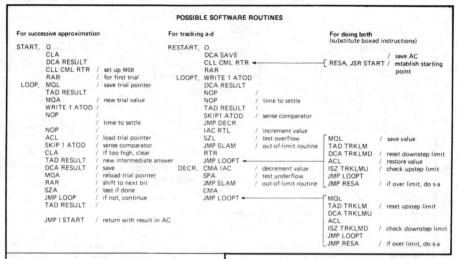

POSSIBLE SOFTWARE ROUTINES

For successive approximation			For tracking a-d			For doing both (substitute boxed instructions)		
START,	O		RESTART,	O				
	CLA			DCA SAVE				/ save AC
	DCA RESULT			CLL CML RTR ◄───────────		[RESA, JSR START /	establish starting point	
	CLL CML RTR	/ set up MSB		RAR				
	RAR	/ for first trial	LOOPT,	WRITE 1 ATOD				
LOOP,	MQL	/ save trial pointer		DCA RESULT				
	TAD RESULT			NOP	/			
	MQA	/ new trial value		NOP	/ time to settle			
	WRITE 1 ATOD	/		TAD RESULT	/			
	NOP	/		SKIP1 ATOD	/ sense comparator			
		/ time to settle		JMP DECR				
	NOP	/		IAC RTL	/ increment value			
	ACL	/ load trial pointer		SZL	/ test overflow	MQL		/ save value
	SKIP 1 ATOD	/ sense comparator		JMP SLAM	/ out-of-limit routine	TAD TRKLM		
	CLA	/ if too high, clear		RTR		DCA TRKLMD	/ reset downstep limit	
	TAD RESULT	/ new intermediate answer		JMP LOOPT ◄───────		ACL		/ restore value
	DCA RESULT	/ save	DECR,	CMA IAC	/ decrement value	ISZ TRKLMU		/ check upstep limit
	MQA	/ reload trial pointer		SPA	/ test underflow	JMP LOOPT		
	RAR	/ shift to next bit		JMP SLAM	/ out-of-limit routine	JMP RESA		/ if over limit, do s-a
	SZA	/ test if done		CMA				
	JMP LOOP	/ if not, continue		JMP LOOPT ◄───────		[MQL		
	TAD RESULT	/				TAD TRKLM		/ reset upstep limit
						DCA TRKLMU		
	JMP I START	/ return with result in AC				ACL		
						ISZ TRKLMD		/ check downstep limit
						JMP LOOPT		
						JMP RESA		/ if over limit, do s-a

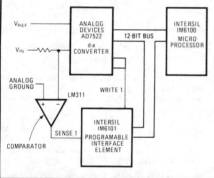

3. Lending a helping hand. The microprocessor can even become part of the converter loop. With the setup shown, the software permits changing from a successive-approximation a-d to a tracking a-d, or even using both methods to their best advantage.

infamous write-only memory. The latch and read-back capability may be provided directly by a number of different programable interface chips, while other interface devices can produce this function via external latches. If a converter has its own latches, they can achieve double buffering or de-skew multi-word data.

A trio of software interrupts

A-d converters offer many more choices of operating modes than d-a converters. If the a-d is operated continuously, the microprocessor can access the most recent data, treating the a-d much like read-only memory. For a nonmultiplexed one-word interface, such a system may be adequate. However, most other interfaces require an interrupt capability.

Interrupts may be of three general types. One, known as the direct-memory-access or non-processor interrupt, steals an entire microprocessor cycle or a portion of one and transfers the digitized data from the a-d directly to a memory location by controlling the bus during this cycle. Because of the amount of hardware required, however, this type of interrupt is largely restricted to disk interfaces, and it is probably of limited use with a-d converters. One exception is the Intersil IM6100/6102 chip pair that provides the necessary hardware for direct-memory access.

The second type, which is called a nonvectored interrupt, causes the microprocessor to stop whatever it was doing after completing the current instruction, save certain vital information in an appropriate place, and jump to a predefined location. This predefined location should contain a routing for polling all relevant peripherals to determine which caused the interrupt so that the right peripheral is serviced. Finally, the interrupt is cleared, the vital information restored, and the microprocessor resumes what it had been doing.

With the third or vectored type of interrupt, the interrupting device sends out the address of its own service routine (the vector) at the appropriate time. This type of interrupt does not require polling of all the peripherals. Both the vectored and nonvectored interrupts can be regarded as software techniques, since the actual data transfer is controlled by instructions.

In systems that might have several peripherals interrupt simultaneously, some priority system is essential. The polling sequence of the nonvectored interrupt performs this function almost automatically, but the other two interrupts usually have hardware provisions for establishing priority. Motorola's MC6800/6820 chip pair is an example of a nonvectored or polling interrupt, while Intersil's IM6100/6101 devices provide vectored priority interrupt, as well as direct-memory-access capa-

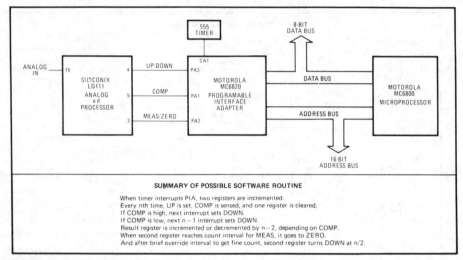

SUMMARY OF POSSIBLE SOFTWARE ROUTINE

When timer interrupts PIA, two registers are incremented.
Every nth time, UP is set, COMP is sensed, and one register is cleared.
If COMP is high, next interrupt sets DOWN.
If COMP is low, next n − 1 interrupt sets DOWN.
Result register is incremented or decremented by n − 2, depending on COMP.
When second register reaches count interval for MEAS, it goes to ZERO.
And after brief override interval to get fine count, second register turns DOWN at n/2.

4. Another approach. The microprocessor can do the digital processing for charge-balancing a-d. However, because the up/down switching for this type of converter must be continued throughout its operating cycle, microprocessor overhead can be substantial.

bility with the addition of some extra hardware.

With any of these interrupt schemes, the a-d converter may run continuously. But every time new data is available, the converter will interrupt the microprocessor, and the data will be transferred to memory. For multiword applications, the word sequence may be controlled by the converter with several interruptions, as in Fig. 1a, or by the microprocessor on one interrupt, as in Fig. 1b. Multiplexer-command words may be sent out during these interrupts, if they are of the software type.

Alternatively, the a-d may be instructed to convert, and the microprocessor is interrupted only after a conversion has been completed. A variation of this technique is depicted in Fig. 2a, which shows how the bidirectional characteristics of the UART are used to send out a multiplex address that triggers a conversion after it has been received. At the end of the conversion caused by the multiplex address, the microprocessor is interrupted with the data. This whole operation could be performed at the ends of a long two- or three-wire system or even over telephone lines if one end of the system is as far away as the other side of the world.

One additional interface possibility is the interrogate-and-wait-till-ready approach. Although this method involves only polling of a status word, rather than interrupt processing, it is limited to use with under-utilized microprocessors or fast a-d converters. However, such an approach does simplify the software, and for one-of-a-kind designs, it may prove cost-effective.

Finally, as might be expected, all the above interfaces can be run by a programable interface device under software control that permits the operating mode of a converter to be changed at any time.

The software depends on the microprocessor, of course. The instruction set uses one of two methods for

transferring data between peripheral devices and memory.

One involves specific I/O-transfer instructions, which usually transfer data between an accumulator or register and the converter register (or a register of the programable interface device). This method has some portion of the I/O-transfer instruction devoted to a peripheral address and another portion for controlling the operation to be performed. Thus, instructions other than those involving only data transfer can be performed — for instance, skip on flag for wait-till-ready routines. Microprocessors that permit this form of software include the Intersil IM6100, DEC's PDP-8 on which it is based, and Intel's 8008 and 8080.

Another way to handle data transfer

The other form of software data transfer involves treating the peripheral device registers the same as memory. In this situation, no special I/O instructions are needed, and both arithmetic and logical operations can be performed directly on the peripheral's data. The simplicity and power of this method has led to its wide acceptance in such minicomputers as the DEC PDP-11, and it has appeared in several microprocessors, too, including Motorola's 6800 and MOS Technology's 650X families.

However, that technique has its drawbacks. The peripheral-device registers occupy what would otherwise be memory space, and only full words (sometimes bytes) can be exchanged or handled between registers. A wait-till-ready routine, for example, requires reading the control words and stripping the relevant bits, as well as test and skip operations.

An additional software concern related to a-d and d-a converters is the ease of working with double-precision

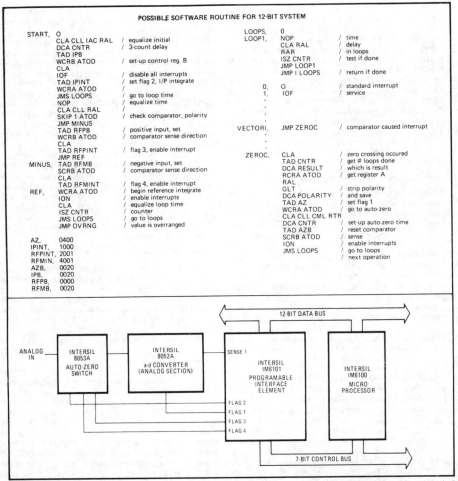

POSSIBLE SOFTWARE ROUTINE FOR 12-BIT SYSTEM

```
START,  O
        CLA CLL IAC RAL     / equalize initial
        DCA CNTR            / 3-count delay
        TAD IPB
        WCRB ATOD           / set-up control reg. B
        CLA
        IOF                 / disable all interrupts
        TAD IPINT           / set flag 2, I/P integrate
        WCRA ATOD           /
        JMS LOOPS           / go to loop time
        NOP                 / equalize time
        CLA CLL RAL         /
        SKIP 1 ATOD         / check comparator, polarity
        JMP MINUS
        TAD RFPB            / positive input, set
        WCRB ATOD           / comparator sense direction
        CLA
        TAD RFPINT          / flag 3, enable interrupt
        JMP REF
MINUS,  TAD RFMB            / negative input, set
        SCRB ATOD           / comparator sense direction
        CLA
        TAD RFMINT          / flag 4, enable interrupt
REF,    WCRA ATOD           / begin reference integrate
        ION                 / enable interrupts
        CLA                 / equalize loop time
        ISZ CNTR            / counter
        JMS LOOPS           / go to loops
        JMP OVRNG           / value is overranged

AZ,     0400
IPINT,  1000
RFPINT, 2001
RFMIN,  4001
AZB,    0020
IPB,    0020
RFPB,   0000
RFMB,   0020
```

```
LOOPS,  0
LOOP1,  NOP                 / time
        CLA RAL             / delay
        RAR                 / in loops
        ISZ CNTR            / test if done
        JMP LOOP1
        JMP I LOOPS         / return if done

0,      0                   / standard interrupt
1,      IOF                 / service
.
.
.
VECTORI,  JMP ZEROC         / comparator caused interrupt
.
.
ZEROC,  CLA                 / zero crossing occured
        TAD CNTR            / get # loops done
        DCA RESULT          / which is result
        RCRA ATOD           / get register A
        RAL
        GLT                 / strip polarity
        DCA POLARITY        / and save
        TAD AZ              / set flag 1
        WCRA ATOD           / go to auto-zero
        CLA CLL CML RTR
        DCA CNTR            / set-up auto-zero time
        TAD AZB             / reset comparator
        SCRB ATOD           / sense
        ION                 / enable interrupts
        JMS LOOPS           / go to loops
                            / next operation
```

ANALOG IN → INTERSIL 8053A AUTO-ZERO SWITCH → INTERSIL 8052A a-d CONVERTER (ANALOG SECTION) → SENSE 1 → INTERSIL IM6101 PROGRAMABLE INTERFACE ELEMENT → INTERSIL IM6100 MICRO-PROCESSOR

12-BIT DATA BUS

FLAG 2
FLAG 1
FLAG 3
FLAG 4

7-BIT CONTROL BUS

5. For dual slope. Designing the microprocessor into a dual-slope converter loop is comparatively easy on the software. In fact, during both the input and reference integration intervals, the microprocessor can service other routines, as well as interrupts.

(or multiprecision) arithmetic for handling, say 10 to 16 bits in an 8-bit machine. For applications involving BCD converters, the degree of difficulty in converting between binary and BCD codes can be a factor in the interface. Some microprocessors, however, offer the ultimate in software simplicity, even including code-conversion instructions—among them, the Intel 4004 and the MOS Technology 650X series.

One factor sometimes overlooked when considering converter speeds is the length of the service routine required to handle the data. This routine usually involves more than simply storing the data in some memory location until it is overwritten by the next value.

A typical service routine could require that a zero correction factor be accessed and subtracted, maybe a scale factor used, and then upper- and/or lower-limit values accessed and compared, or a comparison made with a previous value.

On the basis of an out-of-limit value, a certain rate of change, or a possible maverick reading, a decision might have to be made either to flag an alarm or to adjust some system parameter. Also, a new conversion should be initiated. All this activity can easily take several hundred instruction cycles, especially if double-precision arithmetic is required, and total execution time can run as long as 1 millisecond.

One aspect of the microprocessor-converter interface that does not fit easily into any of the preceding discussions certainly deserves mention is the use of the microprocessor as part of the a-d system.

For successive-approximation conversion, a d-a converter and a comparator can be interfaced to the microprocessor, as shown in Fig. 3. The successive-approximation routine is implemented in software, and the same d-a can be used for analog outputs. For a moderate increase in the software overhead, a tracking a-d converter can be substituted, or better yet, a routine can be used to convert readily from one conversion system to the other, thereby utilizing the advantages of both techniques. Software routines to do this are available in such microprocessor-system libraries as Intel's MCS4 and MCS8.

The integrating converter system

For the under-utilized microprocessor, the same technique can be applied to dual-slope and charge-balancing conversion systems. The digital signals to control the integration steps can be derived from the control signals or one of the data registers of a programable interface device, with the microprocessor counting the time periods. Timing may be accomplished by having a timer interrupt the microprocessor at regular intervals or by counting around instruction loops of known length, although this process may preclude interrupts from other peripherals.

For a charge-balancing device like Intersil's LD111 analog a-d processor, the timer interrupt is virtually mandatory. The up/down switching for this device must be continued through all cycles, including auto-zero, so the microprocessor overhead can be substantial. A suitable interface is shown in Fig. 4, along with a summary of a possible software routine.

Dual-slope conversion (Fig. 5) is easier on the software. During the auto-zero portion of the conversion cycle, no actions are necessary. Since only a minimum time is required, any extra unaccounted time taken by interrupts is not important. During the input-integration interval, other routines and interrupts can be serviced if the time-counter location is incremented and tested after the correct number of instruction cycles. (All routines take a multiple of this number.) If the comparator is set to interrupt on the integrator's zero crossing, other routines and interrupts can also be serviced during the reference-integrate interval of the a-d conversion cycle.

With care in programing, one microprocessor could handle several a-d conversions simultaneously. This type of interface is generating some interest in applications where scale factors are important and where a microprocessor may be waiting for the result, as in point-of-sale terminals.

Interfacing v-f converters

A few words should be said about interfacing with voltage-to-frequency converters, which offer another approach to a-d conversion. These devices do not have much value in microprocessor-based systems because of the asynchronous nature of their outputs. Their value lies in the transmission of single-parameter information over twisted-pair wires to a remote location, where the receiver is a frequency-to-voltage converter or a low-cost digital frequency meter.

If a v-f converter is essential to the application, a programable interface device can communicate with a gated counter, too. But if the microprocessor must do the counting, two sets of interrupts are required—one on each incoming pulse with a routine to increment a memory location, and another at the gating period to transfer the result and reset the counter. The gating timer may be implemented with standard clock-generating chips like the Intersil ICM7038, or by one of the microprocessor peripheral timers, like MOS Technology's 6530 or Intersil's IM6102.

Interfacing an a-d converter with a microprocessor may be a fairly complex job, but new hardware developments are helping to simplify the task. Some converters now provide triple-state buffered outputs that deliver handshake-oriented signals for the microprocessor interface. Some complete data-acquisition subsystems on printed-circuit boards or implemented as compact hand-sized modules can even be plugged directly into microprocessor-based systems.

Easier times ahead

In the near future, converters are likely to offer direct compatibility with UART devices, and converters may be built to contain their own universal asynchronous transmitters or receivers. If bus standards are developed, converters probably will include at least some of the address and handshake signals, in addition to the data-line interface. Also, microprocessors with on-board user-accessible memory are already beginning to appear and will go a long way toward taking the hardships out of interfacing.

Since software is closely tied to the specific application, its development depends on how microprocessors and converters will be used in the future. Additional applications assistance probably will take the form of example interface routines for popular or proprietary microprocessors oriented to generalized tasks. Software optimization may also have some influence on the fine design details of microprocessor-oriented converters, although the increasingly lower cost of ROMs will not permit extensive improvements along these lines to be sufficiently viable. ☐

Straight talk on A/D converter boards

There's a lot more to picking an A/D system than just looking at spec sheets.

Larry Copeland,
Datel Systems, Inc.
Canton, MA

Control engineers are using microcomputers and minicomputers for more and more data acquisition and control applications. In almost all cases, these computer-based systems will require an analog-to-digital (A/D) converter to make analog measurement signals compatible with the digital processors.

As a supplier of A/D converters, we continually find ourselves answering the same questions about speed, accuracy, resolution, expansion and cost. To help clear up some of the myths and misconceptions about converters, this article will explore the topics that seem to concern you.

How much accuracy?

The question of how much accuracy is needed comes up a great deal, especially when a user has an 8-bit microcomputer and, for simplicity, wants to use an 8-bit A/D converter. Users often say that since their process transducers only have ½% accuracy, an 8-bit A/D converter should be just right for the job.

Although Table 1 shows that an 8-bit converter does, indeed, have 0.4% accuracy, it's not that simple. The table assumes an ideal, perfect conversion of signals right at the input terminals of the converter. This does not consider system accuracy, which can be affected by temperature drift, noise, nonlinearity, common mode voltages, power supply rejection, transducer deadband, hysteresis, aliasing errors, and so on.

These errors combine in complex ways to produce an overall system accuracy—or inaccuracy—that can be significant. The resolution and accuracy of a converter must be substantially better than the overall system accuracy, so many users find themselves needing 10- or 12-bit converters, or better.

Even if system accuracy requirements are not difficult to meet, process transducers have dynamic ranges that must be considered. Dynamic range means the difference between the maximum full scale signal and lowest resolvable signal. Many 0.5% accuracy transducers have dynamic ranges of up to 80 to 90 dB, and that requires at least a 12-bit A/D converter (see Table 1). To retain dynamic range, in some applications you should consider a 14-bit or 16-bit converter, or use a programmable gain amplifier (see Glossary).

Obtaining greater resolution is usually done at the expense of conversion speed. Costs go up too. A typical 14-bit A/D requires about 60 microseconds to perform a conversion, and its cost goes up sharply: A 14-bit A/D converter costs $251 vs $124 for a 12-bit device. Sixteen-bit conversions are best done with an integrating type of converter which is economical but very slow—conversions are done in milliseconds. In contrast, a 12-bit conversion can take place in 20 microseconds.

Many customers are curious to know why higher resolution converters are so much more expensive. Increasing an A/D converter from 8-bit resolution to, say, 12 bits is not simply a matter of adding a quad switch and more resistors to the ladder network. The entire A/D converter system must comply with 12-bit performance, including the reference source, thin-film ladder network, multiplexer, sample/hold amplifier, and input differential amplifier.

There are two basic options to trade off resolution, speed and cost:

● Many industrial applications require up to 14 bits of resolution. Yet 14-bit A/D's are fairly slow and quite expensive. A common solution is to take a faster, cheaper 12-bit converter and add a programmable gain amplifier (PGA) "front end." Since 14 bits is 4 times the

resolution of 12 bits, popular PGA's with digitally-coded X1, X2, X4 and X8 gain ranges are ideal.

● If you don't need the speed, a 14- or 16-bit integrating A/D converter will give the required resolution and dynamic range at lower costs. Typically sampling on the order of 50 conversions per second, these converters are slower than successive approximation types.

Noise filtering

An A/D converter very faithfully converts anything you feed it—transducer signals, RF interference, switching transients, ac hum and so on. With its super fast sample/hold circuit, the A/D system will pick off a narrow slice of a composite signal and noise waveform and dutifully convert it to a digital output. It will not tell you which part is signal and which part is noise.

If you have as little as 1% noise in your signal, watch out. That 1% noise will affect 4 or 5 of the least significant bits of a 12-bit converter—so much that you can see them dance. Try it yourself: Set your A/D to sample a noisy input at a modest rate, such as 100 conversions per second, and display the A/D output on the indicator lights on your computer. If you have 1% noise, the last 4 or 5 bits will jump around like crazy.

Glossary for digital data acquisition systems

Accuracy: In a measurement system, accuracy is the amount of deviation or error that the output will vary from an expected ideal or absolute output. Accuracy may be expressed as a portion (percentage, parts per million, dB, etc) of the positive or negative full scale range or as a percentage of any reading between positive or negative full scale (% of reading). Total system accuracy is composed of many error sources including temperature drifts, noise, non-linearity, power supply variation and many more factors beyond the scope of this article. Each element in a measurement system contributes its own errors, and each should be separately specified if they contribute significantly to the degradation of total system accuracy.

Aliasing: A sampling data system, such as an A/D converter, tends to produce false outputs (namely periodic false beat notes) if the sampling rate is insufficient compared to the highest frequency spectra of the input signal. Various solutions cure aliasing, including faster sampling and low pass filtering. A simplified expression of the Sampling Theorem states that the sampling rate must be at least twice the frequency of the highest frequency spectra in a measured signal to avoid aliasing and loss of data.

Dynamic Range: The proportion or ratio between a

full scale signal and the smallest resolvable signal is a system's dynamic range. Generally the signal becomes indecipherable when it approaches the limits of resolution or is buried in noise.

Programmable Gain Amplifier (PGA): This differential instrumentation amplifier changes its amplification on command from a digital code supplied through a program instruction. PGA's are used to fit a wide dynamic range signal into a lower-resolution, lower-cost A/D converter. Generally, PGA's include range decoding. For example, Datel's AM-251B uses two bits to select 4 gains of X1, X2, X4 or X8 corresponding to ranges of ±10V, ±5V, ±2.5V, or ±1.25V. Real-world PGA's are design compromises between stability, common mode rejection, noise, settling time, number of gain steps, size and cost. Generally, a PGA combined with a medium cost A/D has better performance and greater application flexibility than a single high resolution A/D alone.

Resolution: The smallest possible change in the input which can be measured is a system's resolution. The term is akin to the smallest scale graduations on a thermometer, meter face or ruler. In A/D systems, resolution is usually limited by system structural factors, principally the number of bits used to quantize the input signal.

Table 1: Resolution, accuracy, and dynamic range

Digital encoded data	Resolution	Best accuracy as percentage of full scale range	Dynamic range	Best accuracy in parts per million (ppm)	LSB value if full scale +10V
2 BCD Digits	1 part in 100	1%	40dB		100 mV
2½ BCD Digits	1 part in 200	0.5%	46dB		50 mV
8 Binary Bits	1 part in 256	0.4%	48dB		39 mV
3 BCD Digits	1 part in 1000	0.1%	60dB	1000 ppm	10 mV
10 Binary Bits	1 part in 1024	0.1%	60dB	1000 ppm	10 mV
3½ BCD Digits	1 part in 2000	0.05%	66dB	500 ppm	5 mV
12 Binary Bits	1 part in 4096	0.024%	72dB	240 ppm	2.4 mV
4 BCD Digits	1 part in 10,000	0.01%	80dB	100 ppm	1 mV
14 Binary Bits	1 part in 16,384	0.006%	84.5dB	59 ppm	600 μV
4½ BCD Digits	1 part in 20,000	0.005%	86dB	50 ppm	500 μV

Noise filtering obviously is a major concern of our customers. If you have, or expect to have, a noise problem, it's best to filter with hardware. You should filter close to the transducers, if possible, and watch out for periodic high frequency noise (see "aliasing" in Glossary). Most A/D manufacturers can help you out with hardware filtering problems.

You can also filter with software. One easy way to do this is with an averaging method, and if you pick the right number of points to average, it's simple. If you pick any number of points that represents a power of two—such as 2, 4, 8, 16, and so on—then taking the average is simple. After you've summed the inputs, simply shift the sum to the right and you'll have the average. If you're averaging two points, shift right one bit; for four points, shift the sum two bits; for 8 points, shift right 3. This method works because computers operate on binary arithmetic, and each one bit shift to the right represents a divide by 2 operation.

Of course, if you decide to average 27 samples, the arithmetic is no longer easy. Also, if you have a severe

noise problem—such as periodic high frequency noise that produces severe aliasing in the data—you may have to write a numerical analysis program in FOR-TRAN or BASIC to average out the beat notes. In this case, it's better to filter with hardware.

Multichannel converters

Most applications require more than one A/D channel, so almost all converter manufacturers offer multiplexers that provide from 8 to 128 channels on one or two boards. The boards can usually interface directly with a variety of popular mini and microcomputers. Prices vary from vendor to vendor. Table 2 shows Datel Systems' prices for several 8080-based A/D converter

Table 2: A/D converter board costs[1]

Number of channels	Modules required	Total price	Cost/ channel
16	ST-800-16S ($595) 16-channel master board with A/D	$ 595	$37.20
32	ST-800-32S ($650) 32-channel master board with A/D	$ 650	$20.30
64	ST-800-32S ($650) 32-channel master	$1065	$16.62
	ST-800ADX32S ($415) 32 channels, slave mux expander board, no A/D		
80	ST-800-32S ($650) 32-channel master	$1125	$14.08
	ST-800ADX48S ($475) 48 channels, slave mux expander board, no A/D		
128	ST-800-32S ($650) 32-channel master	$1600	$12.50
	(2) ST-800ADX48S ($950) 48 channel expander boards		

For single-ended, 12-bit, 8080-based A/D peripherals

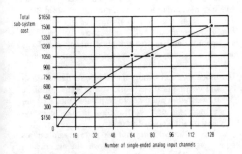

Total sub-system cost

Fig. 1: The cost per channel for A/D converter subsystems increases linearly after the initial master board is purchased. If major components, such as a printed circuit board or chassis, have to be added, the costs can go up dramatically. Although this figure illustrates Datel Systems components, other manufacturers generally are within 10% of these prices (assuming identical configurations).

Cornered by success

One of our customers decided to expand an existing control system by installing a microprocessor-based data acquisition and control system at a remote site. The existing control system, a large minicomputer acting as a central host, already had many input channels installed with direct cables.

From past experience, we felt the customer would probably want to add many more channels, D/A outputs and additional remote site controllers later on. More importantly, we felt he should stick with a microcomputer version of his central minicomputer. This would enable him to use common programming languages, peripheral drivers and communications protocols. But the customer persisted with a low-cost Brand X microprocessor, home-brew chassis, power supply and custom programming. Ultimately, the system got working—sort of.

The remote micro had communication difficulties with the host mini, but the advantages of being able to locally control the process on site had the predictable result: The plant manager was impressed enough to authorize funding for six more remote systems. Now the scramble began. The design engineers had to untangle the software problems and hand-build six more custom units.

We finally convinced the customer to switch to a microcomputer version of his central mini. The off-the-shelf software supplied with the micro solved his communications problems. Then we convinced him to use "packaged" A/D and D/A systems that come complete with power supplies and allow for future expansion. The happy ending was a system that works smoothly, has room for future expansion, and can be duplicated easily for additional applications.

modules. Figure 1 is a graph of cost vs. channel capacity, so you can get a general idea of how much the A/D peripherals will cost for your particular application.

Some companies offer a variety of channel expansion methods, but the variety is not infinite. For example, if your system has reached capacity and you want to add a few more input channels, the manufacturer will have to charge you for the next increment of channel expansion—which may be many more channels than you need. Channel expansion is usually in increments of 16, 32 or 48 channels.

Many customers are concerned about the additional cost of A/D channels and want to specify only the capacity that they need. While this is a good idea, be sure you don't limit yourself. Keep in mind that you will probably think of some other parameter that needs to be measured (if you don't think of it, someone else will).

If your calculations say that you need a certain number of channels, check the manufacturers you are considering to see what their next increment is. For example, if you need 30 channels and are considering a 32-channel A/D from Manufacturer X, is his next increment 48 or 64 channels? Will you have to buy an entire chassis or just an expansion board if you need more channels?

By selecting your multichannel A/D components carefully, you may spend a little more now, but you can also save a great deal if you have to expand in the future.

Getting out of the corner

Multichannel A/D converters that offer speed, accuracy and direct interfacing to your computer are expensive, to be sure. Although we certainly appreciate your need for economy, let me point out one rule of the data acquisition business: Don't paint yourself into a corner!

Stand back from your project for a few minutes and consider a few things. You are not simply buying a processor, data acquisition hardware, transducers and an output terminal. You are buying a system that will provide useful data for a measurement or control application over a long period of time. Don't let the details blind you into not seeing your system's function.

It is false economy to specify an 8-bit micro and an 8-bit A/D converter only to find out six months from now that your system isn't big enough or fast enough to handle the data. Anticipate that others may want to apply your system—or one just like it—to applications you haven't considered. If more people begin using your system, design limitations may begin to cripple it. Something as simple as the number of wires in the cable or the hardware/software methods for multiplexing data can come back to haunt your later on.

And there's always the unexpected. After you've had your system running for awhile, don't be amazed if the plant manager asks you to provide additional inputs from a processing site half a mile away. The half mile may seem insignificant to the plant manager, but you have to solve the communications problem—perhaps with modems, coaxial cable or a microwave unit. If your processor can't handle the additional data acquisition and communications work, you've got a problem. This is exactly the place not to be painted into a corner with a modest processor struggling to handle everything and no simple way to expand.

Anticipate that you may not see all the ramifications of your system design. Try to draw on the experiences of others who have installed systems. Select manufacturers who offer a variety of systems with expandability features, and don't buy a processor or an A/D input system on price alone. If you plan for future problems, maybe they won't be problems. ∎

Application of Analog Conversion Products in Micro-computers

By: GEORGE F. BRYANT
Systems Engineering Mgr.
Datel Systems, Inc.
1020 Turnpike Street
Canton, MA 02021

Introduction

A great many of the applications employing micro-computers also require some form of analog input or analog output.[1] It is estimated that 37% of all computer applications require some form of analog I/O. The majority of these application areas can be classified as Data Measurement/Collection or Process Monitoring/Control.

Since most sensors and control elements are analog in nature, it is obvious that in areas where measurement and control are required, analog signals are most likely to be present and, therefore, must be generated (D-A's) or measured (A-D's).

The actual application determines both the type and number of analog signals involved. In some process control or process monitoring applications, hundreds of control points are being continuously measured. In these applications, the Data Acquisition System is more likely to be a rack mounted system separate from the computer. In other less complex systems, the number of analog signals would be in the area of 4-100 points. Micro-computer systems tend to be smaller in scope; and it is these type applications that are being considered here.

Fewer analog channels allow having the analog circuitry located directly on the same P.C. board as the I/O interface logic. This resulting unit is treated as a standard I/O peripheral and is offered by several manufacturers in many different versions with each version capable of providing many different options.

These peripherals are offered in the following versions:

 a. Analog-in (A-D only) with 8-64 channel input capability.

 b. Multiplexer expander units for applications requiring additional analog channels.

 c. Analog-out (D-A only) with from 4-8 channel output capability.

 d. Analog-out expander boards for multi-channel analog out capability.

 e. Combination A-D/D-A units with 8-32 analog input and 1-4 analog output channels.

Of applications having some form of analog in/out, 45% have analog-in only, 15% have analog-out only and 40% require both analog input and analog output peripherals. The number of analog output channels may be superficially inflated, as in some applications, they are merely used for self-testing or calibrating the A-D section. At other times, the D-A's are used only to reproduce selected analog input channels on a strip chart recorder or CRT.

Typical optional features are listed below:

 a. Single ended or differential analog inputs.

 b. Current loop (i.e. 4-20mA) inputs.

 c. High level analog inputs (0 to +5V, 0 to +10V, ±5V, ±10V).

 d. Low Level (10-100mV full scale) analog inputs requiring instrumentation amplifiers with gains of 100-1000.

 e. Amplifier with software programmable gains of 1, 2, 4, and 8.

 f. Operation under program control, program interrupt or DMA.

 g. With or without DC to DC converter to generate ±15 volts power (from +5V supply) for analog circuitry.

 h. Simultaneous sample and hold circuits on analog input channels.

 i. Different full scale voltage ranges on analog outputs.

 j. Current loop (4-20mA) on analog output channels.

The actual applications described in this paper were selected as typical of those peculiar to micro-computers. These applications may not have been feasible, economically or otherwise, to have been accomplished using a mini-computer. Additionally, the applications were selected depicting different versions and options of the analog I/O peripherals and their employment in different application areas.

Energy

Monitoring Operating Status of
Reactor During Power Station Start-Up

Putting a reactor on-line at a nuclear power station requires a precise procedure with detailed information on the operating condition of many devices. This information must be available at all steps of the start-up procedure.

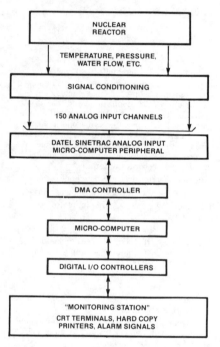

ENERGY

In this application, it was necessary to monitor the status of 150 points. The physical parameters being measured were temperature, pressure, and water flow. The Reactor Vendor chose to use a microcomputer for cost reasons and because the power of a mini was not warranted. The outputs of the transducers were connected to a Signal Conditioning Unit which generated analog voltages in the 0 to +10V range for inputting to the measurement system.

The measurement system operated in two modes:

  a. A slow scan mode to sense long term trends where each sensor was measured four times per hour.

  b. A fast scan mode to look at primary important sensors during start-up or when taking the reactor off-line.

The reactor vendor desired to operate the unit in a DMA mode to poll all units quickly and then release the machine to perform other control functions. The Datel analog I/O boards (ST-800-32S) were capable of being operated in DMA and the ST-800-ADX boards allowed for expansion to 150 channels in increments of 48 channels per board.

This application was as a monitoring station for operator information only and was not used as a control system as there was no feedback to the system.

While the primary function of this system was for monitoring purposes when putting the reactor on or off line, it is now being evaluated as a monitoring system during power station operation. It is extremely important that equipment repair or replacement be performed during scheduled maintenance periods.

If the system is monitoring a group of pumps, and detects excessive wobble on one pump shaft, maintenance personnel can be alerted to replace or repair the pump during the next scheduled maintenance period. If it failed, causing an unscheduled shutdown, the power plant would have to decrease the amount of power it could be depended upon to supply the grid.

By using micro-computers, these monitoring stations can be dedicated to specific groups of equipment and could be spread out over the power station. Employing the monitoring system in this manner, can be proven to be extremely cost effective.

Aviation

Digital Flight Controlled Simulator

This system was developed by the Redundancy Management Laboratory of BMAD (Boeing Military Airplane Development). The application illustrates a system that employs both mini and micro-computers. The Data General NOVA mini-computer was used for central processing and an Intel SBC-80/10 was used for distributed I/O.

This research effort was to investigate system problems associated with *redundant* high reliability digital flight control. As a result of using redundant controls for higher reliability operation, two sets each of NOVA's mini-computers, SBC-80's microcomputers and Datel SineTrac analog I/O peripherals, were employed.

The analog I/O peripherals were connected to an airframe simulator consisting of an analog computer, actuators, and a two axis platform on which sensors were mounted. The system contained 6 analog outputs (D-A's) and 18 analog inputs. The outputs entered an analog computer which drove aircraft actuators connected to the 2 axis platform. The actuators were dual with selection clutches for operation under control of one redundant system or the other.

An operator station is associated with each mini-computer, whereby the operator may input commands to the system to have the system simulate an abrupt altitude change from one position to another. The system would simulate this, via programs in the mini-computer, and measure changes from the sensors mounted on the simulator and generate commands (analog signals) to the simulator to stabilize the airframe.

The data acquisition system samples analog inputs from the simulator which are representative of the following:

    a. Roll information from vertical gyros.

    b. Pitch information from vertical gyros.

    c. Roll rate from rate gyros.

    d. Pitch rate from rate gyros.

    e. Altitude information simulated from the analog computer.

    f. Engine speed information simulated from the analog computer.

The micro-computer does some prescaling and limit checking on the data and sends the results to the mini-computer for processing. The mini-computer contains a full set of flight control equations and after processing the data transmits information back to the micro-computer for stabilizing the simulated airplane.

The micro-computer does some error checking on the data received and outputs to the micro-computer analog output peripheral (D-A). The output of the D-A's contain pitch, roll and throttle information which enter a small analog computer which drives the dual actuators controlling the 2 axis platform.

Manufacturing

Automatic Production Test Equipment

This system monitors the status of 64 products under life test. It can scan 64 similar products at preset time intervals outputting to the operator a hardcopy printout and a visual display of each product's status as it is scanned. Alarm levels are set to flag an item that is out of tolerance.

The parameters being measured are from photocells and pressure and temperature sensors. The signal conditioning section performs two functions:

    a. Amplifies the low level (20mV full scale) input to high level (10V full scale).

    b. Isolates and ground references the signals that had high common mode voltages (up to 1KV) or contained noise spikes of up to 150 volts.

The sequencing logic allows the data logger to make multi readings as each product is individually scanned. At each dual point the sequencer allows several conditions to be read and outputted to the logger. Timing and data channel number information is provided by the microprocessor to the sequencing

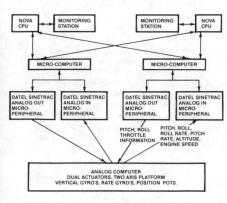

AIRPLANE SIMULATOR

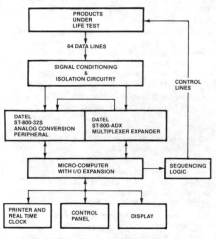

MICRO-COMPUTER CONTROLLED PRODUCT LIFE TEST SYSTEM

MANUFACTURING

logic. The sequencer allows the data to be monitored as various loading and stress effects are changed on the product under life test. In actuality, 64xN readings can be taken, where N represents the number of indexing steps of the load sequencer.

The microprocessor multiplexing technique was utilized because of the off-the-shelf availability of compatible products, namely, the Intel SBC-80/10 Single Board Micro-computer and the Datel Sine-Trac 800 Series Analog I/O System. The in-house availability of a micro-computer software development system and a PL/M high level language compiler allowed us to turn around software for this system rather rapidly.

The block diagram at the upper right hand corner of this page depicts the component parts of the system.

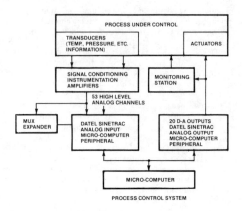

PROCESS CONTROL SYSTEM

Process Control

**Local Microcontrollers Return
Control to Process Site**

This is a process control application for a materials manufacturer who is measuring 53 channels of temperature, pressure, line speed and other types of process data. Low level analog signals from the sensors are signal conditioned by external instrumentation amplifiers to present high level analog signals to the Datel SineTrac Data Acquisition analog input peripheral unit (ST-800-32S). Additional high level analog channels (channels 33-53), are entered through a Datel analog channel expander board (ST-800-ADX). Low level signal input ranges were up to 50mV full scale and each had a bandwidth of less than 20Hz.

The analog channels are selected and digitized under control of the Intel Micro-computer (SBC-80/10). The micro-computer performs some computation and processing operations on the digitized analog data and some switch position inputs. The micro-computer outputs in two ways:

a. It generates 20 analog signals via D-A converters located on Datel analog output peripheral boards (ST-800-DA8). These analog outputs drive actuators in the manufacturing process to complete the real time, computer aided process control loops.

b. Additionally, the computer outputs data to a local monitoring station. Process status is displayed in the form of bar graphs on a color CRT as well as to some digital meters displaying several process variables in engineering units.

By using local micro-controllers at different stages of the process (versus a large remote main frame controlling the whole process), several advantages are realized.

a. It allows local line personnel to correct problems or fine tune the system by manual override.

b. Reduces miles of expensive cabling.

c. Reduces cost.

d. Reduces the possibility of misinterpretation of operation by operators at a remote computer site and allows on-site personnel to diagnose errors or process quality problems.

Environmental

**Air Quality Monitoring and Data
Logging System**

The basic function of this micro-processor based data acquisition system is in the field of air quality monitoring and data reduction. A primary function is to analyze and record wind speed, direction, and radiation in the atmosphere after a nuclear explosion. It can also be employed to measure and record air quality in pollution control endeavors.

It is a self-contained system capable of being battery operated for unattended operation. The system contains the following component parts:

1. A bus orientated micro-computer using both random access and read only memory which stores the operating program.

2. A Datel 16 channel differential micro-computer analog input peripheral (bus compatible to the micro-computer) with 12 bit A-D converter.

3. A 100 year real time calendar clock.

4. Operator control panel with LED displays and thumbwheel switches for operator interaction.

5. 3M cassette tape drive.

6. Operational hard copy line printer.

The inputs to the system are analog signals from analyzers monitoring such parameters as wind speed, wind direction, sulfur dioxide content, nitrogen oxide and other parameters as determined by monitoring application. The analog input peripheral, under control of the microprocessor, digitizes the analyzer information to 12 bit accuracy.

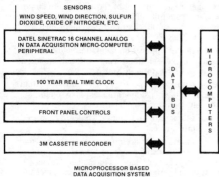

The microcomputer stores the digitized information in random access memory where it is used in one of three ways:

1. It can be displayed on the Front Control Panel which allows for switch selection of the channels's data to be displayed.
2. It can be recorded directly on the tape cassette or sent out to the hard copy printer.
3. It can be used to calculate hourly or daily averages of any parameter and then output that average value.

The real time clock generates time in years, Julian day, hour, minute and second increments. Time can be set by front panel thumbwheel switches and displayed on front Panel LED's.

The Front Panel allows operator intervention for reading the status of selected inputs, read the time, set the real time clock, and actuate a reset pushbutton switch for program restart.

The cassette recorder operates at 30 IPS in an incremental mode with an average capacity of 102,000 bytes. It is servo controlled and has an error rate of 10^{-11}.

Other optional components are:

a. Hard copy line printer.
b. Analog input expansion to 256 channels.
c. Back-up battery pack.
d. Engineering units display.

Weather Research

Global Mapping of Distribution of Physical Structure of Clouds

This research effort is being conducted under the auspices of the NASA Goddard Space Flight Center.

Maps of parameters indicative of cloud physical structure are of principal value in studies of the earth's climate. The parameters to be measured are cloud amount, optical thickness, altitude, temperature, thermodynamic phase and particle number density. Global distributions of these parameters will be assembled according to season and local time and in this format will serve as input data to climate models based on radiative energy balance. This data base will also be of use in meteorological studies of shorter time scale such as severe storm and cloud physical studies.

The cloud climatology experiment combines active and passive remote observation techniques to infer cloud parameters. The passive section consists of a Cloud Physics Radiometer (CPR) which is an 8 channel scanning radiometer with 7 channels in the near infrared and one channel in the thermal infrared. The active section consists of a cloud Lidar System (CLS) which is a two wavelength polarized scanning laser radar. To prove the sensor technique and the utility of the data, engineering models of the CPR and the CLS will be flown on a NASA high altitude aircraft. Results from these flights will be used to design a Space Shuttle (Spacelab) sensor system. A block diagram of the CLS system is pictured here as an application example of a microcomputer with analog I/O.

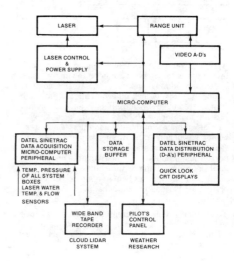

The micro-computer controlled all operating sections of the system. The most important reason a micro-computer was used in this applicaiton was physical size as the entire system was to be installed on an aircraft.

The Data Acquisition micro-computer peripheral monitored the following parameters:

a. All system power supply voltages.

b. Temperature in all system boxes.

c. Pressure in all system boxes.

d. Laser water flow.

e. Laser water temperature.

The Data Distribution (D-A's) micro-computer peripheral is employed as a μP controlled test fixture with quick look CRT terminals.

Medical

Patient Monitoring

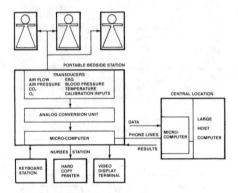

Applying computers for collecting data and monitoring patients has been going on for many years. Previously, in most cases, the monitoring computer has been remotely located requiring the data to be transmitted over considerable distances. Portable bedside monitoring stations become feasible by employing micro-computers and micro-computer analog I/O peripherals. All such applications require these analog conversion products, as the greatest percentage of monitoring instruments provide information in analog form. Additionally, the number of parameters being monitored on each patient lends itself to multi-channel Data Acquisition System applications.

The emergence of the μcomputer has significantly reduced the cost of the monitoring systems, actually making them cost effective versus the very expensive systems of ten years ago. Additionally, by being able to employ a μcomputer at each bedside station, the types of measurements taken can differ, catering to the exact needs of the patient. Monitoring stations can be located right at the bedside with visual terminals or they can be located nearby at the nurses' station.

As a result of the cost effectiveness, success in the field, and the ever increasing demand for health care, the present market of these products has exceeded $200 million in 1976. The market will have a growth rate of 36% through 1980 and reach $292 million by 1980.[2]

The particular application being detailed here is a two-station patient monitoring system installed at St. Vincent's Hospital in New York.

Station #1 monitors post-operative cardiac patients. It is a portable bedside station capable of simultaneously monitoring two patients.

Station #2 monitors patients with acute respiratory insufficiencies.

Up to 16 parameters are measured at the bedside station. Gas flow and pressure transducers as well as gas analyzers are used as measuring devices. The system is supported by calibration devices for flow, pressure and gas analyzing. A tank of a known mixture of oxygen and carbon dioxide are used as calibration standards for the gas analyzers. A source of known positive pressure is used as a standard for the gas pressure transducer. A pump of known positive displacement is used as the calibration standard for the gas flow transducer.

All calibration procedures typically last 30 seconds and are operator initiated via a keyboard and then micro-computer controlled. Long term drifts are manually compensated for on a monthly basis.

The outputs of the sensors are digitized by the micro-computer's analog input peripheral and the data is transmitted via phone lines from the bedside to another micro-computer at a central control location. The second micro-computer interfaces to a large host computer specifically programmed for patient monitoring applications. The host computer is programmed to derive from the transducer data it receives, over thirty physiological functions. These include blood pressure, heart rate, respiratory rate, resistance and compliance of the lungs, maximum inspiratory pressure, oxygen intake, carbon dioxide exhaled, positive and expiratory pressure; and measurement of tidal volume per breath.

This resulting computer information is transmitted via phone lines back to the bedside micro-computer station. There it is available at the nurses' station either on a video display terminal or via a hard copy printer. A keyboard is also located at the station which allows the clinical staff to select which parameters of each patient are to be monitored.

By employing μcomputers directly at portable bedside stations, the potential is there for having these computers operate independently of a host computer. The measurement capability of the analog I/O conversion units, and the computational and storage ability of the computer, allow the displaying of results, providing the attending physician with important up-to-date physiological data. It should be emphasized that computer based patient monitoring does not replace clinical staff, but is a diagnostic tool to aid in clinical decision making.

Communications

Color Correction Of Motion Picture Film For Video Use

This application describes a system for the electronic color correction of video signals produced going from motion picture film to video tape. The main features of this particular system are as follows:

a. Allow for scene by scene correction of hue and saturation of the colors.

b. Allows for the matching of the spectral response in motion picture colors to the spectral distribution of the components in the "film-to-video-converter" (Film Chain).

c. For color correcting at slow film speed prior to the actual reproducing of the film at normal speed. For sharpness and contrast reasons, it is not desirable to reproduce on video tape while running the film at a slow speed.

d. The corrected color data can be stored separately for use at a later date in producing new video tape.

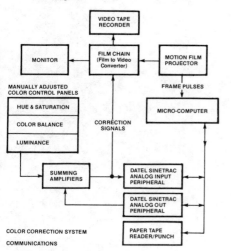

COLOR CORRECTION SYSTEM

COMMUNICATIONS

The main component parts of the system are described below (see block diagram):

a. *Film Projector* on which the film being processed is run. This unit sends signals to the Film Chain Unit and frame signals to the C.P.U.

b. The *Film Chain Unit* is a film to video converter which separates varying primary color components to video signals to form a total luminance signal.

c. *Color Control Panel* which consists of 3 separate panels.

  1. *Color Balance Panel* which contains potentiometers for controlling balance between red, green and blue components of the video signal.

  2. The Luminance Panel allows for manually controlling the gain, gamma and pedestal of the red, green and blue signals.

  3. The Hue and Saturation Panel controls the hue and saturation level of the 3 primary and 3 complementary colors of the video signal.

d. A *Datel SineTrac Analog Input Conversion Peripheral* which digitizes the correction signals from the control panel during the load or set-up mode. The digitized color correction values are stored in the C.P.U.

e. The *Micro-computer* performs the following functions:

  1. Directs the timing operations of the system.

  2. Performs control computations.

  3. Stores corrected digital color data during the set-up mode.

  4. Outputs to D-A's the corrected data during the run mode in sync with the proper film frame or scene.

f. *Datel Analog Output Peripheral* which provides correction signals to the Film Chain Unit during the run mode.

g. Video Tape Recorder records the corrected video tape during the RUN cycle.

The actual system operation sequence is as follows:

The film is run on the projector on a frame by frame, scene by scene basis. Intitially, a standard correction value is selected to provide a picture pleasing to the eye. Incremental corrections (from the color control panel) are added or subtracted on a scene by scene basis to compensate for different lighting, color patterns, cameras, etc.

These corrected values are digitized by the A-D peripheral and stored in the C.P.U. in sync with the frame reference received from the projector. The film can be rerun, stopping on selected frames, until the desired color effect is obtained.

The film is rerun a final time and recorded on video tape. The corrected color signals are sent out from the C.P.U. to the D-A converters to generate the correction signals to the film chain unit (film to video converter).

Summary

The preceding applications illustrate two significant facts:

  a. Micro-computers are not only replacing mini's in some applications, but more importantly, are generating many new market areas.

  b. By putting analog I/O conversion products directly on micro-computer bus compatible plug-in cards, users enjoy the following advantages:

    1. All interfacing logic is predesigned and assembled on the same plug-in card as analog circuitry.

    2. Packaging and interface cabling problems are eliminated.

    3. Interface and support documentation is readily available.

    4. One supplier for both interface and analog conversion circuitry.

    5. Some suppliers offer diagnostic software with the analog I/O peripherals.

    6. Hardware and programmer's instruction manual supplied with peripheral.

Micro-computers are being employed in new market areas for the following reasons:

  1. Most importantly because of their low costs.

  2. Small size and lower power consumption.

  3. Increased dependence on high technology to reduce costs and increase performance in all areas of modern living.

  4. More interest on monitoring our effect on the environment (i.e. air, water, chemicals, contents of food, outer atmosphere, etc.).

  5. Tendency among users to desire local control of each computer application rather than having a large centrally located computer controlling many separate operations. This allows local operators to control, monitor, and visually oversee the actual effect of the computer's operation and, if necessary, diagnose and manually correct any misoperation. These small local controller applications are best illustrated in the Process Control application where many small control computers could replace one large centrally located process control computer. Also, in the Patient Monitoring Application, the bedside portable monitoring stations would be much more effective than one centrally located main frame computer.

As can be seen in these examples, micro-computers in conjunction with their associated analog I/O conversion products, work together to accomplish many most interesting and worthwhile applications.

Footnotes:

  1. Data Acquisition Systems Marketing Report
    Venture Development Corporation
    Wellesley, Mass.

  2. Patient Monitoring Market Report
    Frost & Sullivan
    New York, N.Y.

4. Sample-Holds

Designing with a sample-hold won't be a problem if you use the right circuit

Sample-hold circuits are widely used in analog signal-processing and data-conversion systems to store an analog voltage accurately over periods ranging from less than a microsecond up to several minutes. This capability suits them to numerous applications including data-distribution systems, data-acquisition systems, simultaneous sample-hold systems, a/d converter front ends, sampling oscilloscopes and DVMs, signal reconstruction filters, and analog computation circuits.

Although sample-holds are conceptually simple, their application is full of subtleties. In general, applications that need only slow to moderate speed and moderate accuracy generate few problems, but high-speed, high-accuracy applications are the ones that need careful design. An example of the latter is taking a 10-V sample in one microsecond or less with 0.01% accuracy.

To select the right sample-hold for a particular job, and to apply it properly as well, requires understanding the intricacies of its design and operation.

Basically speaking

A sample-hold circuit is fundamentally a "voltage memory" device that stores a given voltage on a high-quality capacitor. The circuit can take a voltage sample and then "freeze" it for some specified period, while some other circuit or system uses the voltage.

Fig. 1a shows a sample-hold circuit in conceptual form. An electronic switch is connected to a hold capacitor so that when the switch closes, the capacitor charges to the input voltage. When the switch opens,

the capacitor retains this charge and thus holds the desired voltage for a specified period.

There are three important sets of terminals in a sample-hold circuit: the analog input, the analog

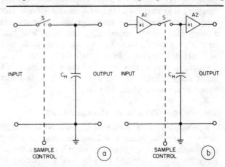

1. **In a basic sample-hold circuit (a),** the switch closes to sample the input voltage. When the switch opens, the capacitor holds the voltage. A practical circuit (b) has unity-gain buffers to charge the capacitor without loading the source and to drive normal loads without changing the voltage stored by the capacitor.

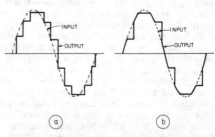

2. **A sample-hold can operate in two different ways.** It can take a quick sample of the input and return right back to hold mode (a), or it can track the input for part of the time and hold it for the rest (b).

Eugene L. Zuch, Product Manager, Datel Systems, Inc., 1020 Turnpike St., Canton, MA 02021.

This first article of a three-part series covers the fundamentals of sample-hold devices, then discusses the various kinds of circuits they use. The second article, to follow soon, will examine operating modes, while the third will give guidelines for selection and describe a number of applications.

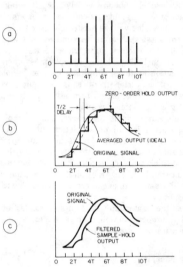

output, and the sample control terminals. Fig. 1b shows a practical circuit that includes input and output buffer amplifiers and a switch-driver circuit. The sample control input closes the switch for sample mode, or opens it for hold mode.

The sample-hold input terminals are usually the input of a high-impedance buffer amplifier since in most applications, such as operating at the output of an analog multiplexer, the source shouldn't be loaded. Likewise, the output has a low impedance so that the sample-hold can drive a load such as an a/d converter input. The output buffer amplifier must also present a very high input impedance, and very low bias current, to the hold capacitor so that its charge doesn't leak off too rapidly. In virtually all sample-hold designs, therefore, this amplifier has a junction-FET input stage. Similarly, the switch must be fast and have very low off-state leakage.

Sample-hold: An energy storage circuit

All sample-holds are basically accurate energy storage circuits. Since the hold capacitor is a key component in an accurate sample-hold, a fundamental question to be answered is: Why use a capacitor to store the energy?

It turns out that certain types of capacitors very nearly approach the ideal. They have extremely low leakage, and therefore very high equivalent parallel resistance. This resistance, commonly specified in megohm-microfarads and known as insulation resistance, is the parallel resistance of a one-microfarad capacitor and is numerically equal to the self-discharge time constant of the capacitor in seconds.

To find the parallel resistance for other capacitor values, divide the insulation resistance in megohm-microfarads by the capacitance in microfarads. Since the parallel resistance can be quite high for smaller value capacitors, most manufacturers specify a maximum "need not exceed" value, generally twice the insulation resistance. This means only that the parallel resistance is not measured or guaranteed by the manufacturer. It may well be as high as calculated.

The self-discharge time constant is the length of time required for an open-circuited capacitor to discharge to 36.8% of its charged voltage. High-quality capacitors used in sample-holds have insulation resistance as high as 10^6 megohm-microfarads, equivalent to a self-discharge time constant of one million seconds, or 11-1/2 days. In other words, this is only 1% droop in almost three hours.

To get back to why capacitors are used for the energy storage, they approach the ideal much more closely than the alternative, which is an inductor. The figure of merit for an energy-storage element is its self-discharge time constant. A high quality short-circuited inductor is hard pressed to give a self-discharge time constant (L/R) as high as 10 seconds, while a capacitor can give a time constant (RC) of 10^6 seconds. (The only exception, a superconducting induc-

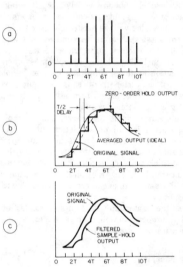

3. A zero-order hold reconstructs an analog signal that's been transmitted as a series of pulse samples (a). It does so by holding the amplitude of each pulse to fill in the spaces between them (b). Practical averaging uses a low-pass filter (c) that has more delay than the ideal averaging shown in (b).

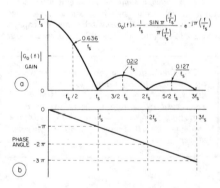

4. The gain response of a zero-order hold (a) in terms of the sampling frequency f_s takes the form of the absolute value of (sin x)/x. The phase response (b) is linear because of the constant time delay.

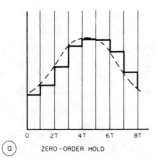
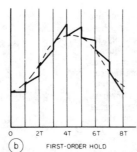
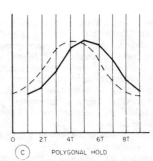

| | O   2T   4T   6T   8T | | O   2T   4T   6T   8T | | O   2T   4T   6T   8T |
| (a) | ZERO-ORDER HOLD | (b) | FIRST-ORDER HOLD | (c) | POLYGONAL HOLD |

5. Three types of holds reconstruct an original signal (dashed curve) differently. The output of a zero-order hold (a) is steady between samples. A first-order hold (b) extrapolates a new slope that's proportional to the dif-ference between the two most-recent samples. Its output error is zero during constant-slope portions of the signal. The polygonal hold (c) interpolates between the two most recent samples.

tor, would, of course, be better than a high quality capacitor, but it would be difficult to package in an ordinary sample-hold circuit!)

Capacitors of certain types are therefore clearly superior to inductors when it comes to approaching the ideal. Acceptable types of capacitors include polystyrene, polycarbonate, polypropylene, and Teflon. In addition, MOS capacitors are excellent for hybrid circuit sample-holds.

Two other storage elements useful in specialized sample-holds are an electrochemical cell such as the Plessey Electro-Products E-Cell, and a register that holds the voltage digitally.

Sample-hold circuits are variously called zero-order-holds, track-and-holds, or sample-and-hold ampli-fiers. Although these terms are generally used in-terchangeably today, some technical distinctions should be pointed out.

Strictly speaking, a sample-hold takes a very fast sample and then goes into the hold mode. This means that the switch closes for only a very short period of time, usually because a pulse transformer drives the switch. A track and hold circuit, on the other hand, can track the input with the switch closed indefinitely and then go into the hold mode upon command.

A zero-order hold may be either a sample-hold or track-and-hold. When a device is called a zero-order hold, that means it's used as a signal recovery filter. There are various types of sample-hold recovery filters such as zero-order holds, first-order holds, fractional-order holds, and polygonal holds.

The term "sample-and-hold amplifier" can refer to either a sample-hold or a track-and-hold, and ori-ginates from the fact that operational amplifiers are used to make sample-hold circuits.

Although there's a technical distinction between the terms sample-hold and track-and-hold, it's auto-matically assumed that both functions are included

in the term "sample-hold," as just about all sample-holds can also track and hold. The few circuits that can only sample for a short time, and cannot track the input, are clearly labeled this way.

To appreciate the difference between true sample-hold operation and track-and-hold operation, see Fig. 2. In Fig. 2a, a sample-hold periodically takes a sample of the input, a sinusoid in this case, and holds it for the rest of the time. In Fig. 2b, a track-and-hold tracks the input for part of the time and holds it for the rest. Here, the track time and hold time are equal.

Zero-order hold

An important sample-hold application is re-constructing, or recovering, an analog signal that has been transmitted as a train of pulse samples, like those in Fig. 3a. To reconstruct the original signal wave-form, a sample-hold, or zero-order hold, retains the peak value of a sample until the next one arrives, thus filling in the spaces between them, as in Fig. 3b. The result is a reasonable reconstruction of the original signal before it was converted to a pulse train. Ideally, the average of the reconstructed waveform, shown dashed in Fig. 3b, is a near-replica of the original waveform, delayed by half the sampling period, T.

If the staircase waveform of the output is objec-tionable, a low-pass filter following the zero-order hold will smooth the waveform further. This filter will add further phase delay, but the resulting reconstruction of the original signal is much better, as Fig. 3c shows. The cutoff frequency of this filter must be determined from the sampling rate and the bandwidth of the signal to be recovered. The lower the cutoff frequency, the better the smoothing.

The zero-order hold is a type of filter. As with other types of filters, its gain-phase characteristics are important to know. These gain and phase terms are plotted in Fig. 4. The zero-order hold is obviously not an ideal filter with its (sinx)/x amplitude response. Nevertheless, it reconstructs signals respectably. Its gain is slightly more than 3 dB down at a frequency of $f_s/2$, and it again goes to zero at integral multiples of the sampling frequency, f_s. There are some undesirable gain peaks at frequencies of $3/2\ f_s$, $5/2\ f_s$, etc. These peaks are frequently attenuated by a low-pass filter following the zero-order hold. A zero-order hold as a filter has a perfectly linear phase response (Fig. 4b), which results in the constant phase delay of $T/2$ for the output signal.

There are also more-sophisticated recovery filters than the zero-order hold circuit. These higher-order hold circuits, known as first-order holds, second-order holds, etc., reconstruct a signal more accurately than a zero-order hold (Fig. 5). A first-order hold does this by retaining the value of the previous sample as well as the present one. It then extrapolates from existing data to predict the slope to the next sample, which hasn't arrived yet (Fig. 5b). When a new sample comes in, it generates a slope proportional to the difference between this sample and the previous one. If the slope of the original signal hasn't changed much, the resulting error is small; for a constant slope, the error is zero. When the original signal reverses its slope quickly, the output "goes the wrong way," causing a fairly large error for one sample period.

An interpolative first-order hold, also called a polygonal hold, reconstructs the original signal much more accurately. This circuit also generates a line segment with a slope proportional to the difference between consecutive samples, but rather than extrapolate into the future, it interpolates between samples already received. Its accuracy is achieved at the expense of a delay of one sample period, which is necessary because a new sample must arrive before the line segment can be generated by starting from the previous sample.

Lots of circuit variety

Sample-holds come in many different circuit configurations, each suited to different speed and accuracy requirements. It's important to know the common configurations and how they operate to choose the proper type and apply it properly.

One configuration is popular because it's accurate and simple. This circuit, shown in Fig. 6a, has a gain of -1 since $R_1 = R_2$; however, making R_2 larger than R_1 gives inverting gains larger than one. When the switch closes, hold capacitor C_H charges to the negative of the input voltage. The switch opens after the capacitor has acquired this voltage to the desired accuracy.

Although potentially very accurate, this circuit is not a fast sample-hold. The capacitor charges slowly since it has a time constant of R_2C_H; with practical values such as $R_2 = 2k$ and $C_H = 2$ nF, the time

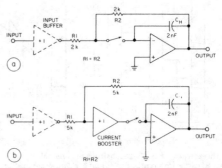

6. **This type of inverting, closed-loop circuit** is both accurate and simple. The charge time constant, R_2C_H, of the basic circuit (a) is much too long for some applications. The current booster in (b) speeds up charging considerably. The input resistance, R_1, may be too low for some sources; the buffer raises it a great deal.

constant is 4 μs. To reach a value within 0.01% of the input requires about nine time constants, or in this case, 36 μs.

Speed can be improved considerably, as shown in Fig. 6b, by adding an amplifier with current gain inside the feedback loop. The operational amplifier must also be able to supply this current to the capacitor. Since these amplifiers have low output resistance, the circuit's time constant is much lower. For example, with the same valued capacitor and an amplifier output resistance of 20 Ω, the time constant is only 40 ns rather than 4 μs. Now, only the amplifiers' output current capability limits charging.

With a maximum output current of 20 mA from this amplifier to charge the capacitor and a 40-ns time constant, the capacitor takes just 1.2 μs to charge to within 0.01% of final value. This is much faster than the 36 μs for the previous circuit. Note that in the latter case, Fig. 6b, R_1 and R_2 can be larger since R_2 no longer determines the charging time constant.

An input buffer amplifier improves this circuit further by boosting the input resistance to a much higher value than that of the input resistor R_1. In fact, the input resistance can be as high as 10^8 to 10^{12} ohms. Such high resistances are required when a sample-hold follows an analog multiplexer. In this case the buffer amplifier must be fast, since its settling time becomes part of the time required to charge the holding capacitor. The buffer can also be added to the circuit of Fig. 6a. Both sample-holds in Fig. 6 are referred to as closed loop, since the capacitor charging takes place within a closed loop circuit.

Fig. 7 shows a noninverting closed-loop sample-hold in which A_1, that is serving as both an input buffer amplifier and an error-correcting amplifier, compares the output voltage to the input voltage, then charges the holding capacitor until this error is reduced to zero.

Amplifier A₁ also gives this circuit a high input resistance.

Thanks to the error-correcting feedback in this sample-hold, A₂ need not be very accurate so long as its gain is roughly unity. Resistor R isolates the output of A₂ from the input of A₁ during hold mode.

This circuit is both fast and accurate; how fast it charges the capacitor depends on the speed of A₁ and its output current capability. Two back-to-back diodes clamp A₁'s output to its negative input so that A₁ remains closed-loop stable when the switch is opened. Note that in this circuit the switch must float up and down with the input voltage, whereas in the circuits of Fig. 6 the switch always operates at virtual ground.

Operational transconductance amplifiers

Fig. 8 shows another type of sample-hold circuit, which is versatile and can be operated in a number of closed loop configurations. This circuit is an operational integrator that can be enclosed in the feedback loop of A₁. In this case, however, A₁ is an operational transconductance amplifier; that is, one that produces an output current proportional to its input voltage. The current charges the holding capacitor while the integrator's input remains at virtual ground.

In this circuit, the two switches operate out of phase. Switch S₁ closes to sample, then S₂ closes to reduce hold-mode feedthrough when S₁ opens again.

This circuit can be connected in different ways as a closed-loop sample-hold: Fig. 9a shows the most commonly used connection, a noninverting sample-hold with a gain of +1; Fig. 9b shows the noninverting connection with gain, and Fig. 9c shows the inverting connection with gain.

Both of the switches in these circuits operate at virtual ground, an advantage in driving the switch and producing an accurate output voltage. This circuit has been successfully used in monolithic, hybrid, and modular sample-hold devices.

Another popular noninverting, unity-gain circuit is shown in Fig. 10. It's basically the same as the one shown in Fig. 1b, with two unity-gain buffer amplifiers. This type of open-loop sample-hold is commonly used in ultra-fast designs. In this case, a pulse transformer drives a fast diode bridge switch.

Normally, the supply voltage back-biases the diodes. Sampling is done by a fast-rise command pulse that turns on the diodes to charge the hold capacitor from the input buffer. Using ultra-fast buffer amplifiers and an appropriate diode-gate switch, such sample-holds can charge the hold capacitor to a full-scale change in as little as 30 nanoseconds. Because of the open-loop configuration, there is no problem with phase delays from output to input caused by a feedback loop. This means that the circuit is both fast and stable.

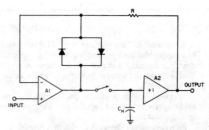

7. **Closed-loop sample-holds can also be noninverting.** In this configuration, A₁ is both an input buffer and an error-correcting amplifier. When the switch closes, current from A₁ charges the hold capacitor until the output equals the input. The pair of diodes clamps A₁'s output to keep it stable when the switch is open.

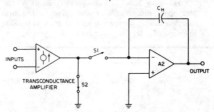

8. **Several closed-loop sample-hold configurations** can be built around this circuit, shown without its feedback connections. Basically, it's an operational integrator driven by an operational transconductance amplifier, A₁.

The input buffer in this circuit is difficult to design, for it must be both fast and stable while driving the hold capacitor load. Sampling switches, however, cause no such problems.

The basic sampling switch circuits commonly use junction FETs, MOSFETs, D-MOS FETs, and diode-gate switches. All of these can be both fast and accurate. The FET-type switches have the advantage of zero offset since they are purely resistive in the closed state. The diode-gate switch does have an offset voltage, however, which is minimized by properly matching the diode forward-voltage drops.

The infinite-hold circuit

All sample-hold circuits have the problem that once they are in the hold mode, the charge will gradually leak off the hold capacitor due to switch leakage, capacitor leakage, and output amplifier bias current. It was mentioned previously that a digital register can store a number equivalent to a voltage value as long as necessary.

The "infinite hold" circuit uses this principle to store a voltage value for any required time without any drift due to leakage. The circuit, shown in Fig. 11, is basically a tracking a/d converter, with its output

Know your circuit

Sample-hold: The generic term used for track-and-hold, zero-order hold, or sample-and-hold amplifier, it describes basically a circuit that acquires an analog input voltage and accurately stores it for a specified period of time.

Track-and-hold: A sample-hold circuit that can continuously follow the input signal until switched into the hold mode.

Signal-recovery filter: A circuit that reconstructs an analog signal from a train of analog samples.

Zero-order hold: A sample-hold circuit used as a signal recovery filter. So called because its output represents the first term of a power-series approximation to the input.

First-order hold, or extrapolative hold: A complex signal-recovery filter that predicts the next sample value by generating an output slope equal to the slope of a line segment connecting previous and present samples. In a sense, it works toward the future.

Polygonal hold, or interpolative hold: A complex signal-recovery filter that generates a straight-line segment output that joins the previous sample value to the present sample. It uses available data to reconstruct the signal more accurately than other hold circuits, but with a one-sample-period delay.

Infinite hold: An analog/digital sample-hold that digitally holds an analog voltage indefinitely without the decay of capacitor storage.

Closed-loop sample-hold: A sample-hold circuit that charges the hold capacitor within a negative feedback loop during sampling to achieve high accuracy.

Open-loop sample-hold: A sample-hold circuit that does not enclose the hold capacitor within a feedback loop.

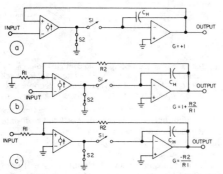

9. **Here are three different ways to connect the input and feedback** to the partial circuit in Fig. 8. The circuit in (c) has unity gain if the input (R_1) and feedback (R_2) resistors have equal values.

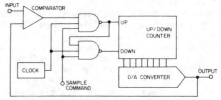

11. **Sometimes called an "infinite hold,"** this circuit can hold a sample indefinitely without the droop that happens with capacitor storage. It's an a/d converter with its output taken from the analog feedback line. A high on the sample command line lets the output follow the input. A low freezes the count inputs, so the count doesn't change.

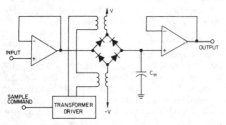

10. **Ultra-fast sample-holds often use a circuit like this.** It has a diode-bridge switch and operates open-loop. The diodes are biased off until a sample command arrives; then the pulse transformer's output turns on the diodes, which connect the input buffer amplifier to the hold capacitor. A 30-ns full-scale change is possible.

from the analog feedback line rather than from the counter. It consists of a d/a converter, up-down counter, clock, and analog comparator. The circuit operates by directing clock pulses into the up or down count inputs of the bidirectional binary counter that controls a d/a converter.

An analog comparator tests the output voltage of the d/a converter against the input voltage and directs the clock pulses to the counter so that the converter's output voltage changes toward the input. When the input voltage is reached, the circuit oscillates within one count of the input value. When the sample command goes low, the counter retains its contents indefinitely until the next sample is taken.

This circuit is not particularly fast since it must go to each new value one count at a time until the input voltage is reached. Different counting techniques will speed it up, however. Its accuracy depends on the resolution of the d/a converter; ±0.01% accuracy requires at least 12 bits. ■■

Keep track of a sample-hold from mode to mode to locate error sources

A complicated process begins when a sample-hold takes a sample. The complications increase when it switches into the hold mode. To this bumper crop of complications, add the actual sample-to-hold transition itself, which, as a complex and important event, must not be overlooked. Understanding the intricate workings of this process is the basis for understanding the sources of error in the system and how to minimize them.

In the sample mode, the sampling switch closes and the circuit charges the hold capacitor to the input voltage. With the capacitor charged, the circuit tracks the input signal as it changes. However, tracking is possible only if the signal doesn't exceed the bandwidth or slew rate limit of the sample-hold. The term "sample mode" applies regardless of how long tracking continues.

The operating parameters that apply to the sample-hold in the sampling mode are specified in the same way as an operational amplifier's. Offset voltage, expressed in millivolts, may be referred to either the input or output, and is usually adjustable to zero with an external potentiometer. Dc gain, the ratio of output to input voltage at dc, is commonly either +1 or −1. With some sample-holds, adding external feedback resistors provides other gains, and some allow trimming external gain to precisely +1 or −1.

Bandwidth, the sinusoidal frequency at which gain is down by 3 dB from its dc value, is measured with a small-signal sine wave below the slew rate limit. The slew rate is the fastest rate at which the sample-

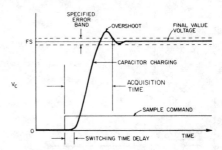

1. **Acquisition time of a sample-hold** starts with the sample command and ends when the voltage on the hold capacitor enters and stays in the error band. Acquisition time is defined for a full-scale voltage change, measured at the hold capacitor.

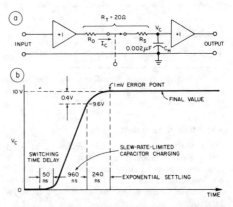

2. **This equivalent circuit for determining acquisition time** (a) shows the importance of the charging time constant, $R_T C_H$. Acquisition time is the sum of the various delays incurred in charging the hold capacitor to its final value (b), and is dominated by slew-limited charging.

Eugene L. Zuch, Product Manager, Datel Systems, Inc., 1020 Turnpike St., Canton, MA 02021.

This article, the second of a three-part series, discusses sample mode, hold mode, and the important transition from sample to hold. The first article covered the fundamentals of sample-holds and discussed the various circuits they use. The third and last article will give guidelines for selecting sample-holds and describe a number of applications.

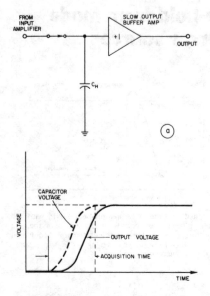

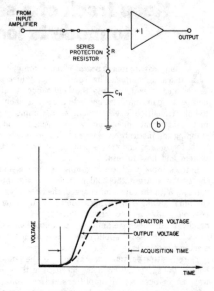

3. **Acquisition time** may be less than or greater than the time it takes the output voltage to settle to its final value. In (a), the capacitor reaches its final value before the output amplifier catches up. In (b), the protective resistor permits the output to settle before the capacitor reaches its final voltage.

---

hold output can change. Specified in volts per microsecond, slew rate is generally determined by the charging rate of the hold capacitor.

Acquisition time counts

The most important specification of the sample-hold in the sample mode is acquisition time—the time required, after the sample command is given, for the hold capacitor to charge to a full-scale voltage change and remain within a specified error band about its final value.

As illustrated in Fig. 1, the definition applies to the capacitor voltage, not the output voltage of the circuit. The reason for this will become clear shortly. The figure shows an initial switching delay following the sample command. After this delay, the hold capacitor charges at a maximum rate which is determined by its charging current.

Initially, as the capacitor voltage attempts to enter the final value error band, it slightly overshoots the band, but then enters and remains within it. The amount of overshoot, generated by a wideband input amplifier driving a capacitive load, depends on this

amplifier's stability. Acquisition time is therefore measured from the beginning of the sample command transition to the point where the signal enters the error band and stays there.

Another useful definition of acquisition time is the amount of time following the sample command transition that the hold command can be given so that the hold capacitor retains the voltage change to the required accuracy. The full-scale voltage change is usually specified as a 10-V change, although other magnitudes may be specifically stated. The error band is commonly specified from 0.2% down to 0.005%, with other values possible. Within this range there are sample-holds available that provide acquisition times from about 10 μs down to 20 ns. Basically, acquisition time determines the maximum sampling rate at which a sample-hold can be operated.

Several circuit limitations determine the achievable acquisition time for a sample-hold: the speed of the input amplifier with a capacitive load, the current available to drive the hold capacitor, the source resistance driving the hold capacitor (both amplifier output and switch), and the value of the hold capacitor. Either the input amplifier or the switch may limit

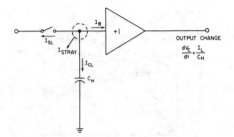

OUTPUT CHANGE

$$\frac{dV_C}{dt} = \frac{I_L}{C_H}$$

4. Hold-mode droop is caused by currents that charge or discharge the hold capacitor. These include switch-leakage, stray-leakage, amplifier-bias currents and leakage within the hold capacitor itself.

the current available to drive the hold capacitor.

Fig. 2 shows the relationship between the acquisition time, the current available to charge the capacitor, and the time constant associated with the hold capacitor. For example, to determine the acquisition time for a 10-V change to within 1 mV, or a 0.01% error band, assume a maximum charging current from the amplifier and switch of 20 mA and a capacitor value of 0.002 μF. The rate of change of capacitor voltage dV_C/dt is

$$\frac{I_C}{C_H} = \frac{20 \times 10^{-3}}{2 \times 10^{-9}} = 10^7 = 10 \text{ V}/\mu\text{s}, \qquad (1)$$

where I_C is the charging current and C_H is the capacitance of the hold capacitor. After a 50-ns switching delay, the capacitor begins to charge at a constant rate of 10 V/μs until it approaches final value and maximum charging current is no longer required. This happens when

$$V_C = 10 - (I_C R_T) = 9.6 \text{ V}. \qquad (2)$$

R_T, the total resistance in the hold capacitor's charging path, is also the sum of the amplifier output resistance (R_O) and the switch series resistance (R_S).

The capacitor charges exponentially over the final 400 mV with a time constant of

$$T = R_T C_H = 20 \times 2 \times 10^{-9} = 40 \text{ ns}. \qquad (3)$$

Since the final value error band is specified as 1 mV, it takes six time constants to reduce the 400 mV error to 1 mV, or 0.25%. Six time constants give a 240-ns exponential settling time. The acquisition time is then the sum of the three times that are indicated in Fig. 2b, or 0.05 + 0.96 + 0.24 = 1.25 μs.

This illustrates a fast sample-hold that acquires to 0.01% accuracy and shows as well that the charging current to the capacitor must be high and the hold capacitor time constant must be low. The same acquisition time limitations apply to the other sample-hold circuits shown in Part 1 of this series, which is why a current booster amplifier is required in one case.

Direct measurement of a sample-hold's acquisition

time is not always possible since in some cases the capacitor voltage is not accessible externally. If a sample-hold has an operational integrator output stage, acquisition time can be measured, but in other circuits it may not be possible because the capacitor is inside the circuit.

The two interesting cases in Fig. 3 illustrate why the acquisition time is defined in terms of the hold capacitor. In Fig. 3a, the output buffer has a slower response time than the input amplifier and capacitor. This lag means that when the capacitor acquires a new voltage, its final value is reached before the output of the sample-hold. The switch can be opened when the capacitor voltage has entered the specified error band even though the output voltage has not. Slightly afterward, the output amplifier settles to the correct output voltage.

Fig. 3b shows the output stage of one of the popular monolithic sample-hold circuits that has a resistor in series with the hold capacitor. This resistor provides short circuit protection to the capacitor terminal. The resistor, however, causes a lag in the capacitor voltage, which means that the capacitor is not fully charged when the sample-hold output voltage has reached final value. To allow the capacitor to charge completely, the sampling switch in this circuit must remain closed longer than indicated by the output voltage. The acquisition time in this case must be measured by starting with a long sample time and then gradually reducing this time until the output starts to show an error. These cases underscore the fact that acquisition time is properly defined at the capacitor rather than at the sample-hold's output.

Then there's hold mode

The second mode of operation for a sample-hold, when the sampling switch is open, is the hold mode. Two important specifications that characterize hold mode are hold mode droop, or voltage decay, and hold-mode feedthrough.

Hold-mode droop, defined as the output voltage change per unit of time while in the hold mode, is commonly specified in volts per second, microvolts per microsecond, or other convenient quantities. Hold-mode droop originates as leakage from the hold capacitor (see Fig. 4). The four leakage components consist of capacitor insulation leakage I_{CL}, switch leakage current I_{SL}, output amplifier bias current I_B and stray leakage I_{STRAY} from the common terminal connection. The rate of voltage change on the capacitor dV/dt is the ratio of the total leakage current, I_L, to hold capacitance C_H

$$\frac{dV_C}{dt} = \frac{I_L}{C_H} \qquad (4)$$

If all the leakage currents don't have the same

Know the lingo

Acquisition time: How long it takes after the sample command is given, for the hold capacitor to be charged to a full-scale voltage change and to remain within a specified error band around its final value.

Aperture delay time: The time elapsed from the hold command to the opening of the switch.

Aperture jitter: Also called "aperture uncertainty time," it's the time variation or uncertainty with which the switch opens, or the time variation in aperture delay.

Aperture time: The averaging time of a sample-hold during the sample-to-hold transition.

Bandwidth: The frequency at which the gain is down 3 dB from its dc value. It's measured in sample (track) mode with a small-signal sine wave that doesn't exceed the slew rate limit.

Effective aperture delay: The time difference between the hold command and the time at which the input signal is at the held voltage.

Figure of merit: The ratio of the available charging current during sample mode to the leakage current during hold mode.

Hold-mode droop: The output voltage change per unit of time while in hold. Commonly specified in V/s, μV/μs or other convenient units.

Hold-mode feedthrough: The percentage of an input sinusoidal signal that is measured at the output of a sample-hold when it's in hold mode.

Hold-mode settling time: The time from the hold-command transition until the output of the sample-hold has settled within the specified error band. It includes aperture delay time.

Sample-to-hold offset error: The difference in output voltage between the time the switch starts to open, and the time when the output has settled completely. It is caused by charge being transferred to the hold capacitor from the switch as it opens.

Slew rate: The fastest rate at which the sample-hold output can change. It's specified in V/μs.

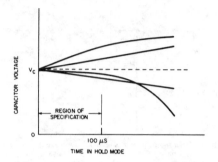

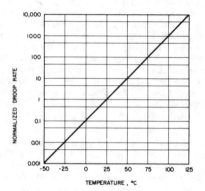

5. **Droop in hold mode** can be positive or negative-going, and may not be linear with time (a). Since most leakage current comes from silicon devices, droop as a function of temperature is predictable (b).

polarity, the result is a somewhat lower droop rate.

To measure hold-mode droop, simply acquire a given voltage and then while watching the output voltage on an oscilloscope, switch into the hold mode. The droop may be positive or negative and is not necessarily linear with time (See Fig. 5a). Several possible droop rates are illustrated. The value measured, which appears on data sheets, is the slope right after initiation of the hold mode when the output voltage feeds an a/d converter or other circuit.

In addition, hold-mode droop changes exponentially with temperature. Most of the leakage that causes this droop comes from silicon devices. Since a device's leakage approximately doubles for every 10 C increase in temperature, hold-mode droop shares this characteristic. Fig. 5b shows a normalized plot of hold-mode droop vs. temperature for virtually any sample-hold. Droop rate is specified on a data sheet at 25 C. To consider an example, a sample-hold with a droop rate of 100 μV/ms at 25 C will have a rate of 3.2 mV/ms at 75 C and a rate of 102 mV/ms at 125 C.

For a given operating temperature, droop rate must be determined based on the required hold time in order to know the resulting error. Of course, below 25 C, droop rate improves by a factor of two for every 10 C. In cases where better droop rate is required, an extra hold capacitor must be added or a better sample-hold selected. Additional capacitance also increases the acquisition time of the circuit.

In the case of monolithic sample-holds, the hold-mode leakage is specified on the data sheet so that the required capacitor value can be figured from the

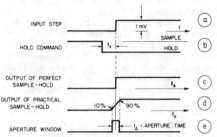

6. **Aperture time can be measured** by repeatedly feeding a tiny step (a) to the sample-hold's input and repeatedly shifting from sample to hold (b) with a varying delay, t_x. A perfect sample-hold would have an output like (c) as a function of delay time t_x, but a real sample-hold averages this step over t_A.

7. **Effective aperture delay time** is the difference between the input amplifier time delay, t_a, and the delay between the hold command and the time when the switch opens (t_d). EADT may be positive, zero, or negative. If t_a is greater than t_d, the hold capacitor sees a delayed version of the input (b), which results in holding an input voltage that occurred before the hold command.

relationships in equation 4.

Since the hold capacitor directly affects both speed and accuracy of a sample-hold, it's useful to have a figure of merit for sample-holds. Increasing the hold capacitance decreases the droop rate, but increases acquisition time. Likewise, decreasing the capacitance increases the droop rate although it does decrease the acquisition time.

The figure of merit is a ratio that measures the improvement in both acquisition time and droop rate together. It is a dimensionless quantity and may have values of 10^9 or more for a high quality sample-hold.

A useful figure of merit sometimes used with sample-holds is the ratio of the current available to charge the capacitor (I_C) to the leakage current from the capacitor (I_L). This ratio is approximately equal to the ratio of slew rate to droop rate:

$$\text{Figure of Merit} = \frac{I_C}{I_L} \approx \frac{\text{Slew Rate}}{\text{Droop Rate}} \tag{5}$$

A source of error in the hold mode, hold-mode feedthrough, or simply feedthrough, is the second specification that characterizes hold mode. This parameter is the percentage of an input sinusoidal signal that's measured at the output of a sample-hold in the hold mode.

To measure feedthrough, apply a 20-V peak-to-peak sinusoid to the input of a sample-hold while it is in the hold mode. A greatly attenuated version of the input shows up at the output, passing through switch capacitance and stray coupling capacitance. The resulting feedthrough can be measured easily with an oscilloscope. Typical values of feedthrough for a well-designed sample-hold are from 0.05% down to 0.005% of the input. Feedthrough is sometimes expressed in dB of attenuation.

Hold-mode feedthrough may vary with frequency, either increasing or decreasing at higher frequencies depending on the particular design of the sample-hold. Feedthrough is a most important specification when a sample-hold follows an analog multiplexer that switches between many different channels. Note that feedthrough can also be measured with a square-wave input rather than a sinusoid, since the square wave contains many harmonic frequencies.

A critical parameter

The most critical part of sample-hold operation is during the short sample-to-hold transition when the sampling switch opens. It's during this transition period that the real subtleties of sample-hold operation appear, including one of the most important parameters associated with this period, called aperture time.

Aperture time is the most misunderstood of all sample-hold specifications. There are actually several related parameters which use the word aperture as part of the specification.

The concept of aperture time in electronics relates closely to the root meaning of aperture: an opening, or hole. In electronic measurements aperture is the "opening" or "window" of time during which a signal is averaged or measured. For example, in an a/d converter, the conversion time is the time required to measure the input signal and is also known as the aperture time of the converter. In fact, a sample-hold is the device that reduces the aperture time of an a/d converter by replacing the converter's time window with the sample-hold's much shorter window.

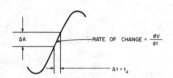

8. Timing uncertainty in the switch and driver circuit produces uncertainty in the held voltage, which for a given period of time, increases with the rate of change of the signal voltage.

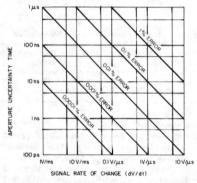

9. To obtain the error due to aperture uncertainty time for a given signal rate of change, a full-log plot is helpful. This plot assumes a 10-V full-scale signal.

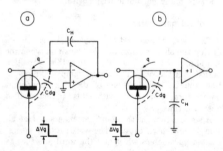

10. Drain-to-gate capacitance, C_{dg}, transfers some charge, q, when a FET sampling switch opens. The resulting voltage step on the hold capacitor, C_H, is small if C_H is large. The switch in the first circuit (a) operates at virtual ground.

Ideally, a sample-hold takes a point sample of the input signal, that is, an accurate sample in zero time. Since this is impossible, the sample is actually taken in the short period of time when the switch opens, during which the signal is averaged. The aperture time

therefore occurs after the signal has been acquired, when the switch rapidly opens.

Aperture time is frequently, but mistakenly, defined as the turn-off time of the switch. If this were true, aperture times would be extremely small since the switch opens very quickly. The confusion stems from the fact that the switch follows a band-limited input amplifier which, even if the switch opening were instantaneous, averages the result over a small period of time.

To interpret aperture time, as in Fig. 6, assume the sample-hold receives a 1-mV input step (Fig. 6a). The hold command transition (Fig. 6b) can be adjusted to occur before, with or after the input step. The timing difference between the two, designated t_x, can be positive, zero, or negative. (For simplicity, assume no delay between the hold command and the opening of the sampling switch.) To make the measurement, feed the sample-hold with repeated input steps and hold commands while slowly varying t_x. As the hold command transition effectively scans across the input step, the sample-hold's output in hold mode changes. Ideally, when hold-mode output is plotted against t_x, it should look like Fig. 6c. Such an output, a perfect sample with no averaging, requires an infinite-bandwidth input amplifier in addition to an infinitely-fast switch.

Since this is not possible, the input step is averaged, or filtered, by both the switch with a non-zero opening time, and by the input amplifier, which has limited bandwidth. The actual waveform therefore looks like Fig. 6d. The filtering action of the switch and input amplifier slows the rise-time of the step to t_A, which is the aperture time or aperture window of the sample-hold as shown in Fig. 6e. Mathematically convolving the input step (Fig. 6a) with the aperture window (Fig. 6e) gives the actual output (Fig. 6d).

In practice, because of amplifier and switch speed limitations, it is extremely difficult to achieve true aperture times less than a few nanoseconds.

Delayed window

Aperture delay time, another frequently used term concerning the sample-to-hold transition, is generally defined as the elapsed time between the hold command and the opening of the switch. Aperture delay time, a pure time delay, can be compensated out by advancing or delaying the hold command. Furthermore, this specification is difficult to measure, if not impossible, since the precise time when the switch turns off cannot be determined directly.

A more useful specification might be called effective aperture delay, and defined as the time difference between the hold command and the time at which the input signal and the held voltage were equal. In other words, effective aperture delay relates the hold command to the point on the input signal which was held (see Fig. 7).

Effective aperture delay really points out the difference between the two delay times snown in Fig. 7. The first is the analog delay through the input amplifier, while the second is the digital delay to the switch opening (Fig. 7a). Effective aperture delay (EAD) is then equal to $(t_d - t_a)$.

Notice that either a positive, negative, or zero value may be obtained depending on which delay is larger. Fig. 7b illustrates negative effective aperture delay. In this instance, time lag in the input amplifier has resulted in holding an input voltage which occurred before the hold command. Knowing effective aperture delay time then is more useful than knowing aperture delay time.

A related specification, aperture uncertainty time, or aperture jitter, is the uncertainty in the time at which the switch opens. Actually, it's the time variation in aperture delay time. If the sampling switch receives the hold command for a series of samples at the same point on a waveform, it will hold slightly different values each time.

Aperture uncertainty time originates in the digital driver circuit and switch. The hold command has a finite risetime and must pass through one or more logic thresholds that have voltage noise. These transitions therefore generate time uncertainties. The significance of aperture uncertainty time is that it causes an amplitude uncertainty in the held output of the sample-hold. This amplitude error, ΔA, shown in Fig. 8, equals the product of the rate of change of the input signal dV/dt, and the aperture uncertainty t_u.

This product is the basis of a graph (Fig. 9) that gives aperture uncertainty vs. signal rate of change for various accuracies. The accuracy is based on 10-volt full scale signals. The surprising fact is that moderate speed signals produce relatively large errors even with small aperture uncertainties. For example, if the aperture uncertainty is 10 ns and the input signal rate of change is $1V/\mu s$, the amplitude error is 0.1% for 10 V full scale. Reducing this error to 0.01% means that the aperture uncertainty time has to be reduced to just 1 ns.

Aperture uncertainty time is generally quite small in well-designed sample-holds since it's possible to achieve values of a few nanoseconds down to tens of picoseconds. As a rough rule of thumb, the aperture uncertainty tends to be 10% or less of the aperture delay time; in some designs it can be as low as 0.1%.

Sample-to-hold offset error develops when the switch opens, as a direct result of a phenomenon called charge dumping or charge transfer.

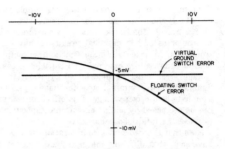

11. **Sample-to-hold offset error varies** with input signal voltage if the sampling switch floats with the signal, but is unaffected by variations in signal voltage if the switch operates at virtual ground.

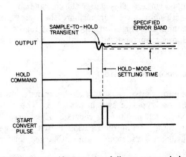

12. **When an a/d converter follows a sample-hold,** the start-conversion pulse must be delayed until the output of the sample-hold has had enough time to settle within the error band and stay there.

There are two types of sample-hold switches; one operates at virtual ground (Fig. 10a), while the other operates at the signal voltage (Fig. 10b). Every electronic switch has a capacitance associated with it. In this case it is C_{dg}, the drain-to-gate capacitance of the junction FET switches shown. This capacitance couples the switch-control voltage on the gate to the hold capacitor.

Since the switch-control voltage must generally be rather large, a significant charge transfers from the hold capacitor to the gate-drive circuit when the switch is turned off. This charge is

$$q = C_{dg} \Delta V_g \qquad (6)$$

where ΔV_g is the change in gate voltage. The error this produces on the hold capacitor is then

$$V_c = \frac{q}{C_H} = \frac{C_{dg}}{C_H} \Delta V_g. \qquad (7)$$

This error typically might be 10 mV assuming 2 pF for C_{dg}, a 10-V ΔV_g, and a 0.002 μF hold capacitor.

Sample-to-hold offset error is one of the undesirable, inherent characteristics of sample-hold circuits. It should be looked for and recognized. The charge transfer that causes this error is expressed in picocoulombs and in practical circuits it may vary from 50 pC down to 0.1 pC. Since monolithic sample-hold circuits require external hold capacitors, their voltage error must be determined by equation 7. Sample-holds with internal capacitors have a specified sample-to-hold offset voltage. This offset, of course, can be decreased by adding an external capacitor to increase the total hold capacitance.

Note that the two switch configurations in Fig. 10 have somewhat different charge transfer characteristics. In the virtual ground switch the charge transfer is constant regardless of the signal voltage, since the gate voltage change is always the same. In the other switch, however, the gate voltage change varies with the signal voltage. This causes the charge transfer to vary with signal level. Furthermore, the drain-to-gate capacitance also varies with the signal voltage, so that the charge transfer itself is nonlinear and even has a "gain error."

Some have curved errors

The output error caused by charge transfer differs for the two types of switches (Fig. 11). The virtual ground switch produces a constant offset error vs. signal voltage, while the floating switch produces a nonlinear error vs. signal voltage. Charge transfer is obviously a limiting factor in a high-accuracy, high-speed sample-hold. It works against attaining both these characteristics simultaneously. Some sample-holds have unique switch designs that minimize or compensate for this charge transfer. In some of them, an externally-adjustable compensation circuit minimizes the charge transfer. If the sample-to-hold offset error is constant with signal voltage, then the error is relatively easy to handle since it can be zeroed with a simple offset adjustment.

Another effect of the sample-to-hold transition is a small transient in the output just after going into the hold mode—the hold mode settling time (Fig. 12b). This is the time it takes the output of the sample-hold to settle within the specified error band after the hold command transition. Notice that the hold mode settling time includes aperture delay time. Fig. 12 shows the small output transient caused by the rapid switch turn-off at the input to the buffer amplifier.

This transient occurs after the output settles to a new value that includes the sample-to-hold offset. Hold mode settling time may be a few nanoseconds to a microsecond or so, depending on the particular sample-hold. It is an important specification because an a/d conversion that follows sampling and holding cannot begin until hold-mode settling is complete without causing a conversion error. As Fig. 12 shows, the pulse that starts the converter is generated after the sample-hold output has settled within the specified error band.■■

Pick sample-holds by accuracy and speed and keep hold capacitors in mind

W hen it comes to selecting a sample-hold device, fortunately there's a fine assortment available: monolithic, hybrid and modular types can all give good performance. There are different degrees of good performance, of course, and for the most part the sample-hold that's finally selected will depend on the degree of speed and accuracy needed. Depending on the type of sample-hold and its application, it may need an external hold capacitor. This capacitor should be chosen with as much care as the sample-hold itself, for its quality directly affects the performance of the sample-hold. There will be more about selecting hold capacitors, but first, it's a good idea to consider error analysis, which is vital in appraising the total error contribution of a sample-hold to a system.

In a given system, of course, the sample-hold is but one of the many sources of error that may also include an amplifier, filter, multiplexer, and a/d converter. Achieving total system accuracy on the order of 0.01% is by no means a trivial task, but quite the opposite. It pays to take a somewhat pessimistic approach in adding up the errors, and follow this by thorough testing of the sample-hold's accuracy in the system. In many cases the results will be a pleasant surprise, because a conservatively-specified device has been chosen. In other cases, it won't be a shock to discover that the analysis is about right because the sample-hold that was selected has been specified right at the edge of its performance.

The best way to handle error analysis is with a

This is the final article of a three-part series on sample-holds. It discusses error analysis and sample-hold selection, selecting a hold capacitor, and describes a number of applications. The first article of the series, which appeared in ED No. 23 (Nov. 8, 1978, p. 84), covered fundamentals and circuit types. The second, in ED No. 25 (Dec. 6, 1978, p. 80), discussed sample mode, hold mode, and the sample-to-hold transition.

Eugene L. Zuch, Product Manager, Datel Systems, Inc. 1020 Turnpike St., Canton, MA 02021.

systematic listing like the one in Table 1, which gives errors for a fast, accurate system with 0.01% error as a design goal. The errors are computed for an assumed operating temperature range of 0 to 50 C and take into account all of the specifications discussed in this series.

What seems to be a large total error in Table 1 shouldn't be alarming. The sample-hold evaluated, designed for use in 12-bit systems, has been conservatively specified. If all the errors add in the same direction, the total error is ±0.036%, but this is an unlikely possibility. Adding the errors statistically (RMS) gives a better figure of ±0.017%, which is a good bit closer to the goal. Since most of the errors are specified as maximums, the typical statistical error is actually close to 0.01%.

Speed and accuracy are the two foremost considerations in choosing a sample-hold, and the key to proper selection is an error analysis that takes the desired sampling rate into account. The circuit configuration, a subject discussed in Part 1 of this series, affects performance in certain applications, so it should be kept in mind as well.

Consider monolithics first

In general, a monolithic device should be considered first, since it will result in the lowest-cost design if moderate performance is acceptable. Moderate performance implies about 4 μs acquisition time to 0.1% and 5 to 25 μs to 0.01%. Monolithic devices use external hold capacitors, so one will need to be selected.

Hybrid microcircuit sample-holds offer a step up in performance without a major increase in size. Acquisition times of 5 μs down to 1 μs, to 0.01% accuracy are available, and even faster acquisition times for 0.1% can be obtained. Most hybrid sample-holds include an internal hold capacitor, so there's no need to select one unless additional capacitance is needed. Many hybrids use MOS-type hold capacitors which offer exceptionally good performance.

Both the newer monolithic as well as hybrid devices equal or surpass the performance of many of the early low-cost modular sample-holds, but they can't match the newer, high-performance modular types. These new modules offer some difficult-to-achieve speed and accuracy specifications such as 350-ns maximum ac-

Table 1. Error analysis of an accurate, high speed sample-hold

Source of error	Error contribution	Comments
Acquisition error	0.01%	Maximum error specified for rated acquisition time.
Gain error	0.00	Externally adjustable to zero.
Offset error	0.00	Externally adjustable to zero.
Nonlinearity	0.005%	Maximum specified.
Droop error	0.01%	For 10 μs hold time. Using 25 C droop of 20 μV/μs max. and multiplying by 10 to give droop of 1 mV at 50 C. This is 0.01% for 10 V full scale.
Gain change	0.004%	Using specified 15 ppm/°C max., × maximum temperature change of 25 C.
Offset change	0.008%	Using specified 30 μV/°C max., × max. temperature change of 25 C.
Dielectric absorption	0.003%	Estimated error voltage during hold time using curve of Fig. 2.
Total	0.036%	
RMS Total	0.017%	

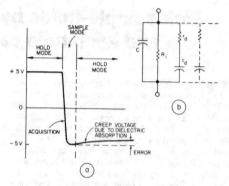

1. **In this example of dielectric absorption error,** the hold capacitor has been sitting at +5 V for some time. Although given enough time to settle completely during sampling, in hold mode, the capacitor's voltage creeps back toward +5 V (a). An imperfect capacitor with dielectric absorption can be modeled (b) by a perfect capacitor, C, the insulation resistance, R_i, and the long-time-constant components r_d and c_d, which simulate dielectric absorption.

quisition time to 0.01%, or 50 ns to 0.1%.

Once a sample-hold has been selected, it may need a hold capacitor. These capacitors have somewhat unusual requirements. Some parameters, such as tempco of capacitance, matter very little, while others, such as dielectric absorption, are very important. Dielectric absorption affects the accuracy of the held voltage, although insulation resistance is quite important as well, for the same reason.

When high accuracy is needed, the range of satisfactory capacitor dielectrics narrows down to those in Table 2, which gives the important specs for them. Note that insulation resistance, which is quite high at 25 C, drops drastically at higher temperatures, such as 125 C. That's because insulation resistance decreases exponentially with temperature.

It won't stay put

If a capacitor is charged to a given voltage, discharged by shorting it, and then open-circuited again, its voltage will begin to creep up from zero toward the original voltage. The capacitor exhibits a "voltage memory" characteristic known as dielectric absorption, which occurs because the dielectric material

doesn't polarize instantaneously—molecular dipoles need time to align themselves in an electric field. As a result, not all the energy stored in a charged capacitor can be quickly recovered upon discharge.

One way to measure dielectric absorption is to charge the capacitor to some voltage for 5 minutes, discharge it through a 5-Ω resistor for 5 seconds, then disconnect it. Measure the capacitor voltage five minutes later. The ratio of the measured voltage to the charging voltage, expressed in percent, is the dielectric absorption.

Even though the time scale in a sample-hold is usually far shorter than 5 min, dielectric absorption is still a source of error and should be taken into account. Assume the hold capacitor has been resting at a given voltage V_0 when a different voltage is sampled and held. Once hold mode begins, the voltage on the capacitor will begin to creep back toward V_0. Thus, the dielectric absorption causes an error as illustrated in Fig. 1a.

Fig. 1b shows a first-order approximation model of an imperfect capacitor, emphasizing dielectric absorption. Resistor R_i represents the insulation resistance and r_d and c_d represent the source of the dielectric absorption. (Actually, to model the absorption accurately, there should be a number of additional, parallel $r_d c_d$ circuits with different values.)

After capacitor C in the model has been rapidly discharged from a previous voltage and then open-circuited, the long time constant of $r_d c_d$ causes some of the charge on c_d to transfer slowly to C, which develops a small voltage.

An accurate approximation to this "creep" voltage

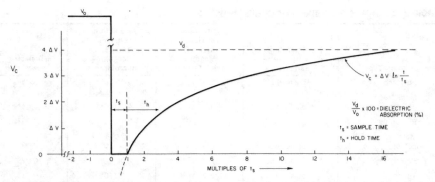

2. **A natural log function of time is an accurate approximation** to the voltage creep caused by dielectric absorption. Before sampling, the capacitor has been holding a voltage V_0. A new sample charges the capacitor to a new voltage (zero, in this case, for simplicity), for period t_s. Once in hold mode, the capacitor reaches a voltage ΔV at time $2t_s$ and continues to creep toward V_0 according to the logarithmic expression.

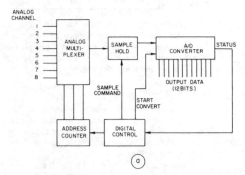

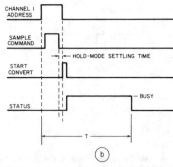

3. **A data-acquisition system scans a number of analog inputs** and converts them, one at a time, to digital form (a). The sample-hold provides an unchanging input to the converter until its conversion is complete. When it's finished, the STATUS line goes low to permit the next input in sequence to be converted (b).

---

caused by dielectric absorption is shown in Fig. 2. The curve is a natural log function of the shorting time, or sampling time (t_s). If the output creep voltage is measured at time $2t_s$, the voltage will be ΔV. If it is measured at $4t_s$, it will be $2\,\Delta V$ and at $8t_s$, $3\,\Delta V$. The equation for the curve is

$$V_c = \Delta V \ln \frac{t}{t_s}$$

where t_s is the sample time and t is the total time, or sample time plus hold time ($t_s + t_h$).

This equation is a good model, providing $V_c \ll V_0$. It does not hold for extremely long time periods, however, since V_c goes to infinity for infinite time. As shown, V_d represents the voltage measured to determine dielectric absorption at a specific time, which is a large multiple of t_s.

Capacitors can be measured and fitted to this curve.

First, determine the value of ΔV from the measured dielectric absorption. The standard tests for dielectric absorption normally specify $t_h \gg t_s$, which is the correct way to make them. Since the equation is logarithmic, there is no asymptote to the curve, which continues to rise. For all practical purposes, however, a hold time much longer than the sample time will give a value for dielectric absorption that's far out on the curve.

Assume that the dielectric absorption is measured as 0.02% for a point at which $t_h = 15t_s$ or $t = 16t_s$. Then

$$\Delta V = \frac{2 \times 10^{-4} \; V_0}{\ln 16}$$

$$= 7.21 \times 10^{-5} \; V_0$$

where the dielectric absorption is defined as V_c/V_0 at $t = 16t_s$. The resulting equation for creep voltage is

Table 2. Sample-hold capacitor characteristics

Type	Operating temperature range (°C)	Insulation resistance at 25 C (Megohm-microfarads)	Insulation resistance at 125 C (Megohm-microfarads)	Dielectric absorption
Polycarbonate	−55 to +125	5×10^5	1.5×10^4	0.05%
Metallized polycarbonate	−55 to +125	3×10^5	4×10^3	0.05%
Polypropylene	−55 to +105	7×10^5	5×10^3 (1)	0.03%
Metallized polypropylene	−55 to +105	7×10^5	5×10^3 (1)	0.03%
Polystyrene	−55 to +85	1×10^6	7×10^4 (2)	0.02%
Teflon	−55 to +200	1×10^6	1×10^5	0.01%
Metallized Teflon	−55 to +200	5×10^5	2.5×10^4	0.02%
			(1) At 105 C	
			(2) At 85 C	

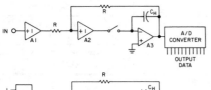

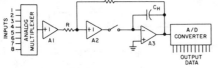

4. **In a single-channel system, the settling time of the input buffer amplifier,** A_1, isn't critical because the amplifier can follow changes in the signal (a). With multiplexed inputs (b), however, the input buffer may take additional time to settle to the new value at the multiplexer's output when it switches channels.

$$V_c = 7.21 \times 10^{-5} \, V_0 \ln \frac{t}{t_s}$$

Two factors reduce considerably the error due to dielectric absorption in typical applications of a sample-hold. First, the dielectric absorption measurement assumes a long initial charging time, say 5 minutes, whereas in a sample-hold a new voltage is held for a relatively short time. Second, the dielectric absorption is specified for a long open-circuit time compared with the shorting time, whereas in a sample-hold the hold time may be only slightly longer than the sample time.

The amount of creep voltage can also be reduced by remaining in the sample mode as long as possible relative to the hold time. The result of these factors is that a capacitor with a dielectric absorption of 0.02%, for instance, may contribute 0.005% or less

error to the sample-hold, as the curve in Fig. 2 shows.

At this point, there may be reason to wonder if all the care and time needed to select a sample-hold is worth it. It certainly is. There's an abundance of applications for these devices.

Take a sample

Undoubtedly one of the most common applications for a sample-hold is in data acquisition systems. A representative system would have an 8-channel multiplexer followed by a sample-hold and a 12-bit a/d converter (see Fig. 3a).

A logic-control circuit steps an address counter to sequence the analog multiplexer through the eight channels of analog data. For each channel the sample-hold acquires the input signal and switches into the hold mode.

After allowing for the hold-mode settling time, a start-convert pulse initiates the a/d conversion, which is performed by successive approximation. After the conversion, the a/d converter's status output goes low.

When the conversion of this channel is finished, the analog multiplexer switches to the next channel while the output register of the a/d converter holds the digital word from the completed conversion. This word is then transferred out to a computer data bus. The sampling and conversion process is repeated for each analog channel in sequence.

From Fig. 3b, T is the time required for the multiplexer and sample-hold to acquire the signal and for the a/d to convert it. Then 1/T gives the throughput rate, or the fastest rate at which the analog channels can be scanned. The rates for practical 12-bit data acquisition systems may vary from about 20 kHz up to 250 kHz corresponding to values of T that range from 50 μs down to 4 μs.

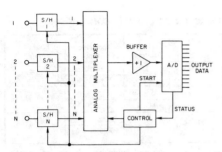

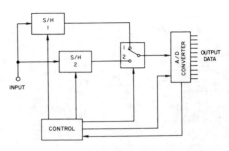

5. **A simultaneous sample-hold system** such as this samples all analog inputs at the same time and holds the samples for conversion. While one of the held voltages is being converted, the others mustn't droop too much.

7. **In an ultrafast a/d conversion system,** acquisition time in a sample-hold takes up a sizable part of the cycle. Interleaving two sample-holds like this lets one of them acquire while the other one's output is being converted.

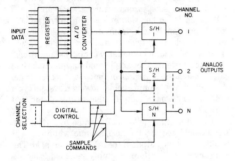

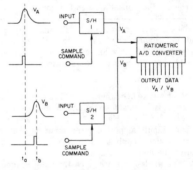

6. **Multiplexed digital data** destined for a number of analog channels are reconstructed and distributed by a system like this one. Once the data for a channel have been converted, the sample-hold for that channel samples the d/a's output and retains it until the next data word for that channel comes in for conversion.

8. **Sample-holds can serve as temporary analog signal-storage devices.** The first sample-hold retains signal V_A's peak value so the converter can divide it by the peak value of input V_B, which comes by later.

Indeed, considering the many applications for sample-holds, a good number are used in conjunction with a/d converters. This is because the sample-hold greatly reduces the converter's aperture time.

There are two important ways to use a sample-hold with an a/d converter, and each imposes a different requirement for the acquisition time. Fig. 4a shows a fast inverting sample-hold used ahead of an a/d converter, which converts just one input signal. The sample-hold continuously tracks the input signal until is goes into the hold mode.

Even while in the hold mode, input-buffer amplifier A_1 continues to track the input signal and only A_2 and A_3 affect the acquisition time. Acquisition is very fast because A_1 doesn't have to settle to a new voltage for every sample.

The same sample-hold can also follow an analog multiplexer, as in Fig. 4b. The required acquisition time will be longer here since A_1 must settle to a new voltage every time the multiplexer switches to a new channel. This means that the settling time of A_1 is now part of the acquisition time.

These two situations are significant because A_1's settling time may be larger than the acquisition time of the rest of the circuit. If it is, there'll be a great difference between the acquisition times of single-channel and multichannel acquisition systems.

Another important consideration in a data-acquisition system is interfacing the sample-hold to the a/d converter. A successive-approximation a/d converter, without an input buffer amplifier (which adds to the conversion time), has a resistor input that goes to an analog comparator's input terminal. Since the comparator is changing state during the successive-approximation conversion, the input impedance to the a/d changes. Since this happens at high speed, there

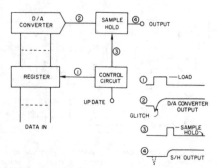

9. **An output developed by many d/a converters for certain input-code transitions** temporarily goes the wrong way. This transient, or "glitch," is undesirable in some applications and can be removed by sampling the converter's output after the glitch has gone by.

may be errors if the sample-hold's high-frequency output impedance isn't low enough. Furthermore, most sample-holds have higher output impedance in the hold mode than in the sample mode.

Sample all at once

Another way to use sample-holds in a data-acquisition system is illustrated in the simultaneous sample-hold system of Fig. 5. Here, data must be taken from all analog inputs at precisely the same time. To do this, the system requires a sample-hold per channel ahead of the analog multiplexer.

All the sample-holds are given the hold command simultaneously; then the multiplexer sequentially switches to each sample-hold output while the a/d converter converts it into digital form. Notice that a high-impedance buffer amplifier is required between the multiplexer and the a/d converter.

For this application, select sample-hold devices that are identical and have very small aperture-uncertainty times. In addition, the aperture delay times should be adjusted so that they all go into hold mode simultaneously. Another important criterion is that the droop rate be relatively low, since the last sample-hold in the system must hold its voltage until all the other outputs have been converted.

In an application which is the reverse of data acquisition, sample-holds can send signals from a channel to many destinations in a data-distribution system. Such a system (see Fig. 6) uses a single d/a converter and storage register together with a number of sample-holds to distribute data to a series of analog channels. As digital data are transferred into the d/a converter and its output changes, the appropriate sample-hold samples the new output voltage and then, once the converter's output has settled, switches into hold mode.

Each sample-hold circuit is updated in sequence as

Table 3. Sample-hold comparison

	Accuracy	Acquisition time	Price
Monolithic	0.1%	4 to 20 μs	$5 to $21
	0.01%	5 to 25 μs	
Hybrid	0.1%	25 ns	$35 to $135
	0.01%	1 to 10 μs	
Modular	0.1%	30 to 200 ns	$43 to $208
	0.01%	0.25 to 5 μs	

new data arrive, and holds its voltage until all the other sample-holds have been updated and the sequence returns to the first one. The sample-holds used must be chosen for the required acquisition time, which depends on the rate of updating each output, and for the desired droop error between updates.

Back on the other side of the coin, ultrafast a/d converters can benefit from working with sample-holds. Interleaving two of them, as in Fig. 7, will eliminate acquisition time delay in many applications.

In such systems, the sample-hold's acquisition time can be a significant portion of the system's cycle time. With interleaved sample-holds, however, system cycle time depends only on the time required for a/d conversion.

Acquisition-time delay is eliminated by having one sample-hold acquire the next sample while the a/d is converting the output of the other sample-hold. The a/d converter, therefore, is simply switched from the output of one sample-hold to the other. The only dead time between conversions is the small delay in the analog switch.

Conversion time can be decreased further, but doing it requires a second a/d converter, with one a/d operating off each sample-hold. The sample-holds then are operated sequentially, and the outputs of the a/d's have to be digitally multiplexed. In this way the throughput time is reduced to half the conversion time of either a/d converter.

In yet another a/d application, a sample-hold can delay or "freeze" analog data that exist only briefly; this information can then be combined with later data. This circuit (see Fig. 8) computes the ratio of two peaks that occur at different times, t_a and t_b.

The first sample-hold stores the peak of signal V_A so that its value will still be available to the ratiometric a/d converter when the peak of signal V_B comes by. The second sample-hold stores the peak while the ratio is being converted to digital form.

Sample-holds deglitch

The list of conversion applications for sample-holds seems almost endless. Even big problems can be solved. For example, major code transitions in a d/a converter can cause unwanted voltage spikes as large as half the full-scale output voltage. These spikes,

175

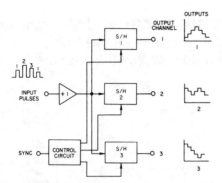

10. **When analog signals are encoded** by pulse-amplitude modulation and then multiplexed, they can be sorted out and reconstructed by a set of sample-holds with properly timed sample commands. The time scale of the input is shorter than that of the outputs.

11. **Cascaded sample-holds acquire a signal quickly** and hold it for a long time with little droop. The first one needs to hold a signal only long enough for the second to acquire it. Typical acquisition would be 5 μs to 0.1%, with a droop rate of 30 μV/s.

commonly called glitches, are caused by switches in the converter that take longer to turn off than to turn on, or vice versa. The point is, in many d/a converter applications such as CRT displays and automatic testing, the converter output voltage should make a smooth, monotonic transition when it goes from one output voltage to the next.

This can be done by processing the d/a converter output with a sample-hold as shown in Fig. 9. First, a digital control circuit transfers the digital data from the register to the d/a converter. With this information at its input, the d/a converter generates a new output containing glitches. Once the glitches have settled, the sample-hold takes a sample of the new analog data and returns to hold mode before the d/a output changes again. The output of the sample-hold now has a smooth, monotonic transition between the old and the new levels.

Keeping up with high-speed analog d/a outputs generally requires ultrafast sample-holds for deglitching. Usually an inverting, current-input sample-hold follows the d/a converter to permit the highest possible operating speed. In fact, some specially designed d/a converters have self-contained sample-holds for deglitching, and not surprisingly, are called deglitched d/a converters.

Putting it all together

Data conversions aren't the only applications to benefit from sample-holds. As Part 1 of this series pointed out, a zero-order hold makes an excellent data-reconstruction filter and is commonly used in pulse-amplitude modulated (PAM) systems such as the one in Fig. 10. Here, time-division multiplexing is used to send a train of amplitude-modulated pulses over a transmission system, each pulse in sequence being the sample from one analog channel.

To demodulate this pulse train, the control circuit synchronously switches on each sample-hold in sequence as the pulse arrives, then returns it to hold mode until the next pulse from that channel arrives. Pulse by pulse, the output of each sample-hold becomes the reconstructed analog signal of the appropriate channel. A low-pass filter can also be added to each sample-hold output to smooth the reconstructed signals further.

In some analog-circuit applications, sampling should be quick, yet the sampled value should hold steady for a long time. Such conflicting needs produce conflicting requirements on the sample-hold. The best solution to the problem is to use two cascaded sample-hold devices, as in Fig. 11. The first sample-hold is a fast unit that acquires the input rapidly and accurately, while the second unit is a slow device with a very long hold time (low droop rate), perhaps on the order of minutes.

Basically, the first sample-hold must acquire the signal and then hold the result long enough for the second sample-hold to acquire it. The errors need to be calculated carefully to be sure of meeting the accuracy requirements. In many cases two monolithic sample-holds in cascade might do the trick. External hold capacitors can then be chosen to give the desired performance.

For example, a 0.001-μF polystyrene capacitor would be a good choice for the first sample-hold to give an acquisition time of 5 μs to 0.1%. For the second one, a 1.0-μF capacitor would give an acquisition time of 10 ms but a hold time of 300 s to 0.1% accuracy. The resulting droop rate would be only 30 μV/s, which is quite low, indeed.■■

Acknowledgement

The author wishes to thank James B. Knitter, Wayne E. Marshall, and Dr. Berry Phillips, whose insights and observations contributed significantly to this series of articles.

Analyzing the dynamic accuracy of simultaneous sample-and-hold circuits is straightforward. A wideband scope and a simple mathematical model supply the answers.

In most simultaneous data-acquisition systems a large number of analog input channels are strobed at precise time intervals and then sequentially digitized by an analog-to-digital converter. To check the multichannel sample-and-hold circuits there are some simple tests the user can perform to verify correct circuit operation.

To start the error analysis, several assumptions can safely be made: All static errors have been eliminated—
- The offset error.
- The gain error.
- The hold step error.

Input voltage, V_{in}, to the sample-and-hold equals the output voltage, V_{out}, from the sample-and-hold. V_{in} is any dc voltage between ± 10 V. The offset error is V_{out} when $V_{in} = 0$, while the gain error is the maximum value of the offset error divided by V_{in} maximum (10 V).

Looking at the dynamic errors

Normally, one sample-and-hold circuit is used for each a/d converter with any multiplexing between input channels done previously. However, for a large number of channels this leads to errors due to the different conversion times of the various channels. In a simultaneous sample-and-hold configuration, a number of input analog channels are strobed at a precise time and the held voltages are sequentially converted to digital form.

At this point the most basic test that can be performed is to simultaneously apply the same voltage waveform to all inputs. Now, if we look at the output for each channel, the digital words representing each voltage should be identical. If the system fails this basic test, the user must search the specification sheets and the circuits themselves for the error sources.

The three major sources of dynamic errors can be traced to the following:

Ralph Johnston, Datel Systems, Inc., 1020 Turnpike St., Canton, Mass. 02021.

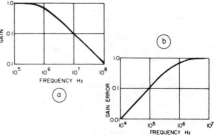

1. **Plots of a single pole transfer function (a) and of the gain-error (b) are shown with a 1-MHz cutoff frequency.**

- A change in the gain during the sample mode as a function of frequency.
- A nonzero hold step as a function of frequency (hold-step error).
- A shift in the effective beginning of the hold-step as a function of V_{out}, dV_{out}/dt, or frequency (aperture-shift error).

The aperture-shift error can be caused by a slowly opening switch or by a pole at the unity-gain -3 dB point (f_{co}) of the unity-gain sample amplifier. The error advances the effective time of the switch opening to a time prior to its actually reaching open circuit. For applications of simultaneous sample-and-hold circuits both the f_{co}'s and the switch opening times, must be matched.

The transfer function during sample

Gain in the sample stage can be represented by a linear transfer function—at least for amplitudes small enough that the amplifier slew-rate doesn't affect the results. Thus, a simple low-pass function with a pole at f_{co}, say 1 MHz, can be represented by the following:

$$\frac{V_{out}}{V_{in}} = \frac{1}{1 + j\dfrac{f}{10^6}}$$

The graph of this typical low-pass filter is shown in Fig. 1a. It has unity-gain transmission and a

1-MHz −3 dB point.

Usually, though, it proves more useful to plot small deviations from unity gain as shown in Fig. 1b. The formula used for this gain-error plot is

$$\text{Gain error} = \frac{V_{out}}{V_{in}} - 1 = \frac{-j\,\dfrac{f}{10^6}}{1 + j\,\dfrac{f}{10^6}}$$

While not usually seen in this form, this type of frequency-response plot is quite valid. From the equation we see, for example, that a circuit band-width of 1 MHz, an input of 10 V at a frequency of 1 kHz results in an error of 0.001 or 10 mV.

By now finding the response of the circuit to a ramp of K V/sec, we can try to match transfer functions of all the channels of the sample-and-hold stages. The gain-error transfer function is put into the s domain using LaPlace transforms and becomes

$$\text{Gain error} = \frac{\dfrac{-s}{2\pi \times 10^6}}{1 + \dfrac{s}{2\pi \times 10^6}}$$

The ramp is also transformed, and becomes K/s^2.

The sample-and-hold: What is it and where is it used?

A sample-and-hold (S/H) circuit holds or "freezes" a changing analog input signal voltage. Usually, the voltage thus frozen is then converted into another form, either by a voltage-controlled oscillator, an analog-to-digital (a/d) converter or some other device.

The simplified block diagram of a lossless (ideal) S/H circuit is shown in Fig. 1. Here the amplifiers are assumed to be ideal—with infinite input impedances and bandwidths, zero output impedances and unity gains. The electronic switch is also considered ideal—with infinite speed, zero impedance in the sample position and infinite impedance in the hold position. Also, the sampling capacitor, C, is assumed to have no leakage or dielectric absorption.

Depending upon cost, the user has three basic methods to choose from when setting up a multiple-signal data-acquisition system. The most basic but also the most expensive scheme is the one shown in Fig. 2a. This circuit uses an individual S/H and a/d converter for each sensor line. Fig. 2b is a low cost alternative in which all the sensor lines are first multiplexed and then fed into a single S/H and a/d converter. Another method, falling between those of Figs. 2a and 2b in cost and performance, is shown in Fig. 2c. Here, the sensor signals are first sampled and then multiplexed and sent to a single a/d converter.

If the S/H circuits were ideal, the only significant errors would occur in the multiplexer or the a/d converters. In a real world situation, of course, the S/H circuits introduce some serious errors into the conversion circuit.

The circuits of Figs. 2a and 2c require additional qualities from the S/H circuits that are not needed for the system of Fig. 2b. Precise matching of the aperture delays and bandwidths is required.

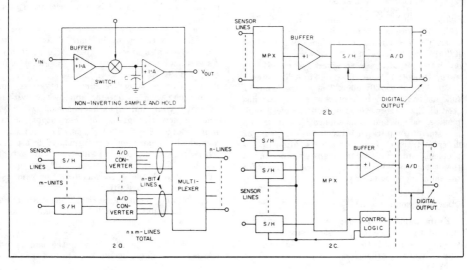

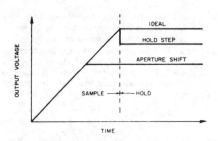

2. **Dynamic errors caused by the hold step** and the aperture shift are hard to distinguish.

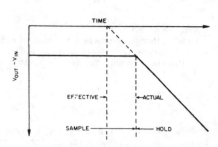

4. **If you use a different scope input,** the effective point of hold initiation can be found by extrapolating back to the zero point.

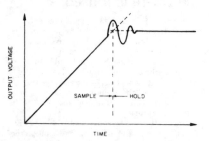

3. **By extrapolating** the two straight-line segments to meet each other, you can find the effective time at which the hold period starts.

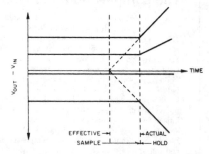

5. **The effective start time** for hold is not affected by the slope of the input ramp—for a first-order analysis.

Taking the inverse transform of the product we get

$$\frac{K}{2\pi \times 10^6} [1 + e^{-(2\pi \times 10^6)t}]$$

as the output error for a ramp input.

The two terms in the result represent a gain error. This error is due to the ramp as a constant $K/2\pi f_{co}$ and a delay of $1/2\pi f_{co}$ seconds. The delay in the output can be considered as an advance in the transition time of sample-to-hold states—but this is not usually done. The inverse transfer function can always be applied after the data has been digitized. However, for multichannel simultaneous sample-and-hold applications it is unnecessarily complicated to keep track of, say, 32 different transfer functions. The solution to this problem is to match all the transfer functions so that the units will deliver identical outputs for the same input waveform.

Other error sources exist

Examination of the output voltage near the time of the sample-to-hold transition shows the errors caused by both a hold step and an aperture shift (Fig. 2).

The hold-step error appears as a sudden change in the sample capacitor voltage at the time of hold. If such an error exists only for a fast ramp input, a probable cause is dielectric absorption in the capacitor.

The aperture shift is a variation, in either direction, of the point in time at which hold occurs. It is also known as aperture uncertainty. As a function of input rate it is somewhat difficult to measure.

To measure aperture uncertainty, use an oscilloscope with a sampling amplifier or with a sensitive, wideband input having good recovery. Then observe the sample-and-hold output for an input slope of 0.5 or 1 V/µs. The resulting straight lines can then be extrapolated to a point where they meet, and the effective hold instant can be found, as shown in Fig. 3. A change of this point with the input waveform, or randomly, is called aperture jitter.

A similar type of measurement uses a scope's differential input. All static and dynamic errors, including linear ones, due to the transfer function can be measured by observing $V_{out} - V_{in}$ as shown in Fig. 4. The slope during the hold period can be extrapolated back to zero to find the effec-

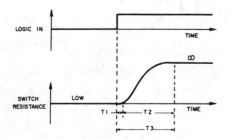

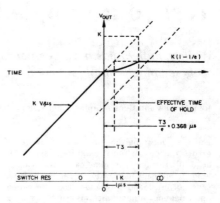

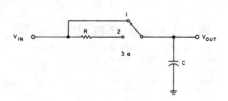

6. **A typical analog switch** introduces a delay in the sample-to-hold transition.

7. **An ideal slow opening switch** can be modeled by using a simple RC network and a three position switch.

8. **The effective time** at which hold commences occurs before the switch is fully opened.

tive time when hold starts. With a single-pole transfer function, the value of $V_{out} - V_{in}$ during sample for an input ramp is proportional to the slope of the waveform. But as shown in Fig. 5, to a first-order approximation, the start of hold is unaffected.

But, there is zero aperture uncertainty with the transfer function representation, thus the effective time of hold initiation occurs before the switch opens! The amount of this shift can be determined as a function of bandwidth. A transfer function with an f_{co} of 1 MHz can be represented by an RC low-pass filter with a resistor of 159 Ω and a capacitor of 100 pF. An input ramp of 1 V/s will cause a capacitor current of 1 mA (CV/t) which in turn causes a resistor drop of 159 mV. Thus the effective time of hold occurs 159 mV/V/μs or 159 ns before the actual switch opening.

The two measurements described are difficult to perform without high performance test equipment. Therefore, most manufacturers' specifications of aperture delay and uncertainty tend to be primarily concerned with the variation of switch resistance after the logic input changes to the hold state. Fig. 6 shows a typical logic switch resistance change during the sample-to-hold transition.

The time T_1 is known as the switching delay or aperture delay and is characteristic of any practical switch. Switching time, T_2, usually is measured from the 10 to 90% points (as for logic circuits) and is sometimes called aperture time. The total switching time, T_3, is also referred to as either the aperture time or aperture delay. If the rise time of the switch varies with the input voltage waveform, or just randomly, the change in T_3 is called the aperture jitter.

To further complicate matters, some definitions do not use switch resistance. Diode-bridge switches are characterized by stored charge and not by changes in resistance. The switch must then be viewed as a black box—apply a ramp voltage to it, open the switch and determine the effective time of opening by observing V_{out} and extrapolating the straight lines as previously described. A second method relying on diode reverse-recovery measurements can be used but is not as accurate.

The example shown in Fig. 7 can demonstrate that the effective switch opening time occurs before the switch resistance reaches infinity. Let V_{in} be a ramp of K V/μs. If, at time t = 0, the switch goes from position 1 to 2, then 1 μs later it goes to position 3, the effective time of hold can be seen from Fig. 8 to occur while the switch is in position 2. The aperture-time advance is fixed for an input ramp but will have jitter for waveforms that have curvature. The effective hold initiation will occur between instants T_1 and T_3. This is why $T_3 - T_1 = T_2$ is often specified as the aperture time. ∎∎

Test your sample/hold IQ

While sample/holds have been around for a long time, don't let their seemingly simple functions contribute errors to your designs.

John M Mills and **Gene Murphy,** Datel Systems Inc

Engineers must become increasingly aware of error sources when designing fast data-acquisition systems; in some cases, the sample/hold circuit that you incorporate can be the main cause of error and frustration. Likewise, when implementing other functions such as peak detectors and D/A deglitchers, you must select the proper device.

Unfortunately, even in today's high-technology marketplace, a certain vagueness still surrounds S/H specifications. One basic ambiguity lies in calling the circuit a "sample/hold" in the first place; by far, the majority of sample/holds on the market today actually operate as (and would be more correctly called) track-and-holds, because you can keep them in the sampling mode indefinitely (tracking). A true sampling circuit samples the signal for a specified amount of time, designated the aperture time. To compound matters, various S/H designs now cause specified acquisition times to assume slightly different meanings depending on design.

Finally, S/H's can do funny things that manufacturers hesitate to specify, let alone mention on data sheets. The following multiple-choice questions, based on various sample/hold concepts,

should help clarify these ambiguities and test your skill. The correct answers, along with a brief discussion of the principles involved, appear on pgs 122-124 .

PENCILS READY? BEGIN!

1. Suppose you wish to use a sample/hold circuit as a deglitcher on the output of a D/A converter. Generally, what basic sample/hold designs from **Fig 1** provide optimum performance?
   a. Open-loop follower
   b. Closed-loop integrator (type 1)
   c. Closed loop
   d. Closed-loop transconductance integrator (type 2)
   e. No advantage among these designs.

2. **Fig 2** shows a basic open-loop-follower sample/hold circuit, with accuracy to ten bits ($\pm 0.1\%$ FS). You'll usually find this design in fast sample/holds. Both the input- and output-follower amplifiers (A_1 and A_2) operate as buffers with settling times of 400 nsec to within 0.1% FS (10V step input) and exhibit single-pole responses. Given that R_{ON} of the

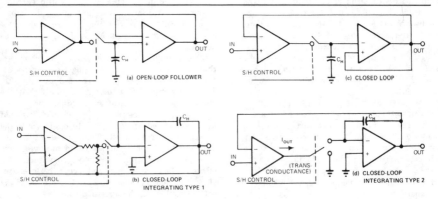

Fig 1—If designing a deglitcher circuit, which S/H configuration would you choose? Note that the closed-loop integrator of **(b)** uses a voltage output to charge the holding capacitor while **(c)** feeds current directly into the capacitor. (See **question 1**)

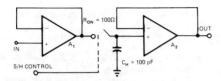

Fig 2—In this open-loop-follower S/H, determine sampling output settling time and output acquisition time. (See **questions 2** and **3**)

sampling switch equals 100Ω and that the hold capacitor has a value of 100 pF, determine, to a first approximation, both the sampling output settling time to 0.1% for a 10V step input and the output acquisition time to 0.1% for a continuous 10V p-p 20 Hz sine wave on the input.
a. 870 nsec, 470 nsec
b. 470 nsec, 870 nsec
c. 570 nsec, 406 nsec
d. 405 nsec, 337 nsec.

3. Suppose that the sample/hold circuit of **Fig 2** is an IC type in which you connect the hold capacitor externally. With C_H=100 pF, the manufacturer specs the following: sample-to-hold offset error of 100 mV and hold-mode voltage droop of 250 mV/sec.
   A. If you change C_H to 2000 pF, what new values do the sample-to-hold offset error and hold-mode voltage droop assume?
   a. 2V, 12.5 mV/sec
   b. 100 mV, 12.5 mV/sec
   c. 5 mV, 5V/sec
   d. 5 mV, 12.5 mV/sec.
   B. Find the input acquisition time to 0.1% FS for a 10V step input with C_H=100 pF and C_H=2000 pF.
   a. 570 nsec, 11.47 μsec
   b. 406 nsec, 1.46 μsec
   c. 570 nsec, 878 μsec
   d. 406 nsec, 1.21 μsec.

4. A sample/hold operates in front of a 12-bit A/D converter that has a 10V FS range and 20-μsec conversion time. This S/H uses FET switches and has a droop rate of 59.5 mV/sec at 25°C. What maximum operating temperature can you choose so that the A/D sees less than 1/2 LSB change on its input?
   a. 60°C
   b. 85°C
   c. 100°C
   d. 125°C.

5. When working with a track-and-hold circuit with a finite sampling time of 50 nsec in an environment with an operating range of −55 to +125°C, what type of holding capacitor

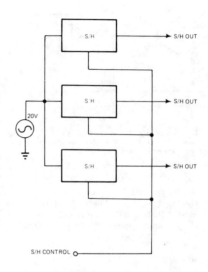

Fig 3—Simultaneous S/H's present special problems of their own. Do you know what they are? (See **question 7**)

gives best performance?
a. Ceramic
b. Teflon
c. Polystyrene
d. Polypropylene.

6. Suppose you're designing a system in which the maximum error introduced by the sample/hold must not exceed 0.01% and you apply a 20V p-p sinusoidal signal to the input. If the only error source consists of a 32-nsec aperture time, what maximum allowable input frequency can you use and remain within error budget?
   a. 1 kHz
   b. 2 kHz
   c. 4 kHz
   d. 7.5 kHz.

7. **Fig 3** shows a simultaneous sample/hold circuit. If you sample a 20V p-p sinusoidal signal with a frequency of 30 kHz, a 10-nsec aperture uncertainty in the S/H causes errors of near what percentage full-scale range between units?
   a. 1%
   b. 0.05%
   c. 0.09%
   d. 0.009%.

8. The sample/hold circuit of **Fig 4** consists of a closed-loop type with an operational-amplifier integrator in the feedback path of

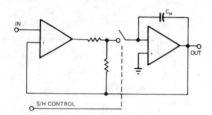

Fig 4—By examining this closed-loop S/H with op-amp feedback, can you describe its general operating characteristics? (See **questions 8** and **9**)

the input buffer amplifier. What relationship exists between (I) the output settling time and (II) the input acquisition time (dependent on C_H) for a 10V step input?

a. I<II
b. I=II
c. I> II
d. Insufficient data.

9. Refer again to the closed-loop integrating S/H configuration of **Fig 4.** What best describes the general characteristics of this type of circuit?

a. Fair accuracy, fast acquisition time, high droop rate
b. Extremely good accuracy, fast acquisition time, high droop rate
c. Extremely good accuracy, slow acquisition time, low droop rate
d. Fair accuracy, slow acquisition time, low droop rate.

10. A sample/hold with unity gain has specified accuracy of 12 bits (ie, gain error in sampling mode=0.01% of reading). In sampling mode this simple S/H exhibits a single-pole transfer function and a 20V p-p −3 dB bandwidth of 500 kHz. If you want to sample a 20V p-p sine wave to 12-bit accuracy, what approximate maximum frequency can you input and still maintain that accuracy?

a. 50 Hz
b. 100 Hz
c. 7.1 kHz
d. 14.14 kHz.

11. Here's a quickie question to complete the quiz: Of the four S/H specs listed below, what is (are) the most commonly omitted parameter(s) on manufacturers' data sheets?

a. Sample-to-hold offset error
b. Hold-mode settling time
c. Output noise, hold mode
d. Output offset voltage drift. □

Presenting the answers to our quiz on sample/holds

Confused? If not, you're an industry expert. Take this opportunity to learn some important facts about these deceivingly complicated devices.

ANSWERS		
1. a, d	4. d	8. b
2. c	5. b	9. c
3A. d	6. a	10. c
3B. b	7. c	11. b, c

This quiz should have given your knowledge of S/H's a real workout. In fact, it should have been difficult—you learn much more from tough exams. Here's how to score yourself (count **3A** and **3B** separately):

11-12 Send your resume to the authors
9-10 Take over your design department
7-8 Collect one "attaboy!"
5-6 Average
3-4 Read up before doing any S/H designs
1-2 Don't let your boss see this.

Now for a more detailed discussion of the answers.

1. Generally, **a** and **d** work best. Although all sample/hold circuits contribute slight errors, open-loop-follower types don't exhibit large hold-to-sample transients (spikes) that generally occur on closed-loop types. And although spiking might not matter for large changes, it becomes extremely important in D/A deglitcher applications where you sequentially increase D/A digital inputs to generate an analog ramp. In this application, the sample/hold samples only 1-LSB changes from input to output, and even in this case the closed-loop types of **b** and **c** generate large hold-to-sample spikes (as high as 7V), possibly worse than the D/A glitches that the S/H tries to eliminate. Because it keeps its loop open during hold, a closed-loop circuit must entirely reacquire the input in sample mode, even with unchanged inputs. Usually this process results in

a spike; however, the closed-loop transconductance integrator of **Fig 1d** won't exhibit large hold-to-sample spikes.

2. The sampling output settling time (ie, keeping the unit in sample mode and observing the output for a 10V step input) depends on the signal going through three separate single-pole stages: the input buffer, the RC network composed of ON switch resistance and hold capacitor, and the output follower. On the other hand, when coming out of a hold state back into sample mode, the acquisition time required for the output to track the slow (20 Hz) sine wave diminishes because the input buffer already tracks the sine wave on its output. You can use the square root of the sum of squares formula as a first approximation for calculating the settling time of such cascaded single-pole circuits. The RC time constant of the switch-and-hold capacitor equals 10 nsec, and its settling time takes seven time constants—70 nsec—to reach 0.1% of its final value.

Thus, sampling output settling time is

$$\sqrt{400^2 + 70^2 + 400^2} = 570 \text{ nsec,}$$

and the output acquisition time is

$$\sqrt{70^2 + 400^2} = 406 \text{ nsec.}$$

3A. With $C_H = 2000$ pF, the sample-to-hold offset error=5 mV and the droop rate=12.5 mV/sec, because both specs vary inversely with C_H. Droop dV/dt equals i/C_H where i represents the current leakage through the hold capacitor (the sum of output-amplifier bias current and switch leakage current). The sample-to-hold offset error consists of the step error that occurs at the initialization of the hold mode generated by dumping charge into the hold capacitor. Because droop $dV/dt = i/C_H$

and sample/hold offset error=Q/C, if you increase C_H by a factor of 20, both droop and offset decrease by 20.

3B. This question is slightly deceptive. The true definition of input acquisition time is the time necessary, in sample mode, for the hold capacitor to acquire a step voltage. If C_H=100 pF as in the initial problem circuit, the time constant RC=10 nsec and 7RC=70 nsec. The input amplifier settles in 400 nsec, and, as before, input acquisition time is

$$\sqrt{400^2 + 70^2} = 406 \text{ nsec.}$$

For C_H=2000 pF, 7RC=1400 nsec, and input acquisition time is

$$\sqrt{400^2 + 1400^2} = 1.46 \ \mu\text{sec.}$$

4. The maximum allowable signal change on the input of the A/D is

$$(0.5)\left(\frac{10V}{2^{12}}\right) = 1.22 \text{ mV,}$$

and maximum allowable slew rate equals

$$\frac{1.22 \text{ mV}}{20 \ \mu\text{sec}} = 61 \text{V/sec.}$$

This value also represents the maximum allowable droop rate for the sample/hold. Because the S/H uses FET switches, the droop rate doubles every 10°C. Taking this into consideration, apply the following formula:

$$DR_{max} = DR_{25°C} \times 2^{(\Delta T/10°C)}$$

$$61\text{V/sec} = 59.5 \ \frac{mV}{sec} \times 2^{(\Delta T/10°C)}$$

And because ΔT=100°C, T_{max}=125°C.

5. A major error source in sample/holds with finite sample time periods comes from the storage capacitor's dielectric-absorption characteristic. Teflon exhibits the lowest dielectric-absorption property at 125°C and thus makes the best choice. This characteristic, also called dielectric hysteresis, determines the length of time a capacitor requires to discharge; a high dielectric-absorption value means that the capacitor won't react to sudden step changes in storage charge and also that high temperatures can cause extremely high sampling errors. The nearby **table** lists breakdown characteristics of commonly used capacitor types.

6. A sample/hold amplifier, actually a form of analog memory, ideally stores (in hold mode) an

CAPACITOR BREAKDOWN CHARACTERISTICS		
TYPE	TEMPERATURE RANGE	DIELECTRIC ABSORPTION
CERAMIC	UNACCEPTABLE	0.01-0.02%
POLYSTYRENE	TO 85°C	0.01-0.02%
POLYPROPYLENE	TO 100°C	0.03-0.09%
TEFLON	TO 125°C	0.01%

instantaneous voltage (sample value) at a desired instant in time. The constraint on this time is aperture uncertainty. To compute the error (for sinusoidal waveforms), you must observe the following formula:

$$E = \left(\frac{dV}{dt}\right)T$$

where E=voltage error or change, dV/dt=signal slew rate and T=aperture time. During time T, the maximum allowable change on the input of the sample/hold equals (0.01%×20V)=2 mV. Also note that for sinusoidal waveforms, the maximum slew rate occurs at zero crossings.

Any sinusoidal input signal follows the form

$$V_{in} = V\sin(2\pi ft),$$

and in this case E=10V for a 20V p-p signal. Taking the first derivative, which represents slew rate, find

$$\frac{dV}{dt} = (2\pi f)V \cos(2\pi ft).$$

Then you know that zero crossings occur at

$$t = \frac{n}{2f} \ (n = 1, 2, 3 \ldots).$$

Thus,

$$dV = (2\pi fV)dt.$$

To find the maximum allowable input frequency, use this equation and solve for f:

$$2mV = 2\pi f(10V)(32 \text{ nsec})$$

$$f = 0.995 \text{ kHz.}$$

7. Find the answer in the same manner as in the previous question, but here the key lies in knowing how to use the 10-nsec value in relation to this circuit.

You know that

$$E = \left(\frac{dV}{dt}\right)T$$

where

$$\frac{dV}{dt} = (2\pi)(30 \times 10^3)(10)$$

$$= 1.8 \times 10^6 \text{V/sec.}$$

But because $T = 10 \times 10^{-9}$ sec, $E = 18$ mV; converting the value, you find that

$$\text{Error} = \frac{1.8\ mV}{20V} = 0.9 \times 10^{-3} = 0.09\% \text{ FS range.}$$

Aperture uncertainty is the variance of the aperture time, the uncertainty in the time interval. This parameter varies from unit to unit and typically ranges from 0.5 to 10 nsec. In this question, you see that aperture uncertainty becomes very important to consider in simultaneous S/H applications. This approach gives you a better grasp of worst-case errors. To conclude, aperture time is an important parameter to consider when sampling one channel with a fast-changing signal, and aperture uncertainty becomes important when performing simultaneous sample-holds.

8. Settling time and acquisition time tend to assume the same value because the output as well as the input controls the charge on the hold capacitor for closed-loop circuits.

9. Extremely good accuracy, slow acquisition time and low droop rate best describe the characteristics of closed loop integrating-type S/H circuits. High tracking accuracy results from a configuration that acts like one amplifier during the sampling time. Also, because an integrator is used, the sample/hold switch operates at ground potential, eliminating leakage problems through the feedback hold capacitor and thus reducing the droop rate i/C.

10. A single-pole transfer function with gain=1 and a -3 dB BW=500 kHz has the input/output relationship

$$\frac{V(out)}{V(in)} = \frac{1}{1 + j\left(\dfrac{f}{5 \times 10^5}\right)}$$

To maintain 12-bit (0.01%) accuracy, V(out)/V(in), or gain, should not degrade more than $(1-0.01\%) = 0.9999$. Thus,

$$\frac{1}{1 + j\left(\dfrac{f}{5 \times 10^5}\right)} \leq 0.9999,$$

or f, the maximum sampling frequency, should not exceed 7071.6 Hz.

11. Data sheets will most likely omit **b** and **c**.

Generally, the p-p output noise in hold mode runs well below the specified linearity of the particular sample/hold, and its omission usually causes few problems. But this noise could cause slight linearity problems if you input its signal into an A/D. A more important missing sample/hold specification, hold-mode settling time, is defined as the time for the output to settle to the sample/hold accuracy after being given the logic command to switch into hold mode. This hold-mode settling time could cause annoyances in D/A deglitcher (display) applications, but bigger headaches can result if you use the sample/hold with an A/D converter. Here, if you begin the conversion process (A/D clocking) before the sample-to-hold transient has settled to the LSB level, you run the risk of getting bad codes, especially noticeable at the half-scale level for successive-approximation-type A/D's and at lower voltages for counter-comparator types. The hold-mode settling time can run as high as 1 µsec for the slower closed-loop-type S/H's, while it usually runs only tens of nanoseconds for high-speed S/H's. □

Authors' biographies

John M Mills, regional sales coordinator for Datel Systems Inc, Canton, MA, formerly worked as an applications engineer for Analog Devices, Norwood, MA. He earned his BSEE at Northeastern Univ in Boston, where he's now studying for his MBA. An outdoor-sports enthusiast, John enjoys softball, golf, cross-country skiing and handball.

Gene Murphy, a senior applications engineer, has been with Datel Systems for three years and possesses a BSEE degree from Worcester Polytechnic Institute, where he is now completing his thesis for an MS in Management Science and Engineering. Among his hobbies he lists music and cosmology.

5. High Speed Operational Amplifiers

High-speed op amps—
they're in a class by themselves

The same special characteristics that make fast op amps useful in difficult applications can also create problems for unwary designers.

Gene Zuch and **Jim Knitter,** Datel Systems, Inc.

Fast operational amplifiers are not like other op amps. In addition to good dc characteristics such as high open-loop dc gain, low bias currents and low input offset drift, fast op amps have specially designed ac characteristics that come into play at high frequencies. Proper application of these amplifiers involves the selection of gain-bandwidth product, slew rate, settling time and output current. In addition, you must pay particular attention to many small circuit details like power-supply bypassing, proper routing of grounds, short lead lengths and minimization of stray capacitance. Poor design practice invariably produces an oscillator instead of a high-speed amplifier.

You can't ignore op-amp characteristics

Operational amplifiers offer designers one fundamental attraction: The characteristics of the closed-loop feedback circuit are determined almost exclusively by external circuit elements rather than by the op amp itself. Precise control of gain, offset, linearity, temperature stability, etc., in amplifier design itself thus reduces the user's task to the proper selection of the passive circuit components used around the op amp. Unfortunately, this simple relationship in general doesn't hold true for high-speed op amps: They're more difficult to handle than their low-frequency counterparts, and a detailed knowledge of their characteristics becomes essential:

Open-loop gain and bandwidth—Refer to **Fig. 1's** gain-frequency (Bode) plot. The open-loop

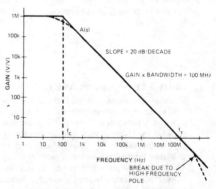

Fig. 1—Well designed high-speed op amps have a smooth 20 dB/decade roll-off. Additional amplifier poles should not occur until well beyond f_T.

gain must be very high in a fast operational amplifier to reduce errors at the device's summing junction. Open-loop gain typically runs between 10^5 and 10^8 V/V in a good quality, high-speed op amp. As illustrated, the gain is flat from dc out to a corner frequency (100 Hz in this case); then it decreases with increasing frequency. For well-designed amplifiers, gain decreases at a fixed rate of 20 dB/decade of frequency, a roll-off rate that assures stable closed-loop operation and also produces the best settling-time performance.

The gain-frequency plot crosses the gain-of-one axis at unity gain frequency, f_T. This frequency should be as large as possible for a wide-bandwidth amplifier; 100 MHz is common. Along the 20 dB/decade slope of the gain roll-off, the product of gain and frequency remains constant and equal to f_T. Therefore, the value of f_T is frequently referred to as the gain-bandwidth product of the amplifier.

Smooth roll-off is generally maintained out beyond f_T for most fast amplifiers. Another op-amp pole usually occurs at a higher frequency as a result of a nonideal amplifier circuit, but if this frequency is considerably greater than the circuit's closed-loop bandwidth, the extraneous pole will have very little effect on high-frequency performance.

Slew rate—The ability of a high-speed op amp to reproduce fast, large signal outputs depends primarily on its specified slew rate, the maximum rate at which the output can change, expressed in

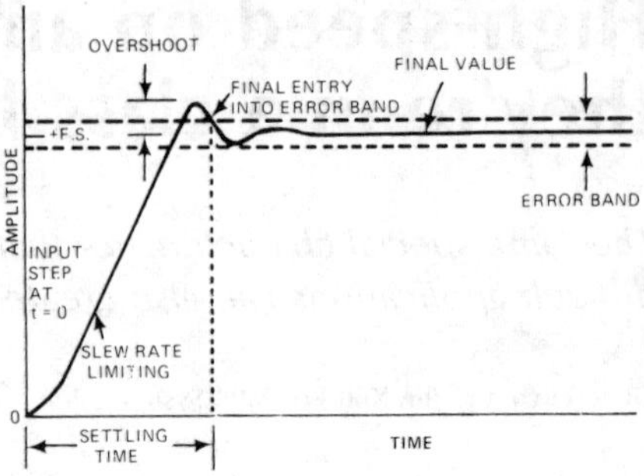

Fig. 2—**Slewing time must be included** in settling-time measurements.

V/μsec. When the output must respond to a step-input change, slew-rate limitation causes a longer large-signal settling time than you might expect from the bandwidth characteristics alone. Slew rates of modern high-speed op amps equal or exceed 1000 V/μsec.

Settling time—In servo theory this term specifies the maximum time required to achieve an accuracy of 5% or so after a step input is applied to the servo. With regard to op amps, it refers to the time required for much greater accuracies, typically 0.1% to 0.01% of F.S., and is best defined as follows:

"Settling time is the elapsed time from the application of a step input to an amplifier to the instant when the output has entered into and remained within a specified error band around its final value." Note that settling time must be specified with both the error band and the magnitude of the step change given. Almost all cases specify a F.S. output change of 10V.

Fig. 2 illustrates a typical settling response for a high-speed op amp. Usually the amplifier's output first goes into slew-rate limit, overshoots its final value, then enters the specified error band and remains there until it reaches the final steady-state level. (One word of caution: Measure settling time from t=0, the instant that the input step was applied. Some manufacturers play "specmanship" games and fail to include the amplifier slewing time in their measurements.)

You can't predict amplifier settling time from bandwidth and slew-rate specifications alone: It's a measured, as well as designed-in, parameter. You can usually tell an op amp specifically designed for fast settling time from one that's not: The former's settling-time spec will be fairly predictable from bandwidth and slew-rate considerations; the latter's won't.

Today's fast op amps ARE fast

Modular op amps introduced in the late 1960's featured settling times as low as 1 μsec to 0.01%, and they quickly became popular in 12-bit data-acquisition systems. Early in the 1970's, ultrafast modules became available, boasting even faster settling times, 100 MHz gain-bandwidth products and 1000 V/μsec slew rates. More recently, hybrid units have achieved such performance levels, as shown below.

BASIC CHARACTERISTICS OF A TYPICAL HIGH-SPEED OP AMP (AM-500)	
DC OPEN-LOOP GAIN	10^6 V/V
GAIN-BANDWIDTH PRODUCT	130 MHz
SLEW RATE	1000 V/μSEC
FULL POWER FREQUENCY (20V p-p)	16 MHz
SETTLING TIME, 10V TO 1%	70 nSEC
SETTLING TIME, 10V TO 0.1%	100 nSEC
SETTLING TIME, 10V TO 0.01%	200 nSEC
INPUT OFFSET DRIFT	1 μV/°C
OUTPUT VOLTAGE	±10V
OUTPUT CURRENT	±50 mA

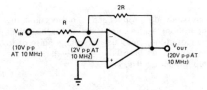

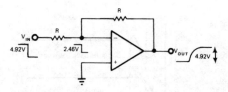

Fig. 3—The summing junction is NOT a virtual ground in high speed op-amp applications. Thus the amplifier must be designed with a large input dynamic range (IDR), or distortion, limiting or clipping will result.

Fig. 4—Staying within an amplifier's IDR avoids slew-rate limitation problems and produces a smooth output response.

Low output impedance and high output current—High-speed operational amplifiers almost always are designed to give low output impedance and relatively high output current. Low output impedance proves critical to stability for driving capacitive loads, while high output current (20 to 100 mA) is required for both driving capacitive loads at high speed ($I=Cdv/dt$) and for driving relatively low-value feedback and load resistors. (Good high-frequency design practice keeps all impedances as low as possible to cut phase shifts from parasitic capacitances.)

Why is input dynamic range important?

Fig. 3 shows a simple, high speed op-amp circuit with an inverting gain of 2 to illustrate an important device characteristic. The signal input is a 10V p-p sine wave at 10 MHz; the output, an inverted 20V p-p sinusoid. If we assume that the amplifier has the Bode plot shown in **Fig. 1,** then its open-loop gain at 10 MHz is 10. So for a 20V p-p output, the voltage at the op amp's summing junction must be 2V p-p. This is a rather large signal; in fact, most general-purpose op amps couldn't handle such a high level without distorting, limiting and/or clipping. Therefore, high-speed op amps must possess a large input dynamic range; i.e., significant peak-to-peak voltages applied directly across the device's input terminals must not cause the output to slew-rate limit or distort. Calculation of a high-speed op amp's input dynamic range is straightforward (see **box** at right).

Knowing the input dynamic range of an operational amplifier can help you determine how to best utilize the device while carefully avoiding slew-rate limitation problems. For instance, **Fig. 4** shows an op amp connected as a unity-gain inverter. If we assume that this device has an input dynamic range of ±1.23V (as calculated in the **box**), then the circuit can reproduce a 4.92V input step as a −4.92V output step without slew-rate limiting. (Observe that the 4.92V input

step appears at the summing junction divided by a factor of two by the two equal-value resistors.)

To further appreciate the significance of input dynamic range, you must understand that within this input range the op amp's output rate of change is in direct proportion to the input voltage. Therefore, the output can make a large voltage transition in the time required to make a small voltage transition. **Fig. 5** illustrates three

---

IDR is a function of SR and GB

The input dynamic range (IDR) of a high-speed op amp is related to the unit's slew rate (or full-power frequency) and its gain-bandwidth product. To compute IDR, assume that the output is at its full power frequency and amplitude (i.e., it's producing the largest and fastest output possible without distortion), then calculate the open-loop gain at this frequency, and finally plug these values in the following formula:

$$IDR = (V_{pp} \times FPF)/GB$$

where V_{pp}=peak-to-peak full-power voltage, FPF=full-power frequency and GB=gain-bandwidth product.

If the full-power frequency is not known, you can use an alternate equation:

$$IDR = V_{pp} \times SR/(20\pi GB)$$

where SR=slew rate.

EXAMPLE

What is the input dynamic range of the amplifier described in the previous **box** (the AM-500)?

$$IDR = (20 \times 16 \text{ MHz})/130 \text{ MHz} = 2.46V \text{ p-p}$$
(or ±1.23V).

Thus, within an input range of ±1.23V, the op amp won't go into slew-rate limitation.

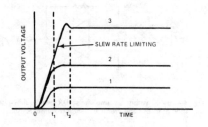

Fig. 5—Rise times for pulses of varying heights remain constant as long as you observe IDR limits.

values of output steps for a fast op amp. Output steps 1 and 2 have identical rise times; since they lie within the IDR, they aren't slew-rate limited. Because Output 3 is generated outside the IDR, however, slew-rate limiting occurs, and the output takes considerably longer to reach its final value. Further, the waveform exhibits some overshoot, a common problem under slew-rate limit conditions.

It's no trivial task to design an op-amp input circuit that has good dc characteristics, plus good input dynamic range, plus the response needed to avoid slew-rate limiting. One approach combines the low-drift characteristics of a bipolar input op amp with the excellent IDR of an FET in a fast-feedforward design **(Fig. 6)**. This circuit produces very wide bandwidth, high slew rate and fast settling time. It also provides extremely high open-loop gain and very low input offset-voltage drift (typically 1 μV/°C).

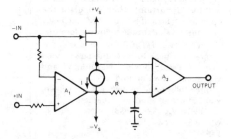

Fig. 6—Fast-feedforward amplifier design combines a low-drift, bipolar IC op amp with an FET feedforward stage to produce excellent dc and ac characteristics.

Your choice should start with bandwidth

When you select a high-speed operational amplifier, first determine your application's bandwidth requirement. The minimum closed-loop bandwidth is a function of both the op amp's

gain-bandwidth product and its noise gain in the application. "Noise gain" is defined as the gain of the closed-loop amplifier to voltage noise or to any other signal inserted in series with one of the amplifier inputs **(Fig. 7)**.

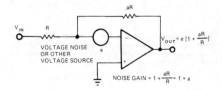

Fig. 7—Noise gain and signal gain differ. In an inverting circuit the noise gain equals the signal gain plus one.

The noise gain drawn on the Bode plot of an op amp determines the −3 dB closed-loop bandwidth. In **Fig. 8,** for example, closed-loop gain equals 99, giving a noise gain of (1+a) or 100. When plotted on the diagram, this noise gain gives a closed-loop 3 dB bandwidth of 1 MHz for the 100 MHz gain-bandwidth amplifier illustrated. (Note that for the common unity-gain inverting amplifier, the noise gain is 2; therefore the closed-loop bandwidth of such a circuit built with a 100 MHz op amp would equal 50 MHz, not 100 MHz.)

A single pole simplifies response calculations...

If an op amp has a true single-pole response (as many do), you can calculate its step response for the closed-loop circuit by the expression:

$$E_{OUT} = aE_{IN}(1 - e^{-2\pi f_T/(1+a)})$$

and the output error is then

$$\epsilon = e^{-2\pi f_T/(1+a)}$$

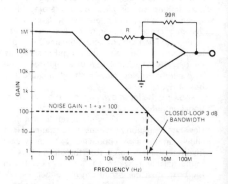

Fig. 8—If the op amp exhibits a single-pole response, you can compute its settling time from frequency and noise-gain data. This approach works best at high noise gains.

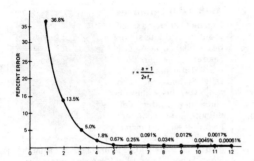

Fig. 9—**Output error decreases** predictably as a function of the number of time constants when the op-amp circuit exhibits a single-pole response.

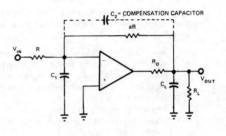

Fig. 10—**Three sources of extraneous poles** appear in this diagram: input capacitance, load capacitance and the op amp itself. C_2 compensates for output ringing and is best chosen via experiments with the actual circuit components and layout.

From the latter equation you can readily compute the settling time to various accuracies. For greatest convenience, perform this computation in terms of the time constant $\tau = (a+1)/2\pi f_T$, where a is the closed-loop gain. The amplifier configuration of **Fig. 8,** for instance, has a time constant (τ) of 159 nsec.

Fig. 9 shows the number of time constants necessary to reach a given error, assuming a single-pole response. Thus, the amplifier configuration of **Fig. 8** would take nine time constants or 1.44 μsec to settle to 0.01% . If the same amplifier (GB=100 MHz) were connected as a unity-gain inverter, its closed-loop bandwidth would equal 50 MHz, giving τ =3.2 nsec and a settling time to 0.01% of 28.8 nsec.

Using the ideal single-pole response with no slew-rate limiting to determine settling is a valid approach. At worst it gives a first approximation of the settling time, and this approximation gets closer at high noise gains. Given an op amp designed and specified for fast settling, you can obtain an even closer approximation by adding to the computed settling time that estimated extra time required to slew to the final voltage.

...but multiple poles often occur

In some cases the op-amp circuit is not really a single-pole system. **Fig. 10** shows three typical situations that add a second pole to the circuit. C_1 represents the input capacitance of the amplifier plus any stray capacitance from the summing junction to ground, as well as (where applicable) the output capacitance of the device driving the op amp. C_1 combines with resistances R and aR to produce a pole located at $-aRC_1/(a+1)$ on the real axis of the s-plane. The finite output resistance of the amplifier, R_0, and load resistance R_L com-

bined with output capacitance C_L can add another pole located at $-R_0R_LC_L/(R_0+R_L)$. And the op amp itself can add a third extraneous pole if it has an extraneous high-frequency pole in its response as noted.

In general, one of these "extra" poles will be dominant; i.e., closer in frequency to the amplifier's unity-gain frequency than the others. This dominant pole, of course, converts our first-order system into a second-order one and brings up the possibility of complex conjugate poles that produce ringing.

When ringing occurs, the amplifier must be compensated by a feedback capacitor **(Fig. 10).** You can determine experimentally the optimum value for this compensation capacitor by observing the step response and adjusting a trimmer to eliminate the ringing. Normally you want a damping ratio of one, but in some applications you may actually prefer a small amount of overshoot.

Calculations reveal that if the frequency of the second pole is at least 4× the op amp's closed-loop bandwidth, the damping ratio will equal or exceed one, and overshoot won't occur. Since often you can quickly approximate the frequency of the extraneous pole, you can use this relationship to predict ringing in the circuit.

In the common situation where input capacitance C_1 causes the second pole, a good starting value for compensation capacitor C_2 is $C_2=C_1/a$. Increase C_2 as necessary above this value to achieve a damping ratio of one. (The other two possible extraneous poles, even when they don't dominate, may still add some phase lag to the amplifier. This possibility explains the somewhat higher value of C_2 often needed to give the required compensation.)

Success is just a design tip away

We conclude our discussion by offering six brief, but important, hints on applying high-speed op amps:

- Keep all component leads as short as possible, particularly at the summing junction. Also, diligently strive to keep stray capacitance at the summing junction to an absolute minimum.
- Separate signal grounds from power grounds, connecting them only at one common physical point.
- If you must locate the source or load some distance from the op amp, use properly terminated coaxial cable for best response.
- If you mount the op amp on a pc board, incorporate a ground plane into the board's design for best performance.
- Make the input and feedback resistors as small as possible consistent with input-source drive capability and amplifier-output drive capability. A value in the range of 500 to 1000Ω is commonly used for the input resistor.
- Use good power-supply bypass capacitors and connect them right at the amplifier power-supply pins. We recommend tantalum capacitors in parallel with ceramics. □

Authors' biographies

Eugene L. Zuch is a prolific author and thus should be familiar to many EDN readers. As product-marketing manager at Datel Systems, Inc., Canton, MA, his duties include new-product definition, introduction and technical support materi-al, plus publicity and advertising. An MIT man (BSEE, MSEE and BS in management from the Sloan School), Gene holds one patent and is a member of the IEEE, Tau Beta Pi and Eta Kappa Nu. He also is a Registered Professional Engineer.

James B. Knitter designs high-speed amplifiers, sample/holds and A/D converters as a senior staff engineer at Datel Systems, Inc. He attended Worcester Polytechnic Institute and Northeastern University, holds one patent and lists golf (10 handicap), bicycle touring and travel among his leisure pursuits.

Unity-gain buffer amplifier is ultrafast

by James B. Knitter and Eugene L. Zuch
Datel Systems Inc., Canton, Mass.

Applications where transmission-line drivers, active voltage probes, or buffers for ultrahigh-speed analog-to-digital converters are needed can use a stable buffer amplifier capable of driving a relatively low-resistance, moderate-capacitance load over a wide range of frequencies. The circuit shown in (a) fulfills these requirements. With a bandwidth of 300 megahertz, it exhibits no peaking of its response curve, having a gain of virtually 1 (0.995) under no-load conditions and 0.9 under a maximum load of 90 ohms.

The circuit is a variation on a basic emitter-follower network, which is inherently capable of wideband performance. However, no feedback loops are needed anywhere within the circuit to boost the gain at the high frequencies, and dispensing with them contributes to the stability of the circuit. Also, using two matched npn-pnp transistor pairs ensures close tracking between input and output voltages (a task normally addressed by suitable feedback circuitry) as well as low offset-voltage drift (20 microvolts/°C).

The complementary-transistor pairs are 2N4854s wired for active current sourcing and sinking so that bipolar input signals can be processed. Each transistor has a typical β of 100. With the npn and pnp input-bias currents tending to cancel each other, the resultant input-bias current of the amplifier is ± 5 microamperes.

Layout is critical to the stability of the circuit. The buffer should be constructed as shown in (b). The two transistor pairs are mounted close together, in holes drilled in a copper-clad circuit board as shown. The flanges on the TO-99 cases encapsulating the 2N485s should be soldered to the copper, which serves as a ground plane. The collector of each transistor must be bypassed by a 0.1-microfarad ceramic-chip capacitor mounted close to the transistor. This is done by standing the capacitors on end, with the bottom contact lead soldered to the ground plane and the top contact lead soldered to the collector.

All leads must be less than ½ inch in length and be as

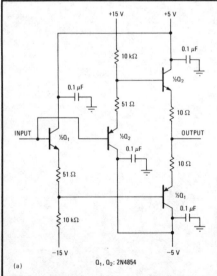

Wideband buffer. Emitter-follower configuration yields unity gain from dc to 300 megahertz. Absence of feedback in circuit contributes to buffer stability. Use of matched npn-pnp transistor pairs ensures almost perfect input/output signal tracking (a). Component layout is critical for circuit stability (b).

CHARACTERISTICS OF UNITY-GAIN BUFFER	
Input impedance	500 kilohms (dc)
Input bias current	±5 µA
Input capacitance	16 pF max
Input/output voltage range	±3 V
Output offset-voltage drift	±20 µV/°C
Output impedance	10 ohms
Load resistance	90 ohms max
Gain, no load	+0.995
Bandwidth, −3 dB	300 MHz
Power supply, quiescent	±15 V dc at 1.5 mA ± 5 V dc at 4.5 mA
Power consumption	90 mW

directly wired as possible. One-eighth-watt resistors are used throughout and are soldered to the transistor leads as close as possible to the case. For clarity, not all components are shown. For coupling to or from the amplifier, subminiature radio-frequency connectors can be mounted at the input and output ports of the buffer.

Typical characteristics of the unity-gain buffer circuit are listed in the table. □

6. V/F Converters

Voltage to frequency converters

Eugene L. Zuch, Product Marketing Manager, Datel Systems, Inc., Canton, MA

Voltage-to-frequency converters in recent years have become quite popular due to their low cost and application versatility in a variety of electronic control and measurement systems. Getting down to basic definitions, a voltage-to-frequency (V/F) converter is an electronic circuit that converts an input voltage into a train of digital output pulses at a rate that is directly proportional to the input.

A V/F converter with its transfer function is illustrated in Fig. 1. An important characteristic of the transfer function is its high degree of linearity; that is, the relationship of input voltage to output pulse rate is very nearly a straight line function. Another important characteristic is that the output pulses are at levels that directly interface with standard digital logic circuits such as DTL, TTL and CMOS.

Not many years ago, V/F converters were infrequently used rack-mounted instruments, both bulky and expensive. About five years ago they first became available as low-cost modular devices that were easy to use and had excellent linearity and stability characteristics. As a result, the application of V/F converters increased rapidly.

A more recent development has been the introduction of monolithic V/F converters: miniature low-cost devices. Fig. 2 shows examples of both modular and monolithic high-performance V/F converters.

How and why V/F converters are used

The important feature of V/F converters is that they convert analog signals into digital form: a train of serial pulses. Since the output data is in digital form, generally at TTL compatible voltage levels, the analog input has been converted into a noise-immune

output that can be transmitted over considerable distances. The transmission can be accomplished by a twisted pair cable or coaxial cable.

Fig. 3 illustrates a common application of V/F converters where the output of a transducer is locally amplified and then converted to a digital pulse train by the V/F. This pulse train is sent to a central location where the data is recorded and processed. In Fig. 3(a) the pulses are counted over a fixed period of time by a digital counter. The output can then be converted to hard copy by a digital printer. Fig.

Fig. 2. Monolithic and modular V/F converters.

3(b) shows the analog data reconstructed by the use of a frequency-to-voltage (F/V) converter. Back in analog form, the data can be recorded on an analog chart recorder.

A common application is to transmit temperature or pressure data from an industrial process in this manner. The only restriction on the analog data to be transmitted is that it not change too rapidly for the V/F converter to follow.

V/F as an A/D converter

A V/F converter is actually the front end of an analog-to-digital

(A/D) converter. A/D converters change an analog input voltage into an equivalent parallel digital output code word for computer processing. Since a V/F converter changes the analog input into a train of pulses, it is only necessary to convert the pulse train into a parallel digital code word. This is done by counting the pulses for a fixed period of time, as illustrated in Fig. 4.

Fig. 4 shows a complete A/D converter with a V/F converter as the analog front end. Following the V/F is a NAND gate controlled by a precision timer which gates the pulses through to a counter. The counter counts the pulses until the timer turns them off at the gate and then holds the output as a parallel digital word. As with other A/D converters, a trigger pulse initiates a conversion by triggering the timer and resetting the counter to zero.

The timer circuit must generate a precise, stable timing pulse to control the count. For example, if the V/F converter has a full-scale pulse rate of 10 KHz and the timer circuit is set to produce a precise 0.4096-second pulse, then the full scale output of the counter is 4096 counts: equivalent to 12 bits (2^{12}) binary resolution. The circuit of Fig. 4 is then that of a complete 12-bit A/D converter.

With a good quality V/F converter, this circuit will match the performance of many commercial 12-bit A/D converters. Its only disadvantage is a relatively slow conversion time of 0.41 second. Nevertheless, in many control and measurement applications this speed is sufficient and the circuit has the additional advantage of excellent noise rejection at the input by virtue of its 0.41-second signal averaging time.

To obtain faster conversion times one must use faster V/F converters at the analog input. V/F converters today are available in a number of full-scale frequency ranges with 10 KHz and 100 KHz being the most popular; but there are also V/F's with 1 MHz and up to 10 MHz outputs available. If, for example, a 1-MHz V/F converter were used in the circuit of Fig. 4, then a 12-bit conversion could be done in just 4.096 msec, or 100 times faster than with a 10-KHz V/F converter.

The A/D converter circuit shown in Fig. 4 is called a *charge-balancing,* or *quantized feedback,* A/D converter, since this is the circuit technique employed in the V/F converter. This type of A/D converter falls into the general class of integrating A/D converters, which includes methods known as single-slope, dual-slope, and triple-slope A/D converters.

Integrating A/D converters are all relatively slow devices but have two important characteristics. First, they integrate input noise to give a relatively noise immune conversion. Second, the linearity curve for these converters is a smooth one with slight curvature. This curvature, illustrated in Fig. 5, is the nonlinearity of the converter and is the maximum deviation from a straight line, expressed in percent.

How V/F converters work

The charge-balancing, or quantized feedback, technique used to

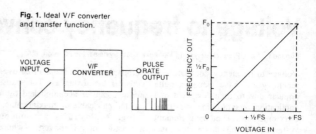

Fig. 1. Ideal V/F converter and transfer function.

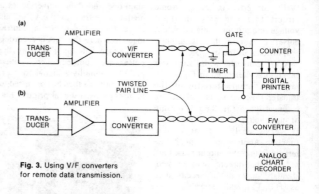

Fig. 3. Using V/F converters for remote data transmission.

make a V/F converter is shown in Fig. 6. This is a unique method of realizing voltage to pulse rate conversion with a very high degree of linearity. The circuit consists of an operational integrator with a pulse generating feedback loop around it.

The circuit operates as follows. A positive input voltage causes a current to flow into the operational integrator through R_1. This current is integrated by the amplifier and capacitor to produce a negative-going ramp at the output. When the ramp crosses the comparator

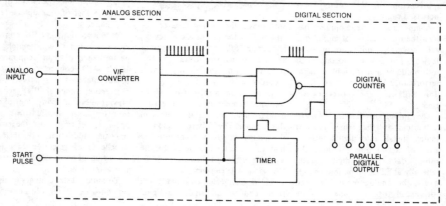

Fig. 4. The V/F converter used as an A/D converter.

threshold voltage at ground, the comparator output changes state and causes a pulse timing circuit to generate a narrow voltage pulse.

This pulse controls switch S_1, which switches from ground to a negative reference voltage for the duration of the pulse. During this time a narrow pulse of current flows out of the integrator through R_2. This current pulse is also integrated by the operational integrator, and causes a rapid ramp up in the output voltage for the duration of the pulse. This process is then repeated, creating a sequence of pulses that are also buffered as the output of the V/F converter.

A higher input voltage to the charge-balancing circuit causes the integrator to ramp down faster, thereby generating pulses at a higher rate from the pulse timer circuit. Likewise, a lower input voltage causes the integrator to ramp down slower and generates pulses at a lower rate than before.

The term "charge-balancing" is appropriate since the feedback loop, which is closed around the integrator, causes an average of the current pulses (through R_2). Each current pulse through R_2 is a fixed charge of value:

$$Q = \frac{V_{REF}}{R_2} \times \tau = \tau I_2$$

where τ is the width of the pulse.

"Quantized feedback" is a term that describes the feedback around the integrator, which is in the form of quantized current pulses rather than a continuous current. The linearity, and hence accuracy, of the V/F converter circuit depends on both the linearity of the integrator, the constant width of the pulses generated, and on the switching characteristic of S_1.

Calibrating a V/F converter

In applying V/F converters, optimum accuracy in a given application is desired. This is achieved by properly calibrating the converter for both zero and gain in the given application. Fig. 7 shows the connections required for a monolithic V/F converter. This

device requires a bias resistor, compensating capacitors. It has output pull-up resistor, and two provision for both an external zero

Fig. 5. Nonlinearity of charge-balancing A/D converter.

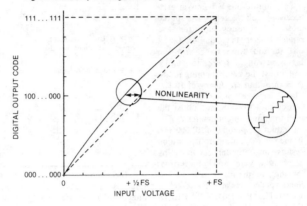

Fig. 6. Charge-balancing V/F converter circuit.

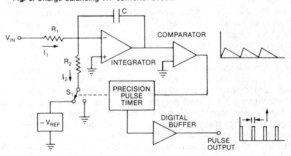

Fig. 7. Calibration of low-cost monolithic V/F converter.

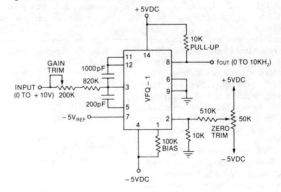

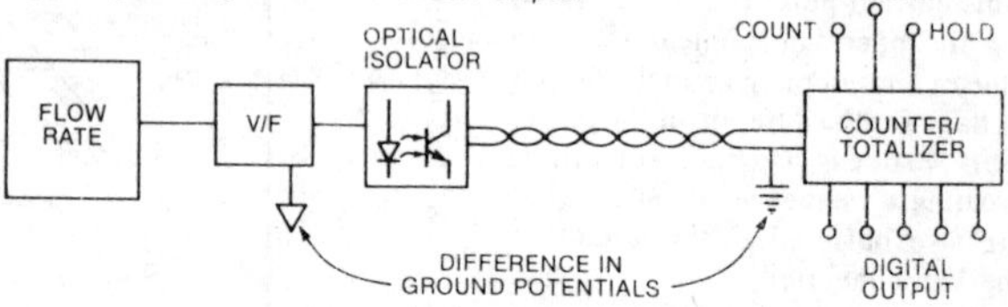

adjustment and external gain adjust-ment. The connection shown is for a 10-KHz full-scale output frequency with a +10V full-scale input.

To calibrate this V/F converter, a precision voltage reference source and a frequency counter are required. Set the counter for a one-second time base and the precision voltage source to +0.01V and adjust the zero trimming pot to give an output frequency of 10 Hz. Then set the precision voltage source to +10.000V and adjust the gain trimming potentiometer to give an output frequency of 10,000 Hz. Proper zero and gain calibration results in optimum accuracy by eliminating zero and gain errors, leaving only the nonlinearity.

Some applications of V/F converters

REMOTE TRANSDUCER READ-OUT IN A HIGH NOISE ENVI-RONMENT

Fig. 8 shows a V/F converter located at a transducer site. Because of the high electrical noise environ-ment, a differential line driver and receiver are used to transmit the pulse data over a twisted pair line. At the readout location is a gate, timer and counter. In this case a BCD counter is used, which goes to a driver and then an LED decimal display. If the timer is set to generate pulses at desired intervals, then the display is automatically updated.

INTEGRATING A REMOTE TRANSDUCER OUTPUT

A most useful application of a V/F converter is as a zero drift digital integrator. Fig. 9 shows a V/F converter that transmits a fluid flow rate in digital form. In this application there is a difference in ground potentials between the remote location and the measure-ment location. Therefore an optical isolator is used to isolate between the two grounds and transmit the pulses.

At the measurement location, if the pulses are counted for fixed intervals the result is flow rate. If, however, the counter is allowed to

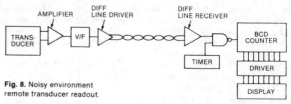

Fig. 8. Noisy environment remote transducer readout.

Fig. 9. Digital integration of transducer output.

run for a long period of time, it totalizes the pulses to give the integral of flow rate, or total flow. The V/F converter is a perfect integrator when its output is totalized. A 10-KHz V/F, for example, produces one output pulse for every millivolt-second of input signal.

MULTIPLE REMOTE MONITOR

Another type of remote monitor, shown in Fig. 10, automatically scans a number of transducer outputs in sequence, transmitting the measurement results to a central location for display or recording. This is done by using an analog multiplexer in conjunction with a synchronized set of counters and a single V/F converter. An additional line is required for clock pulses to synchronize the counters at both locations.

At the remote location, the channel counter steps the multiplex-er input decoder through the various channels in sequence. At the central location the clock drives a digital divider and a counter. The divider gates the pulses from the V/F converter to a BCD counter. The channel counter drives a decoder and display indicator that shows which transducer output is being displayed.

FUTURE PROGRESS IN V/F

At this point, V/F converters have a bright future indeed. The advent of low-cost, high-performance mon-olithic units means that remote industrial monitoring with a V/F converter per transducer will be a growing application area. At the same time higher performance modular devices will find applica-tion in higher speed requirements.

Fig. 10. Multiple transducer remote monitor.

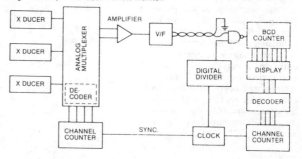

Voltage-to-frequency converters: versatility now at a low cost

Modular units that fit in your hand and go for less than $50 are moving into low-cost instruments and systems, putting their excellent linearity and temperature stability to wider use

by Eugene L. Zuch, *Datel Systems Inc., Canton, Mass.*

☐ Voltage-to-frequency converters can be purchased today for one tenth the price they were going for as rack mounted instruments less than three years ago. This, together with the v-f converter's long-prized linearity and temperature stability, accounts for the heightened interest they now enjoy among systems designers.

There are other reasons as well. The converter's recent evolution into a modular component package gives it a size advantage that widens the range of applications. One such application—not to be overlooked for certain data acquisition or control functions—involves the v-f converter's capability to interface between analog and digital circuits. By the same token, high common-mode voltage isolation, ratiometric measurements, and analog-signal integration also represent fertile areas for v-f applications. It has already been put to use in instruments that include low-cost 3½-digit multimeters, high-performance digital panel meters, and hand-held probe-type digital multimeters.

While the modular component v-f converter is relatively new, the basic technique of translating a given voltage level into a frequency signal is not. Until fairly recently, however, v-f converters have been available only in the form of rather expensive instruments.

A v-f converter accepts an analog voltage or current input and generates an output train of digital pulses at a rate directly proportional to the amplitude of the input. In its most basic form [see Fig. (a) in the accompanying panel, "Converting v-to-f: three techniques"] conversion is accomplished by allowing the incoming voltage to charge a capacitor until it reaches a value equivalent to a reference voltage. At that point, a comparator triggers a monostable multivibrator which puts out a constant-width pulse. Other variations [panel figures (b), (c) and (d)] provide improved linearity and stability, or permit output pulses to be synchronized to a clock.

Datel Systems Inc. uses the charge-balancing technique in its v-f converters [see panel Fig. (c)]. And, by changing the connections at the external pins, the same module becomes a frequency-to-voltage converter. The f-v connections remove the logic buffer and permit an input pulse to be delivered to the timing circuit, and voltage to be taken from the output of the op amp.

The v-f converter has as its key characteristics good linearity—typically 0.002% to 0.05% over the input-output operating range—and excellent temperature stabil-

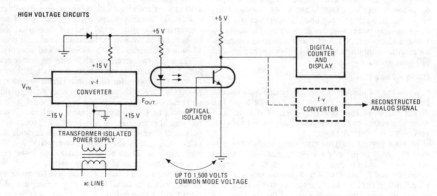

1. Isolation. Because the v-f converter has a serial output, the pulses can be transmitted through a single optical isolator. The v-f converter is floated at the high common-mode voltage at which the measurement is made. It is also powered by a floating and isolated supply.

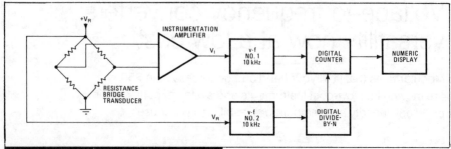

RATIO MEASUREMENTS USING N = 500				
V_I	V_R	TIME BASE (SEC)	OUTPUT RATIO	OUTPUT + DECIMAL
0.1 V	10 V	0.1	10	0.010
1 V	10 V	0.1	100	0.100
10 V	10 V	0.1	1,000	1.000
10 V	1 V	1	10,000	10.000
10 V	0.1 V	10	100,000	100.000

2. Ratiometric measurements. One converter is used as the input v-f, a second converter is used as a reference and is followed by a divide-by-N digital circuit. The output of the divide-by-N is used as the time base for the digital counter.

ity—typically 10 to 100 parts per million per °C over the operating temperature range. The analog input range is 0 to +10 V or 0 to –10 V for voltage inputs and 0 to +1 mA or 0 to –1 mA for current inputs; there is an input overrange of 10%. The most popular models today are units having output pulse rates of 0 to 10 kHz and 0 to 100 kHz. The outputs are usually constant-width pulses compatible with diode-transistor, transistor-transistor, or C-MOS logic levels, permitting a direct interface with digital circuits.

On the input side, v-f converter modules take analog inputs in the –10 V to +10 V range, making them directly compatible with analog modules and ICs such as operational amplifiers, sample and holds, analog multipliers, etc. In addition, they also operate from standard ±15 V op amp power supplies drawing only a moderate amount of current. V-f converters also have provision for external trimming for precise calibration of zero-and full-scale values.

Using v-f as a-d

While the v-f module is a relatively slow way to convert a-d, the cost is low and accuracy can be high. The digital output of the converter is in serial form, and must be counted over some period to give a final conversion value in parallel form.

To get a complete digital measuring instrument, it is only necessary to precede a v-f converter with a signal conditioning circuit, such as a high input impedance amplifier, and follow it with a digital counter and display. Then, if the time base for the counter is set to one second, the actual output pulse rate of the v-f converter will be displayed. If a 10 kHz converter is used, a full-scale value of 10,000 would be displayed with a one-second time base; with a 10-second time base a full scale value of 100,000 would be displayed, although the

counting time would be too long for many applications.

It is useful to discuss the characteristics of v-f converters in terms of well known a-d converter specifications. For a v-f converter, conversion time is determined by the time base, one second being a convenient time base for many applications. For faster conversion time, a 0.1 second time base could be used, giving a full-scale count of 1,000 for a 10 kHz converter. With a 100 kHz converter, the full-scale count is 10,000.

For an a-d converter, resolution is expressed in bits and is determined by the number of parts into which the full-scale range is divided. By comparison, a 10 kHz v-f converter has a resolution of 1 part in 10,000, assuming a one-second conversion time. This is equivalent to a resolution of greater than 13 bits (1 part in 8,192). A 100 kHz converter with a one-second time base gives greater than 16-bit resolution (1 part in 65,536).

Linearity is another important a-d converter specification. A good a-d converter has a linearity of ±½ LSB (least significant bit) over its full-scale input range. For a 10 kHz v-f converter with a typical linearity figure of 0.002%, the linearity is equivalent to that of a 14-bit a-d converter. Therefore, a 10 kHz v-f converter, as described, has equivalent performance to at least that of a 13-bit a-d converter in both resolution and linearity.

The 100 kHz converters, while offering better resolution, have generally worse linearity than 10 kHz converters. The reason for this is that circuit parasitic time constants vary with pulse duty cycle. At high output pulse rates the small variations in pulse width with duty cycle will be proportionately more significant, thus increasing the amount of non-linearity. Therefore, the best resolution and linearity are achieved with slower pulse rates, namely the 10-kHz converters with a 10-second time base. These achieve better than 16-bit resolution with better than 14 bits of linearity.

A 10-second time base is prohibitive for many applications, but is obtainable by using a sample-and-hold circuit with a long holding time. A large holding capacitor is needed to make voltage decay negligible.

Another useful way of looking at v-f converters is in terms of dynamic range. This specification is critically dependent on linearity. Some v-f converters become

Converting v-to-f: three techniques

In its simplest form, Fig. (a), v-f conversion involves a current source driving a capacitor that charges linearly to a threshold voltage level determined by V_{REF}. At this voltage level, the comparator changes state and triggers a monostable multivibrator which puts out a constant-width pulse. At the same time a switch is used to discharge the capacitor and the cycle repeats itself. If the current source is designed to be proportional to input voltage, v-f conversion takes place.

A better implementation of the ramp-threshold method in Fig. (a) is the variation shown in Fig. (b). Here an operational integrator is used with a bipolar-transistor switch across the integrating capacitor. Starting with a negative input voltage, the circuit integrates in a positive direction until the reference voltage level is reached. The comparator then trips and triggers the monostable multivibrator, while at the same time resetting the integrator to zero by means of the saturating transistor switch. The disadvantage of this circuit is that it seldom offers better than a fraction of 1% linearity.

For higher linearity, the charge-balancing method is preferred, Fig (c). Here voltage or current is fed to an operational integrator. The output of the integrator goes to a precision pulse-timing circuit whose output drives a pulsed current source that pulls current pulses out of the summing junction of the integrator. The current pulses occur at a rate that exactly balances the positive input current to the integrator.

This technique also can be used for frequency-to-voltage conversion by opening the feedback loop at the output of the integrator and connecting the input pulses directly to the timing reference circuit, Fig. (e). In this case, the input resistor of the integrator is also connected back to the output to form a single-pole low-pass filter which averages the train of input pulses.

Still another form, the "delta-sigma" converter, Fig. (d), is used when output pulses must be synchronized to a clock. Current pulses are generated by a D flip-flop when the integrator output is high and when a clock pulse is present. Note here the assumption that a negative input current or voltage is used, and that the pulsed current source is operating in a direction opposite that of (c). Output pulses are a result of ANDing the Q output of the D flip-flop with input clock pulses. As a result the output pulses are both proportional to the input voltage and synchronous with the clock.

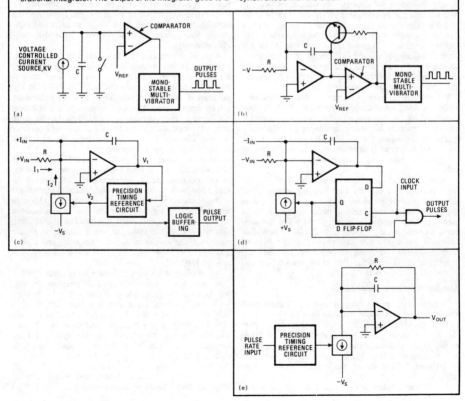

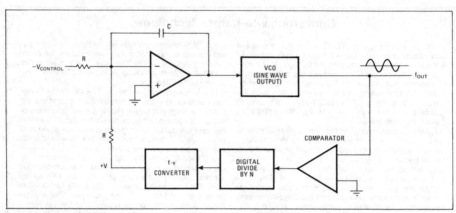

3. VCO Improvement. A frequency-to-voltage converter is the key to a low-cost voltage-controlled oscillator. A special feedback control loop forces the VCO output to track the superior linearity and stability of the f-v converter.

nonlinear near zero and, therefore, the dynamic range is limited. A 10-kHz v-f converter that holds its linearity down to zero can be calibrated externally from an input of 1.0 millivolt to its full-scale value of 10 V. This is a dynamic range of 4 decades, or 80 dB. Similarly a 100-kHz converter has a dynamic range of 5 decades, or 100 dB, if its linearity is maintained through zero. One mV is chosen as a practical lower limit because of drift in the zero-adjust potentiometer, long-term drift of the circuit, and noise at the input to the integrator.

V-f converters have two other significant features when considered for analog conversion. First is their monotonicity. (A monotonic a-d converter is one that has a continuously increasing output for a continuously increasing input over the full input range of the converter.) A v-f converter is naturally monotonic because its output pulse rate must increase with increasing input voltage.

Second is the excellent noise rejection inherent in using a reasonably long time base like one second. Random and periodic noise are effectively integrated over the conversion period. Periodic noise, such as a 60 Hz power pick-up, is effectively integrated when the conversion period is long compared to the 60 Hz period of 16.66 ms. For a 60 Hz noise that is integrated over an unsynchronized 1-second measurement period, the noise rejection is approximately 46 dB; for a 0.1-second period the rejection is 26 dB.

Monitoring from a distance

Remote data monitoring is one application well suited to the v-f technique. Remote monitoring can be a difficult problem, especially when analog signals pass through an environment with high levels of electrical noise, as in a manufacturing facility where there is heavy equipment. If a high degree of accuracy must be maintained, analog signal transmission becomes prohibitive.

An obvious solution is to transmit the signals in digital form. This can be done by applying the analog signal to an a-d converter. The digital pulses can then be transmitted in parallel or serial format. If transmitted serially, the pulses will have to be transformed ultimately into parallel form at the receiving end for display or storage.

A superior solution in terms of cost is to use a v-f converter to transmit the data directly in serial form. This is a simple and effective way to achieve an accurate system of 10 to 13 bits resolution (0.1% to 0.01%) if the data rate is slow. At the monitoring end, the pulse train can be simply counted for a one-second period and then displayed to show the analog value. This can be done with a low-cost 4-digit counter if a 10 kHz v-f converter is used. The cost of the v-f converter is less than half that of a good 12-bit a-d converter.

Some instrumentation problems involve parameters that must be derived from high-voltage measurements. In these circumstances, transmission of the desired information back to normal ground-potential circuits requires some form of isolation. One answer to this is to use an isolation amplifier powered from a non-isolated supply. If the data eventually is desired in digital form, the output from the amplifier would then go to an a-d converter. The cost of an isolation amplifier and a good quality 12-bit a-d converter (0.024% accuracy) runs around $200.

An effective alternative is to use a v-f converter with a floating power supply while optically coupling the digital data back to ground-level circuitry. The v-f converter output is a serial pulse train and, therefore, requires only one low-cost optical isolator for a total of roughly $60. The isolated power-supply cost must also be factored in. This can be relatively low (around $50) if the voltage is not too high (up to 1,500 V peak). For slow data rates this part of the system, shown in Fig. 1, is currently available for slightly over $100.

An interesting variation that would reconstruct the original analog signal is shown dotted in Fig. 1. This might be useful for a feedback control system. Another f-v converter hooked up to the isolator output reconstructs the signal into analog form.

Measuring the ratio

Ratiometric measurements are important for applications in which a transducer output might be affected by variations in the exciting power-supply voltage, as, for example, in a resistor bridge. This can be overcome by a measurement system that determines the ratio of transducer output to excitation voltage.

There are several ways of taking this measurement. One is simply to use a digital multimeter with ratiometric option. Such an option is usually obtainable on the more expensive models of digital multimeters, and sometimes on digital panel meters and a-d converters. But, in general, this capability is limited to high-priced models of a-d converters or digital panel meters, and the range is usually quite limited. Many models permit only a ±10% variation in the reference voltage to achieve ratiometric operation; some models go up to about ±50%. This means that ratios with wide dynamic range cannot be measured at all by conventional means.

A simple and inexpensive way of using two v-f converters for accurate ratio measurements over a dynamic range of up to 1,000 to 1 is illustrated in Fig. 2. The resistance-bridge transducer is excited by reference voltage V_R which also goes to the input of v-f converter No. 2. The output of the bridge is amplified and goes to v-f converter No. 1. The resulting pulse rate is fed to a digital counter circuit. The output pulse rate of v-f No. 2 representing V_R is fed to a divide-by-N circuit, and the resulting pulse train is used as the time base for the counter. The parallel output of the counter drives a numerical display. Since the counting time is one half the output period of the divide-by-N circuit, the output count = $2N V_1/V_R$.

The value of N can be chosen so that the time base is one second or less. The table in Fig. 2 gives the results for different values of V_1 and based on the use of a 10 kHz v-f converter with N equal to 500. The ratio measurement can be made over a dynamic range of 1,000 to 1 while keeping the time base one second or less. If the time base is allowed to go to 10 seconds, the dynamic range can be increased to 10,000 to 1. The time base can also be shortened by a factor of 10 by using 100-kHz v-f converters.

Integrating analog

Accurate analog integration over a wide dynamic signal range is difficult, especially over an extended period like several minutes. The problem is drift error in the operational integrator. In the end a very expensive, low-input current amplifier with low drift must be used along with an expensive, stable capacitor that has low leakage and low dielectric absorption. Even with the best of components, the operational integrator cannot work well when the integration period exceeds 10 minutes. A simple alternative is an analog/digital integrator using a v-f converter. The analog signal is applied to the input of a v-f converter, and the output goes to a counter operated in the totalizing mode to give a total count equal to the time integral of the signal.

$$\int V(t)\, dt = k \int f\, dt = k \int dN(t)\, dt/dt = kN$$

where N is the total count and k is a constant.

Because of the superior linearity, the integration is accurate for a signal dynamic range of 10,000 to 1. Since the output is an accumulated pulse count, there is no integrator drift as there would be with an operational integrator. Also, the counter can be stopped at any time for an indefinite period without affecting the integrated value. The limitation on the total integral is the total count capacity of the counter. Therefore, counter capacity must be based on the signal values and period of integration.

The actual integration time can be days if a counter has sufficient capacity. Assume, for example, a signal with an average value around 2 v but with occasional high peaks up to 10 v (full-scale input of the v-f converter). The output frequency of a 10 kHz converter is then 2 kHz, on average. If an 8-decade counter is used (99,999,999 full scale count), the integration period can be as long as 50,000 seconds, or 13.88 hours. The counter itself can be made from low cost ICs and be operated manually or by an external logic signal.

F-v useful, too

-Applications using the counterpart to v-f converters, the f-v converter, can include frequency measurements in flowmeters and tachometer problems in motor speed controls. Output pulse rates from these devices are used to develop an analog voltage proportional to speed or flow. The voltage, in turn, is usually fed back to regulate the process or system. The f-v converter basically is an analog pulse counter as the output voltage is linearly proportional to input rate—with excellent temperature stability. Once the pulse rate is in analog form at the f-v converter output, other analog operations can be performed. Subtracting the output of two f-v converters gives an analog frequency difference, a quantity more difficult to obtain by other means.

Another application of the f-v converter is in stabilization and linearization of a voltage-controlled oscillator. VCOs with a high degree of linearity and low temperature coefficients are quite expensive, especially if a wide variation of output frequency is needed. Very high quality VCOs use an oven-controlled inductance-capacitance element (LC) to stabilize the frequency. On the other hand, low cost VCOs have only moderate linearity and temperature stability.

A low-cost VCO can be combined with a low-cost f-v converter to achieve a linearity of better than 0.005% and a temperature coefficient of 20 ppm/°C maximum. As shown in Fig. 3, the f-v converter is used in a feedback loop to control the VCO frequency. Of course, if a pulse output is satisfactory for a system, a v-f converter could be used directly. A large proportion of VCOs, however, are used with sinusoidal outputs and, in addition, at frequencies higher than those available in v-f converters. □

Consider v/f converters for data-acquisition systems. They offer high resolution and accuracy when used as analog-to-digital converters.

Examine the performance specifications of voltage-to-frequency converters before you pick an analog-to-digital converter for your application. Three relatively inexpensive (under $100) methods—the successive-approximation, dual-slope and voltage-to-frequency conversion schemes—can deliver equal accuracy, but each is used best in a different application (Table 1).

Look at the key converter specifications (Table 2) to evaluate the performance of v/f converters compared to the two other methods. Some of the most commonly specified parameters are resolution, linearity, conversion time, temperature stability and monotonicity (no missing codes).

V/f conversion: an alternative a/d method

Seldom used until a few years ago, v/f conversion techniques are rapidly becoming popular as an alternative to successive-approximation or dual-slope techniques. There are several ways to build a v/f conversion circuit, but the charge-balancing method (Fig. 1a) is the most popular. If V_{in} is positive, the integrator output ramps down until its output voltage V_1, crosses the comparator's threshold (ground, in this case) and causes the comparator to change state. The transition, in turn, triggers a precision timing circuit that delivers a constant-width pulse. The pulse gets fed to two places: a buffer circuit that then feeds the output; and the integrator, where the pulse causes the integrator output to rapidly ramp up (Fig. 1b).

The timing circuit is, in effect, a precision one-shot multivibrator that is stable with both time and temperature. The reference current, I_{ref}, must also be stable, and a precision regulator with a voltage reference source is included for that purpose.

Since the reference current is pulled from the integrator summing junction for a fixed amount of time, and at intervals determined by the input voltage, the positive-input current feeding the integrator balances the current pulses being pulled out. The integrator can be made extremely linear and, when combined with the charge-balancing feedback loop, can achieve non-linearities as low as 0.005%.

To form an a/d converter with the v/f technique, the output of the v/f circuit must feed a counter that is gated for the desired maximum count (for a converter with a 10-kHz output, a four-digit BCD counter or a four-stage binary counter can be used).

Nail down the definitions first

Before you start comparing specifications, make sure the specs are defined. Resolution tells you the smallest quantity the converter can distinguish. Even though the quantity is usually an analog voltage the resolution is given in terms of bits: 8, 10, 12 or more.

The usable resolution of a converter can be less than the stated resolution. However, because it's a function of linearity and stability, the usable resolution can often change with time and temperature.

In the v/f form of an a/d converter, the resolution is determined by the full-scale frequency, the time base and the capacity of the counter used (Fig. 2). If a 10-kHz v/f converter is used with a time base of 1 second and four decade counters, its resolution is one part in 10,000, or four binary-coded decimal (BCD) digits. Successive-approximation or dual-slope converters with straight binary coding would have to deliver a digital output of at least 13 bits to come close (13 bits = 1 part in 8192). A v/f-based a/d converter can also deliver straight binary. To make a 12-bit unit, use three 4-bit binary counters and set the time base equal to 0.4096 seconds.

In dual-slope converters, resolution is also a function of integration time, clock frequency and counter capacity. Successive-approximation units use weighted current sources, and the number of sources determines the resolution. The higher the number of bits, the harder it becomes to maintain the linearity of the weighted sources.

Eugene Zuch, Senior Engineer, Datel Systems, 1020 Turnpike St., Canton, MA 02021.

Table 1. Typical converter applications

A/d converter type	Common applications
Successive approximation	High-speed data-acquisition systems Pulse-code-modulation systems Waveform sampling & digitizing Automatic test systems Digital process control systems
Dual slope	Digital multimeters Digital panel meters Laboratory measurements Slow-speed data-acquisition systems Monitoring systems Ratiometric measurements Measurements in high-noise environments
Voltage to frequency	Digital multimeters Digital panel meters Remote data transmission Totalizing measurements Measurements in high-noise environments High-voltage isolation measurements Ratiometric measurements

Table 2. Comparison of a/d converter types

Specification	Successive approximation	Dual slope	Voltage to frequency
Resolution	12 bits	12 bits	12 bits
Missing codes	none by careful design	none, inherent	none, inherent
Nonlinearity	±0.012% max.	±0.05 to 0.01% max.	±0.005% max.
Diff. nonlinearity	±1/2 LSB	≈ 0	≈ 0
Tempco	10 to 50 ppm/°C	10 to 50 ppm/°C	10 to 50 ppm/°C
Conversion time	2 to 50 μs	5 to 77 ms	0.041 to 0.41 s
Noise rejection, 60 Hz	None	40 to 60 dB	33.8 dB*

*For 0.41-s conversion time.

Linearity is the acid test of any a/d converter specification since resolution can be unusable if linearity error doesn't hold to less than ±0.5 LSB (1 LSB at the worst). At a fixed temperature, linearity is the only error that remains after offset and gain errors have been adjusted out.

The linearity error of a converter is the maximum deviation of the output values from a straight line drawn from zero to the maximum output. For 12-bit a/d converters a "good-quality," successive-approximation unit has a non-linearity of about ±0.012%. a dual-slope unit about ±0.05 to ±0.01% and a v/f converter about ±0.01 to ±0.005%.

The nonlinearity characteristic of successive-approximation converters differs fundamentally from that of the dual-slope or v/f. Typical non-linearity curves are shown (slightly exaggerated) in Fig. 3.

Both the v/f and dual-slope converter linearity characteristics tend to have a bow that is caused by the operational integrators used in the con-

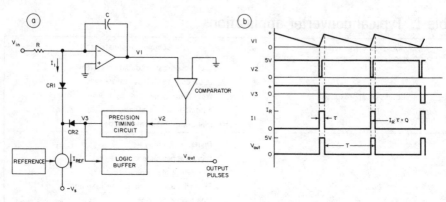

1. **The basic charge balancing v/f converter** (a) uses an operational integrator with a precision timing circuit con-

nected in a feedback loop. The output pulse width (b) is proportional to the charge stored in the capacitor.

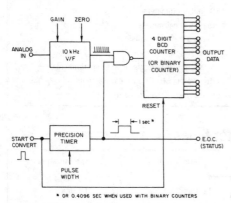

2. **By using a v/f converter and a precision timer,** you can build an a/d converter that delivers a BCD output.

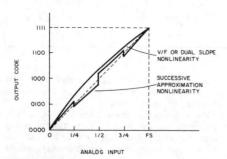

3. **Nonlinearities of v/f and dual-slope a/d converters** appear as a slight bow in the curve. However, successive-approximation nonlinearities make the curve jagged.

verters. By contrast, the successive-approximation converter's linearity is determined by the major-carry transitions of the weighted current sources. These points are located chiefly where 1/2 and 1/4-scale current values are switched in or out during the conversion process.

As shown in the graph of Fig. 3, a jump in the curve signifies when a major-carry current value is slightly off its correct value. A very linear converter restricts these jumps to very small amounts ($\pm0.012\%$ for a 12-bit converter).

Don't let the converter slow you down

The v/f converter takes the longest to do a complete conversion. The time base used in Fig. 1 is 1 second for a single conversion—rather slow for most applications. Dual-slope converters are faster, with conversion times ranging from 5 ms to 100 ms.

Successive-approximation converters are the fastest of the three, with conversion times as short as 2 μs for 12-bits. Most successive-approximation converters have conversion times between 3.5 and 50 μs.

However, if time isn't a problem, you can increase the time base to 10 seconds, add another decade counter and, voila: a converter with a resolution of one part in 100,000. Such a long conversion time could cause difficulty in many applications. And, the linearity of the 10 kHz unit would not be commensurate ($\pm1/2$ LSB) with the increased resolution.

Since the time for conversion can be made equal to the inverse of the line-voltage frequency, the dual-slope converter can be designed to reject much of the noise caused by the power line. The integrating technique used by dual-slope and v/f converters gives them the ability to reject

Successive approximation and dual slope conversion methods

The successive-approximation approach is the most widely used (Fig. A) of the three most popular conversion schemes. It compares the output of an internal d/a converter against the input signal, one bit at a time. Therefore, N fixed time periods are needed to deliver an output N bits long, but the total time needed is independent of input-voltage value.

The first step after the start pulse in a successive-approximation conversion cycle is turning on the MSB, which sets the d/a converter's output at half-scale (Fig. B). This analog signal is then fed back to the comparator. The MSB is left on if the d/a converter's output is smaller than the analog input, and turned off if the output is larger.

Next, the second bit is turned on, and the quarter-scale value added to the d/a converter output and the comparator again does its job. This process continues until the LSB has been tested and the final comparison made. When the process is complete, the converter signals this by changing the state of its end-of-conversion (status) output. The final digital output can then be read from the output of the successive-approximation register of the converter.

Successive-approximation converters can achieve conversion speeds of 100 ns/bit in medium-priced ($250 to $350) 8 and 10-bit units. Converters with 12-bit outputs are typically available with conversion times ranging from 2 to 50 μs.

Dual-slope units slow the pace

The dual-slope converter uses a simple counter to indirectly measure the input signal after an operational integrator converts a voltage into a time period (Fig. C). This scheme is the second most commonly employed method and is used, almost exclusively, in such instruments as digital multimeters and panel meters.

The conversion cycle begins when the analog-input signal is switched to the input of the operational integrator. The voltage is integrated (Fig. D) for a fixed time period determined by the clock frequency and the counter size. At the end of the period, the integrator input is switched to an internal reference whose polarity is opposite that of the original analog input. The reference is then integrated until the output reaches zero and triggers the comparator.

During the second integration, the clock is gated into a counter chain that accumulates the count until the comparator inhibits the clock. When the clock signal stops, the conversion is complete.

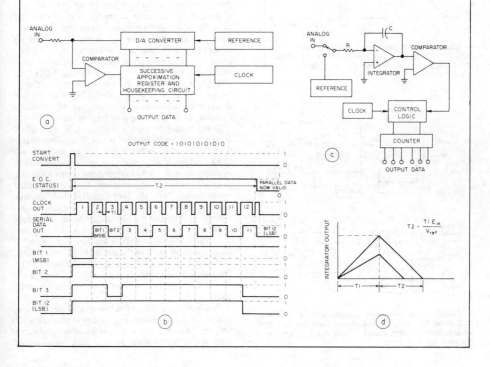

high levels of input noise.

For these two integrating converters, the longer the signal is integrated, the better the noise attenuation. When the integration period equals a multiple of the inverse of the line frequency (for dual-slope units), the noise rejection becomes infinite at integral values Tf_n, where T is the integration period and f_n is the noise frequency (Fig. 4). V/f converters don't, in general, use a period that is a multiple of any periodic noise, and so the asymptote of the noise-rejection curve is used to determine the rejection at a given Tf_n.

The v/f converter's noise-rejection asymptote rises by 20 dB per decade, and, for a 60-Hz power

line and a 0.41-s conversion time, the rejection can be computed at 33.8 dB. Dual-slope converters have rejection ratios as high as 60 dB when conversion is synchronized with the noise frequency.

Successive-approximation converters have no noise-rejection capability whatsoever. Input noise at any time during the conversion process can cause significant conversion errors. (Noise feeds directly to the comparator and can change the decision point.) The only way to minimize noise is to add an input noise filter to the converter.

Temperature coefficients change converter specs

Operation at different temperatures can tremendously alter converter performance, no matter which converter type you select. These changes affect offset and gain, two important converter parameters. Even though offset and gain are adjusted during calibration, they can change significantly with temperature.

Offset is a function of current-source leakage, comparator bias current and comparator input voltage offset. Gain (sometimes called scale factor) is a function of the voltage reference, resistor tracking and semiconductor-junction matching—and is usually the most difficult parameter to control. Absolute accuracy is affected by offset and gain changes, so if these change during operation, output errors will occur.

And, if the linearity degrades, a converter can actually skip output codes (become nonmonotonic). (An a/d converter is said to have no missing codes when, as the analog input of the converter increases from zero to full scale or vice-versa, the digital output passes through all of its possible states.) Both the dual-slope and v/f converters are inherently monotonic because of their integration techniques and the use of counting circuits to deliver the digital output.

The successive-approximation a/d converter, on the other hand, is more prone to missing codes. The code jumps occur when the analog transitions between adjacent output codes become greater than 1 LSB. Because the jumps can be greater than 1 LSB, another spec differential nonlinearity, becomes very important. Differential nonlinearity is defined as the maximum deviation of the size of any adjacent code transitions from their ideal value of 1 LSB.

A specified differential nonlinearity of ± 0.5 LSB tells you that the magnitude of every code transition is 1 LSB ± 0.5 LSB, maximum. The differential nonlinearity can reach a maximum of ± 1 LSB before converter performance is in doubt.

Picking the right converter for your application is no easy matter. For example, digital multimeters typically use a dual-slope converter since high speed isn't necessary but high noise rejec-

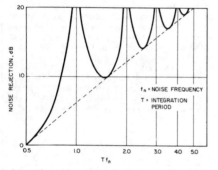

4. **Integrating a/d converters** can have exceptional noise-rejection capability if you merely adjust their measurement cycle to equal the period (or a multiple) of the noise frequency to be rejected.

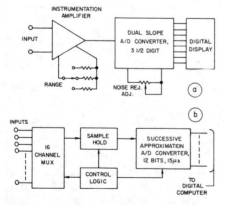

5. **Simple digital measuring systems** can be built with dual-slope (a) and successive-approximation (b) converters. Both systems shown usually require signal conditioning for each input.

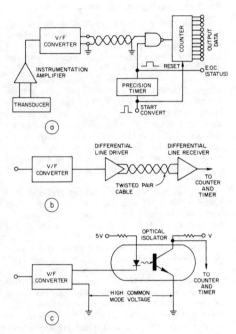

6. **V/f converters can be used** in simple, remote data-gathering applications since only a twisted pair of wires is needed to transmit the signals (a). Differential line drivers can be added if long transmission distances are required (b), or an opto-isolator can be used to eliminate large, common-mode voltage problems (c).

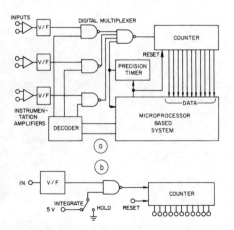

7. **A microprocessor or computer-based controller** can be used to make a multiple-channel data-collection system with a v/f converter at each point (a). If manual switches are used instead of a timer, you can turn a v/f-based a/d converter into an "infinite" integrator (b).

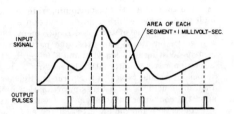

8. **The integration process in a v/f converter** can be defined in terms of millivolt-seconds for each pulse delivered. To get the total area, simply multiply the total count by 0.001.

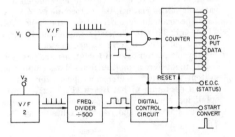

9. **If you use two v/f converters,** you can make a high-accuracy, ratiometric a/d converter. Because of the wide frequency span covered, the dynamic range of the converter can reach 10,000:1.

tion is. However, in other applications, such as in fast-throughput data acquisition, the successive-approximation converter must be used.

Dual-slope converters are widely used in applications requiring human interface in measurement and control. A simple digital measurement system (Fig. 5a) that uses a 3-1/2 digit, BCD-output converter can handle various signal inputs. The instrumentation amplifier used on the front end offers flexible gain settings with a single resistor value change.

The converter can be either a modular unit manufactured by several vendors or one made from the various IC building blocks. In many industrial and even in some lab environments, pick-up from 60-Hz radiation or magnetic coupling can cause measurement problems. By including a conversion time adjustment, you can synchronize the clock to the 60-Hz line and obtain noise rejection of more than 40 dB.

When multiple channels of data must be handled and you need all the data quickly, use the speedy successive-approximation converter. The circuit shown in Fig. 5b is a commonly used system organization for multichannel data acquisition. Although various analog-input devices might be slow in responding—and not require a fast a/d converter—the fast scanning rate of the multiplexer may require a new conversion every 2 to 30 μs. Because of the speed requirement, the a d converter can be an expensive part of the system—costing between $100 and $300 by itself.

You do have an alternative to sending analog signals over long cables to a central multiplexer. Instead of using a successive-approximation unit split the converter into an analog front end (a v f converter) and the digital receiving end (the timing and counting circuits) as in Fig. 6a.

To get even better noise immunity, you can use several simple circuits to manipulate digital levels. Cable runs of several thousand feet are possible if you let the v/f circuit feed a differential line driver that, in turn, feeds a twisted pair terminated in a receiver (Fig. 6b). When electrical isolation is critical, use optocouplers to separate the transducer output from the long lines (Fig. 6c). This is especially important if large ground potential differences are present.

Other converter-system variations are possible. You can design a multichannel data-acquisition system to operate under microprocessor control with a minimum of hardware (Fig. 7a). Simple totalizing a/d converters can be built by using manual start/stop and reset switches (Fig. 7b).

Drift-free integration is only one bonus

Unlike analog integrators that must use "super high quality" components when the integration period extends past several minutes, the v/f integrator uses inexpensive components and can even hold its value indefinitely.

A 10-kHz v/f converter delivers a pulse every 0.1 ms if the input is 10 V, or a pulse every 1 ms if the input drops to 1 V. You can manipulate these facts and say that the converter generates an output pulse for every millivolt-second of input signal. The output-pulse count then represents a piece-by-piece addition of input voltage/time area (Fig. 8). The integral of the signal with time is the total count multiplied by 0.001 volt-seconds.

You can put together a ratiometric a/d converter (Fig. 9) by combining two v/f converters and a divide chain. Input V_1 acts as the numerator and V_2 as the denominator, while the divide chain acts as a scale factor.

Since the gating pulse is half the output period, N, of the divider circuit, the counter output is

$$\text{Count} = 2NV_1/V_2.$$

If you use 10-kHz v/f converters, the time base period is no longer than 1 second for ratios of up to 1000 to 1. Unlike other ratio-measurement methods that have rather limited dynamic ranges, using two v/f converters permits a possible dynamic range of 10,000 to 1. ▪▪

Sending transducer signals over 100 feet?

Try voltage-to-frequency converters.
They should give you the accuracy you need.

Eugene L. Murphy,
Applications Engineer, Datel Systems, Inc.

A common problem confronting system and instrument engineers is the measurement of low level transducer analog output signals after transmission over long wires (100 ft or more). Fortunately, the problems can be resolved by both traditional and newer, less known methods. The need for the remote monitoring of signals can be for many reasons such as safety, due to potential hazards at the actual monitoring site, for temporary test setups at a nearby remote position, and of course, for normal control applications and systems.

Remote monitoring can be a difficult problem, especially when analog signals pass through an environment with high levels of electrical noise, as in a manufacturing facility where there is heavy electrical equipment. If a high degree of accuracy must be maintained, analog signal transmission becomes especially prohibitive beyond a few hundred feet.

One obvious solution to the noise problem would be to transmit the signals in digital form. This can be done by applying the analog signal to an analog-to-digital (A/D) converter. The digital pulses can then be transmitted in either parallel or serial format. If transmitted serially, the pulses may have to be transformed ultimately into parallel form at the receiving end for display or storage.

A better solution, in terms of cost, is to use a voltage-to-frequency (V/F) converter to transmit the transducer data directly in serial form. This is a simple and effective way to achieve an accurate system of 10 to 13 bits resolution (0.1% to 0.01%) if the data rate is slow. At the receiving end, the pulse train can be simply counted for a 1 second period or less and then displayed to show the analog value. While this may be the "best approach" for many applications, direct analog signal processing using instrumentation amplifiers is far from extinct.

Here then are some important points, suggestions, and applications to aid in selecting the most effective method for your needs using commercially available

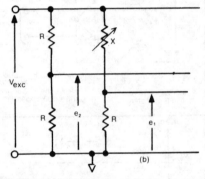

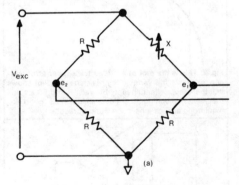

Fig. 1: Here is a typical transducer bridge circuit (a) and its equivalent circuit (b). The variable resistor, X, is the actual monitoring transducer in the bridge.

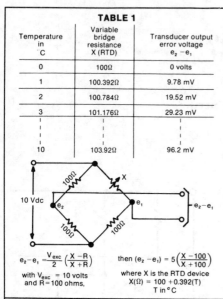

TABLE 1

Temperature in °C	Variable bridge resistance X (RTD)	Transducer output error voltage $e_2 - e_1$
0	100Ω	0 volts
1	100.392Ω	9.78 mV
2	100.784Ω	19.52 mV
3	101.176Ω	29.23 mV
⁞	⁞	⁞
10	103.92Ω	96.2 mV

$$e_2 - e_1 = \frac{V_{exc}}{2}\left(\frac{X-R}{X+R}\right)$$

with V_{exc} = 10 volts and R = 100 ohms,

then $(e_2 - e_1) = 5\left(\frac{X-100}{X+100}\right)$

where X is the RTD device
X(Ω) = 100 + 0.392(T)
T in °C

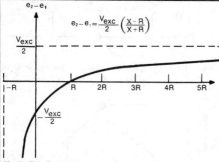

$$e_2 - e_1 = \frac{V_{exc}}{2}\left(\frac{X-R}{X+R}\right)$$

Fig. 2: This is the plot of a bridge transducer error voltage, $e_2 - e_1$ vs. the variable leg resistance, X. Plot shows that there is excellent linearity between R and 5R for this transducer, meaning that the transducer is good for monitoring applications in the linear portion.

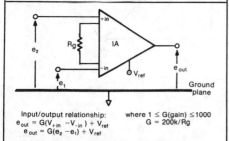

Input/output relationship:
$e_{out} = G(V_{+in} - V_{-in}) + V_{ref}$
$e_{out} = G(e_2 - e_1) + V_{ref}$

where $1 \le$ G(gain) ≤ 1000
G = 200k/Rg

Fig. 3: Simple sketch of instrumentation amplifier illustrates the input and output signals. The resistor, Rg, is used to adjust the instrumentation amplifier's gain.

modular building blocks driven by transducers. So let's start at the beginning, with the transducers.

Transducer signal source

Transducers often take the form of a Wheatstone bridge as shown in Fig. 1. With the advantages of high null resolution and means for temperature compensating, the bridge has the ability to measure a minute voltage differential appearing across it in the presence of significantly larger excitation and noise voltages. In other words, the output is differential:

$$e_2 - e_1 = \frac{V_{exc}}{2} - V_{exc}\left(\frac{R}{X+R}\right) = \frac{V_{exc}}{2}\left(\frac{X-R}{X+R}\right)$$

where V_{exc} is the bridge excitation voltage and X is the variable resistor branch.

The resistor X might be a strain gage element or a resistive thermal device (RTD[1]) which changes in a near-linear manner with temperature. We will use the latter as the X element in the Wheatstone bridge plot in Fig. 2. Note the excellent linearity between the values $X = R$ through $X=5R$. A commercially available platinum RTD[1] with suitable linearity exhibits nominal 100 ohm resistance at 0°C and a temperature coefficient of +0.392 ohms/°C; the output of a 100 ohm bridge between 0°C and 10°C using this device is shown in Table 1. With only millivolts of output, this circuit will serve as a signal to be measured over long lines.

Amplify first

To be useful, the millivolt-level differential output of the bridge must usually be amplified to levels well above ambient noise. Specifically designed for this task, the instrumentation amplifier (IA) in Fig. 3 will boost the differential bridge output by 1000 times or more. The actual gain is a function of the values selected for the external gain setting resistor, Rg. This resistor enables the user to set the full scale output to a convenient value. It is possible to use a variable resistor here for final trimming.

Another benefit of the instrumentation amplifier is that it amplifies on the difference in voltage between the signal and signal-return leads. Interference signals on both leads in the same phase are not amplified. This is known as common-mode rejection (CMR) and is the principal advantage of using these amplifiers. It is this property that enables the amplifier to ignore ground loop voltages due, for example, to the long wires while responding to differential signals as mentioned above for transducer outputs.

The RTD measurement system, shown in Fig. 4 illustrates the need for shielding and bypassing techniques to minimize RFI (radio frequency interference) and line frequency (60 Hz) interference. The need to keep the bridge/amplifier ensemble in close proximity to one another, to bypass the amplifier power supply input terminals *at the amplifier socket* and to return the shield to the single point input reference ground are crucial to the success of this system.

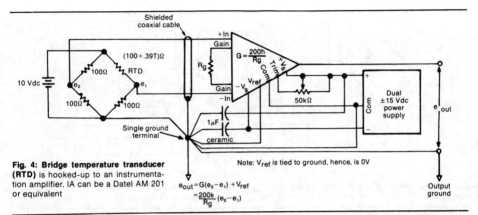

Fig. 4: Bridge temperature transducer (RTD) is hooked-up to an instrumentation amplifier. IA can be a Datel AM 201 or equivalent

$$e_{out} = G(e_2 - e_1) + V_{ref}$$
$$= \frac{200k}{R_g}(e_2 - e_1)$$

Note: V_{ref} is tied to ground, hence, is 0V

Fig. 5 shows an IA transmitting its output, the amplified bridge signal, over long wires to a monitoring instrument. It is a fairly common practice to use twisted and often shielded pairs of wires. Unfortunately, the capacitive effect of these wires degrades the amplifier's frequency response, and encourages undesirable oscillation. In other words, this can distort the desired information being transmitted.

Permissible capacitive output loading of the instrumentation amplifier will vary from supplier-to-supplier; typically this will range from 300 to 10,000 pF (picofarads). Shielded twisted pairs of wire may have 25 pF of capacitance per foot. So, in a 100 ft. run, equivalent capacitance would be 2500 pF. This is certainly not a limiting factor, but it is one that must be seriously considered, especially when faced with longer telemetry distances.

A small series resistance, on the order of 50 ohms to 200 ohms, can be placed in the amplifier output to maintain stability with capacitive loading. Series resistance incurred with shielded twisted pairs of wire, (or any good transmission line) is negligible; a practical value is 50 ohms per mile, roughly 1 ohm per 100 ft.

You can see that direct analog measurement approach is vulnerable to all forms of electrical noise—RFI, EMI and power line interference. Further, capacitive loading can create amplifier instability and the long lines, which can act as antennas, will themselves induce undesired extraneous signals.

Finally, the amplifier can be scaled higher in order to boost desired signals to the level of volts, improving CMR capability while reducing the amplifier frequency response. But this can be an advantage in low frequency because high frequency noise will be partially filtered.

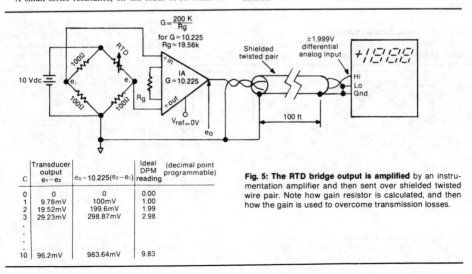

Fig. 5: The RTD bridge output is amplified by an instrumentation amplifier and then sent over shielded twisted wire pair. Note how gain resistor is calculated, and then how the gain is used to overcome transmission losses.

C	Transducer output $e_1 - e_2$	$e_0 = 10.225(e_2 - e_1)$	Ideal DPM reading	(decimal point programmable)
0	0	0	0.00	
1	9.78mV	100mV	1.00	
2	19.52mV	199.6mV	1.99	
3	29.23mV	298.87mV	2.98	
.				
.				
.				
10	96.2mV	983.64mV	9.83	

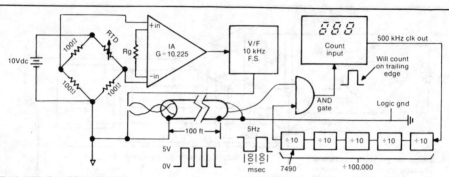

Fig. 6: With the addition of a V/F converter, transducer bridge output can be sent over greater distances. A low priced DPM will display the information through the addition of a divider and a AND gate.

Digital or analog readout?

Acknowledging that "moving pointer" readouts (or analog meters) cost less, some features of the digital panel meter (DPM) can far outweigh the analog meters:

● The DPM provides unambiguous readings with up to 0.01% resolution, with no guessing.

● The DPM presents a high input impedance to its signal source, making long line measurements less of a chore.

● Many DPM's can be manipulated by digital signals to perform a surprising array of tasks.

In its simplest form, the DPM uses the single slope conversion method. It is, in fact, nothing more than a "dumb" counter which can be made "smart" by externally controlling the interval over which pulses are counted. This feature allows the DPM to perform like a frequency meter. (See right hand portion of Fig. 6.) This method can serve as a basis for digital transmission of analog data. But first, why should we transmit digitally?

Digital vs. analog data transmission

The wide noise margin and the relatively large amplitude of logic levels make digital transmission highly immune to the effects of noise. For example, millivolt-level analog signals can be represented by transistor-transistor logic (TTL) digital signals that vary between 0 to 0.8 volts for ZERO levels and 2.4 to 5.0 volts for ONE logic levels. Commercially available V/F converters can produce this type of output in the form of a digital pulse train with a rate proportional to the analog input amplitude (voltage).

Most V/F's have a 0 to 10 volt full-scale analog input and they output either 0 to 10 kHz or 0 to 100 kHz digital pulse trains. The 10 kHz full-scale units are very popular because of their extremely good linearity (accuracy) performance. Linearity for the 10 kHz full scale (F.S.) units is ±0.005% or ±½ Hz. Thus, if 5 volts are applied to the input, the output pulse train will be a 5 kHz ±½ Hz rate, which is very accurate. For simple systems, the hook-up is not very difficult. It can often be "cook booked" from literature readily available from the module manufacturers.

To recap briefly, the information from the transducer is amplified to a high level (1-10 volts); it is then used to drive the input of the V/F converter. The output of the converter is then transmitted via wires to an indicator, which is most commonly a DPM.

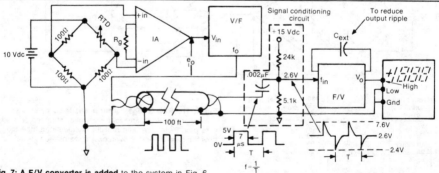

Fig. 7: A F/V converter is added to the system in Fig. 6. This addition presents an analog signal to the DPM, eliminating the need for a divider or AND gate. It also makes analog control signals available for other applications.

While it is not intended to be covered here, if you had long wire runs of several hundred feet and more, you should use a differential line driver to drive the twisted pair. Then, at the other end of the line, you would use a differential line receiver to feed the digital counter.

Mating the V/F to the frequency meter

Fig. 6 shows the entire signal processing system using an instrumentation amplifier to amplify and scale the transducer output, a v/F converter to time encode and digitally transmit the amplified analog signal, and a DPM to present a properly scaled numerical display of the transducer voltage (temperature). This circuit features a 2.4 volt noise threshold. Over long distances it is advisable to include a line driver at the v/F converter output and a line receiver at the corresponding AND gate input; these drivers minimize the edge-rounding that can be caused by capacitive storage in a system.

Another approach—somewhat more complex—presents a DPM with an analog input signal in the manner shown in Fig. 7. Here, a v/F converter drives an F/v converter (the v/F counterpart) over long lines and the F/v drives the analog inputs of the DPM. This circuit rejects up to 1.8 volts of noise and is recommended for applications where the conditioned analog signal, the DPM input, must also be available for other system functions.

Other applications using the F/v converter can include frequency measurements in flow meters and tachometer problems in motor speed controls. Output pulse rates for these devices are used to develop an analog voltage proportional to speed or flow. The voltage, in turn, can be fed back to regulate the process or system. Basically, the F/v converter is a temperature stable analog pulse counter with an output voltage that is proportional to input rate. Once the pulse rate is in analog form at the F/v converter output, other analog operations can be performed.

Because the v/F converters perform integration, they actively reject time varying signals that are symmetrical about zero. This feature provides even higher noise immunity in system applications.

All the components mentioned are readily available products that can be obtained from numerous sources in a variety of forms, performance levels and prices. Further, applications assistance and notes are offered by most manufacturers to help you with your requirements. ∎

References

1. 1975 Omega Temperature Measurement Handbook, Copyright 1974 by Omega Engineering, Inc.
2. "Voltage to frequency converters: versatility now at low cost" by Eugene L. Zuch, Electronics, May 15, 1975.
3. Transducer Measurements, Second Edition, by Kenneth Arthur, Tektronix, Inc., copyright, 1971.

Frequency converter is a dual operator

by Eugene L. Zuch
Datel Systems

Voltage-to-frequency converters are analog/digital interface devices that generate digital output pulses at a rate linearly proportional to the input voltage. Universal voltage-to-frequency converters have pin-programmable input/output features that make them extremely versatile devices for a wide variety of applications. They operate:

- As voltage-to-frequency or frequency-to-voltage converters with either positive or negative voltage or current inputs; or with either positive or negative going output pulses.

- As an F/V converter with either positive or negative output voltage. They are compatible with DTL/TTL, CMOS, or other high level logic circuits.

The key specifications of Datel's 10 kHz and 100 kHz universal V/F converters are given in Table 1.

The main advantage to using a universal type of V/F converter is its flexibility. Since it is pin-programmable, it isn't necessary to stock various models for different applications.

A typical V/F/V converter using charge balancing is shown in Fig. 1. When operating as a V/F converter, the V_{OUT} terminal is connected to the Pulse In terminal. Therefore, the timing reference circuit is triggered by the integrator output as it passes through a threshold level. The timing reference circuit generates a precise, constant width pulse that is converted into a current pulse by the charge feedback circuit. The the current pulse, or charge, is pulled from the integrator input terminal. The rate of charge generation exactly balances the input current into the integrator; therefore the output pulse rate is linearly proportional to input voltage or current. The voltage pulses from the timing reference circuit are fed to a special logic buffering circuit. This circuit programs the pulse output level and polarity. It also short-circuit proofs the unit.

The second amplifier in the diagram is a unity gain amplifier, and is used to invert inputs when the module is used as a V/F converter or to invert outputs when used as an F/V converter. In the F/V mode, pin 26 is connected to pin 1 and the input pulses are applied to the Pulse In terminal. Thus, the 10k input resistor at the +V_{IN} terminal is effectively in parallel with C and the integrating amplifier acts as a low pass filter that filters the current pulses from the charge feedback circuit. An external capacitor can be connected between the +I_{IN} terminal and V_{OUT} to increase the filter's time constant.

The universal V/F converter's usefulness centers around its analog/digital interfacing capability. The V/F converter is like an A/D converter with serial output pulses.

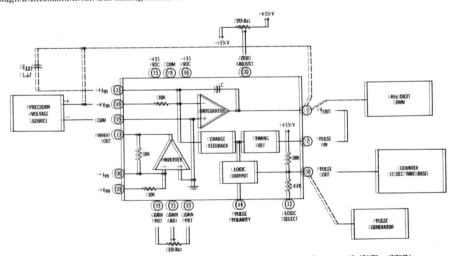

Fig. 1. The inverting amplifier shown in color switches the converter between the V/F and F/V modes. External connections also in color are used when calibrating the converter in the V/F mode. F/V calibrations are illustrated by dashed lines. Note the 10k gain pot and the 20k zero adjust pot are used in both calibration procedures.

TABLE I
SPECIFICATIONS OF UNIVERSAL V/F CONVERTERS

Specification	VFK-10K	VFK-100K
Input voltage	0 to +10 v, 0 to −10 v	
Input current	0 to +1 ma, 0 to −1 ma	
Input Z (voltage)	10 k ohms	
Frequency range	0 to 10 kHz	0 to 100 kHz
Nonlinearity, max	±0.005%	±0.05%
Gain Tempco, max	±20 ppm/°C	±100 ppm/°C
Zero temp drift	±10 μv/°C	±10 μv/°C
Outut pulse width	75 μsec	7.5 μsec
Output loading	12 TTL loads	
Power requirement	±15 vdc at 25 ma	
Case size	2″ x 2″ x 0.375″	
Price (1 to 9)	$59	$79

A 10 kHz V/F converter has a resolution of one part in 10,000, equivalent to a resolution of better than 13 binary bits (one part in 8192). The worst case linearity is 50 ppm, also equivalent to that of a 13 bit A/D converter. The gain temperature stability of 20 ppm/°C for the Datel VFV-10K, combined with the resolution and linearity figures, makes this unit equivalent to a high quality A/D converter. However, this is based on slow conversion rates, and is not useful where high data conversion rates are required, although somewhat faster conversion times are possible by sacrificing resolution. Alternatively, a faster unit, such as the 100 kHz converter, can be used with a 0.1 second time base to give the same resolution as the 10k unit, but it does not have as good linearity.

The lower operating limit of these units is about 1 millivolt. This is due to the resolution of the zero adjustment, long term stability, temperature drift, etc. The useful dynamic range of both the 10 kHz and 100 kHz models is 10,000:1, or 80 db.

Calibrating a V/F/V converter

In general, calibration is done in a manner similar to that of A/D converters with external gain and zero adjustments made by trimming potentiometers. The calibration steps for the V/F mode are as follows:

- Connect the unit as a V/F converter with zero and gain trimming potentiometers as shown in Fig. 1.
- Connect a precision voltage source to the input and a digital counter set to a one second time base to the pulse output.
- Set the precision voltage source to +10.000V and adjust the gain trimming potentiometer to give an output count of 10,000 (VFV-10K) or 100,000 (VFV-100K).
- Set the precision voltage source to +0.010V and adjust the zero timming potentiometer to give an output count of 10 (VFV-10K), or 100 (VFV-100K).
- Repeat the +10.000V adjustment.

When used in the F/V conversion mode, the unit can be calibrated in the V/F converter mode and reconnected as an F/V converter; or the module can be directly calibrated as an F/V converter using the following procedure:

- Connect the module as shown in Fig. 1 with an external 1 μf (film type) integrating capacitor.
- Connect a pulse generator to the pulse input and set to give +5 v negative going pulses 50 μsec wide for the VFV-10K or 5 μsec wide for the VFV-100K. Connect a digital counter to the output of the pulse generator and set the pulse rate to 10 kHz for the VFV-10K or 100 kHz for the VFV-100K.
- Connect a 4½ digit DVM to the voltage output terminal; adjust the gain trimming potentiometer to give +10.000V output on the meter.
- Set the pulse generator output to 10 Hz for the VFV-10K and 100 Hz for the VFV-100K and adjust the zero trimming potentiometer to give +0.010V output.
- Repeat the +10.000V adjustment.

In the calibration procedure as a V/F converter, the module was shown connected as a positive input, voltage to frequency converter. By using the current input terminal, the unit becomes a positive input, current to frequency converter with a current range of 0 to 1 ma. For negative input voltages and currents, the inverting amplifier is connected ahead of the integrator. Since this amplifier has both current and voltage inputs, the ranges are 0 to −10V for voltage and 0 to −1 ma for current.

Operating point

The Logic Select terminal (pin 12) selects the logic level used, either the 5 v levels for DTL/TTL or the 15V levels for CMOS and high level logic. Other arbitrary logic levels between 5V and 15V can be obtained by leaving the Logic Select pin open and connecting an external resistor from the Pulse Out pin to ground. The outputs are summarized in Table II. For a given logic level V_L, the value of this resistance is derived from the equation:

$$+V_L = \frac{15\ R_{ext}}{R_{ext} + 10k}$$

TABLE II PULSE OUTPUT PROGRAMMING				
Pulse Type	Pulse Output		Logic Select	Pulse Polarity
Positive going 5 v pulses	+5 0	⊓⊔⊓⊔⊓	Ground	+15 v
Negative going 5 v pulses	+5 0	⊔⊓⊔⊓⊔	Ground	Open
Positive going 15 v pulses	+15 0	⊓⊔⊓⊔⊓	Open	+15 v
Negative going 15 v pulses	+15 0	⊔⊓⊔⊓⊔	Open	Open

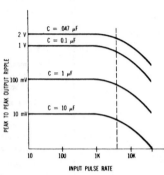

Fig. 2. Output ripple characteristics of the F/F/V-10k.

where R_{ext} is the external resistance between pin 10 and ground.

The Pulse Polarity terminal is connected to 15V or left open, depending on whether the output pulse is positive going from ground or negative going from a positive level.

When used as a F/V converter, the feedback loop is opened and the input pulses are fed directly to the input of the timing reference circuit. These pulses must be negative going pulses from a high state greater than 2.0V to a low state less than 0.8V. The pulse width must be between 10 and 60 μsec for the VFV-10K and 1 and 6 μsec for the VFV-100K. For wider pulses and other waveforms, input conditioning is necessary.

Acts as a filter

Again, in the F/V operating mode, the integrator circuit is used as a single pole, low pass filter with a time constant determined by the 10k ohm resistor and capacitor C. The converter's output ripple magnitude (Fig. 2) depends on the input pulse rate and the value of C (Fig. 1). The capacitor values shown include an internal value of 0.047 μf. Increased external capacitance gives better filtering but sacrifices response time. When C = 1 μf, the peak to peak ripple component is 100 mV maximum with a step response time of about 22 msec.

A V/F converter can be used to transmit data to other locations with very high noise immunity. For example, information from a transducer is amplified to a high level (1 to 10V) and is used to drive the input of the V/F converter. The converter feeds a twisted-pair cable that carries the signal through the noisy environment. At the other end of the line, a differential line receiver feeds a digital counter and display, or alternatively an F/V converter. The counter and display read out data directly.

In some cases, however, it might be desired to reconstruct the original analog signal. This is done by using an F/V converter with an appropriate external capacitor to convert the digital pulses back to the analog signal. Using differential line drivers and receivers results in very high noise immunity to common mode noise.

A universal V/F converter can be used to transmit data directly from an industrial transducer with 4 to 20 ma output current. The V/F converter differential line driver ahead of a is offset by a 2.5V reference voltage applied to the inverting input amplifier, and the output of this amplifier is fed through a 10k ohm resistor to the summing junction of the operational integrator and pins 1 and 2 are shorted. A 665 ohm load resistor is connected across the transducer's output. Because of the offset, a 4 ma transducer output corresponds to a zero input to the V/F converter, and a 20 ma output corresponds to a full scale input of 10V. The digitally transmitted data from the transducer can then be read out at the other location on a digital counter and display.

The universal V/F converter has 4 inputs (+A, +B, −C, −D) including both the integrator and inverting amplifier inputs. If the inverting amplifier is used, it must have its output connected either to the $+V_{IN}$ input or through a 10k ohm resistor to the $+I_{IN}$ input. Additional input resistors added to the $+I_{IN}$ terminal result in the algebraic summation and subtraction of the input signals. The output frequency, assuming a 10 kHz model, is:

$$f = 10 \text{ kHz} \left[\frac{A+B-C-D}{10V} \right]$$

In addition to the straight summation shown, summation with gain can also be achieved. In this case, the inverting amplifier is used as a gain stage rather than as an integrator. This is done by hanging input resistors with values less than 10k ohms on the $-I_{IN}$ terminal. Gain for a given input signal is $G = -10k/R$.

A number of data channels can be read out by a single digital counter and display. The counter/display, for a low cost system, is simply switched from one channel to another. Each data channel has its own V/F converter that is programmed for the particular transducer or signal used. Therefore gain, addition or subtraction, inversion, etc., can be individually accomplished for each separate information channel.

Test your
V/F converter IQ

While V/F's aren't new, today's designs transform them into highly versatile, low-cost building blocks. Do you know how to use them?

Eugene L. Zuch, Datel Systems, Inc.

A basic understanding of the operation and characteristics of the modern voltage-to-frequency converter is a must for system or circuit design engineers. Based on an old method, V/F's in modular or IC form combine latest component and design technologies into "data converters with a difference." Not only do they compete for traditional analog-to-digital interface applications with successive-approximation and dual-slope type converters, they also compete with discrete circuits of many types for cost-effective solutions to general-purpose problems.

Unfortunately, though, V/F converters aren't widely appreciated and are often misunderstood. To correct this situation we present, as a test of skill and (hopefully) a source of inspiration, 14 multiple-choice questions based on the unit described in the box. The correct answers, along with brief discussions of the principles involved, appear elsewhere in this issue. Good luck!

Given: a typical V/F converter

Voltage-to-frequency converters generate a train of output pulses with a frequency linearly proportional to the input voltage. The input range, generally 0 to +10V, interfaces with such analog circuits as op amps, multipliers and sample/hold amplifiers. The output, which typically has a F.S. range of 10 or 100 kHz, is DTL/TTL or CMOS compatible to interface directly with digital logic.

V/F converters list among their most important features high linearity, excellent temperature stability and low to moderate cost. When used with a precision timing circuit, gate and counter, they make a complete A/D converter with high resolution, linearity and stability, but not high speed.

Table 1 lists the key specifications of a typical commercially available V/F converter—the Datel Systems' VFV-10K.

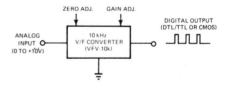

TABLE 1 — KEY SPECIFICATIONS, VFV-10k

INPUT VOLTAGE RANGE	0 to +10V
INPUT OVERRANGE, MIN.	10%
INPUT IMPEDANCE	10kΩ
OUTPUT FREQUENCY	0 to 10kHz
FREQUENCY OVERRANGE, MIN.	10%
PULSE WIDTH	70 μsec
RISE & FALL TIMES	200 nsec
SETTLING TIME TO 0.01%	1 PULSE AT NEW FREQUENCY
OUTPUT COMPATIBILITY	DTL/TTL OR CMOS
FULL SCALE ERROR	ADJUSTABLE TO ZERO
OFFSET ERROR	ADJUSTABLE TO ZERO
NONLINEARITY, MAX.	0.005%
TEMPCO OF ZERO, MAX.	±30μV/°C
TEMPCO OF GAIN, MAX.	±20 ppm/°C
POWER REQUIREMENT	±15V DC @ 25 mA

1. Which of the following circuit techniques has no relation to V/F conversion?
   a. Charge dumping
   b. Voltage-controlled oscillator (VCO)
   c. Charge balancing
   d. Variable transconductance

2. Assuming that the linearity of the V/F converter of **Table 1** holds all the way down to zero input voltage (which it does), and that the input offset voltage can be accurately zeroed for an input as low as +1 mV (which it can), what dynamic range of the output frequency can be realized?
   a. 60 dB
   b. 66 dB
   c. 80 dB
   d. 100 dB

3. The V/F converter is useful for high noise-immunity remote data transmission because:
   a. It amplifies the input signal but not the noise
   b. It integrates the input signal, rejecting noise
   c. It transmits the data in the form of digital pulses that are relatively noise immune
   d. It can be used with an optical isolator at the output for high common-mode rejection

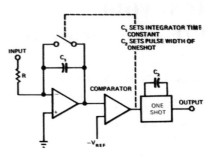

Fig. 2

5. In the V/F converter diagrammed in **Fig. 2**, how does the stability of capacitors C_1 and C_2 affect the accuracy of the converter?
   a. C_1 directly affects the accuracy but C_2 does not
   b. C_2 directly affects the accuracy but C_1 does not
   c. Both C_1 and C_2 directly affect the accuracy
   d. Neither C_1 nor C_2 directly affects accuracy

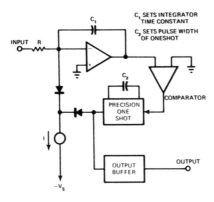

Fig. 1

4. In the V/F converter of **Fig. 1**, how does the stability of capacitors C_1 and C_2 affect the accuracy of the converter?
   a. C_1 directly affects the accuracy but C_2 does not
   b. C_2 directly affects the accuracy but C_1 does not
   c. Both C_1 and C_2 directly affect the accuracy
   d. Neither C_1 nor C_2 directly affects accuracy

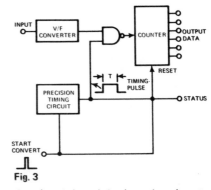

Fig. 3

Questions **6** through **9** refer to the voltage-to-frequency type A/D converter illustrated in **Fig. 3**. The V/F converter used is described in **Table 1**.

6. To make a 12-bit binary A/D converter, we use a 12-bit binary counter. Assuming that the V/F is calibrated to give exactly 10 kHz at F.S. (+10V) input, what should be the width of the pulse from the timing circuit?
   a. 0.4096 sec
   b. 1.000 sec
   c. 2.048 msec
   d. 40.96 msec

7. To change the circuit of **Fig. 3** into a 4-digit BCD A/D converter, which of the following changes must be made?
  a. Change the V/F converter to a 100-kHz unit and the counter to a 4-decade BCD counter
  b. Change the counter to a 4-decade BCD counter and the timing pulse width to 1.000 sec
  c. Change the timing pulse width to 1.000-sec
  d. Change the counter to a 4-decade BCD counter, and NAND gate to a NOR

8. For the 12-bit A/D converter described in **Question 6**, what is the approximate linearity?
  a. ±1/10 LSB
  b. ±1/4 LSB
  c. ±1/2 LSB
  d. ±1 LSB

9. Voltage-to-frequency A/D converters possess good noise rejection characteristics since they average the input signal during the conversion time. Assuming a 10-sec conversion time (or counting time) for this type converter, what is its noise rejection for 60-Hz input noise?
  a. 26 dB
  b. 33.8 dB
  c. 35.6 dB
  d. 41.6 dB

10. Which of the following is an advantage of the successive approximation A/D converter over the voltage-to-frequency A/D converter?
  a. Noise rejection
  b. Inherent monotonicity (no missing codes)
  c. Excellent temperature stability
  d. None of the above

11. Differential nonlinearity for an A/D converter is defined as the maximum deviation of any bit size from its theoretical value of 1 LSB over the full conversion range. Since a voltage-to-frequency A/D converter has a smooth, bow-type linearity characteristic, its differential nonlinearity is approximately:
  a. Zero
  b. ±1/2 LSB
  c. ±1 LSB
  d. Cannot be determined

12. One of the applications for a V/F converter is a voltage-controlled oscillator (VCO) with either pulse- or square-wave output (**Fig. 4**). How does the V/F converter basically differ from a VCO?
  a. The V/F converter is linear over its full operating range and the linearity holds down to zero
  b. The V/F converter is smaller and cheaper
  c. The V/F converter has a pulse output, whereas a VCO has a sine-wave output
  d. No difference

13. Which of the following characteristics do voltage-to-frequency and dual-slope A/D converters have in common?
  a. Excellent noise rejection
  b. Inherent monotonicity (no missing codes)
  c. Slow conversion time
  d. All of the above

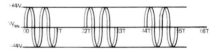

Fig. 5

14. **Fig. 5** shows a pulsed sine wave with a peak-to-peak amplitude of 8V. This waveform is squared by an analog multiplier and then integrated by applying it to a 10-kHz V/F converter and counting output pulses for a specified period of time. If the capacity of the counter is 10 BCD digits, what is the length of time over which the waveform can be integrated?
  a. 6944.4 hrs.
  b. 3472.2 hrs.
  c. 2777.7 hrs.
  d. 1000 hrs.

References
1. E. Zuch, "Designer's guide to V/F converters," Datel Systems, Inc., Canton, MA
2. E. Zuch, "Voltage-to-frequency converters: versatility now at low cost," *Electronics*, May 15, 1975, pg. 91.
3. S. Connors, "Voltage-to-frequency converters: A/D's with advantages," *EDN*, June 5, 1974, pg. 49

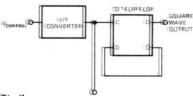

Fig. 4

Presenting: the answers to our quiz on V/F converters

To ace this exam you need more than just a passing familiarity with V/F's. Our explanations should help clear up any misconceptions.

ANSWERS

1.	d	8.	b
2.	c	9.	d
3.	c	10.	d
4.	b	11.	a
5.	a	12.	a
6.	a	13.	d
7.	b	14.	a

Fourteen questions do not an expert make. But if you've answered all of our queries correctly, consider yourself very well versed on at least the basics of V/F converters. (An average score is 6-8 correct.) This quiz, combined with a careful reading of the reference articles, should give you an excellent grasp of the subject.

Our comments to the questions follow.

1. Variable transconductance is a circuit technique used for analog multiplication, division and other nonlinear functions. It has no relation to V/F conversion.

2. The analog input range is 1 mV to 10V; the corresponding output frequency range, 1 Hz to 10 kHz. This represents a dynamic range of 10,000:1 or 80 dB.

3. Although **b** and **d** are true statements, they do not explain the V/F's high noise immunity in the transmission of remote data. Rather, the reason for **c** is that the analog information is converted into a digital pulse train, which has relatively high noise immunity compared to an analog signal.

4. **Fig. 1** diagrams a charge-balancing V/F converter. C_1 determines the amplitude of voltage transition at the integrator output but does not affect the accuracy of the output pulse frequency. C_2 directly affects accuracy because the average current pulled out of the integrator's summing junction is directly determined by the width of the pulse from the one shot.

5. A charge-dumping V/F is shown in **Fig. 2**. Here C_1 directly affects accuracy since it determines how fast the output of the integrator gets to the trip point of the comparator. C_2, on the other hand, merely sets the output pulse width and has no effect on accuracy.

6. A 12-bit binary A/D converter has a total of 4096 output states. Therefore, the pulse width must be 0.4096 sec to produce this number of states from a 10-kHz pulse rate.

7. The 4-decade BCD converter has 10,000 output states, so it needs a 1.000-sec timing pulse width and a 4-decade BCD counter.

8. The V/F converter used has a nonlinearity of 0.005% max. that corresponds to about 1/4 LSB out of 12 bits (1 LSB in 12 bits is 0.024%).

9. Noise rejection of an averaging type A/D converter is 20 log $2Tf_n$, where T is the averaging or conversion time and f_n is the noise frequency. Therefore, 41.6-dB rejection of 60-Hz noise is correct, based on the noise rejection asymptote. Note that this doesn't assume that the 1.000-sec conversion time is a precise multiple of the 60-Hz period. If it were an exact multiple, the noise rejection would be infinite.

10. Choices **a**, **b** and **c** are characteristics of integrating and voltage-to-frequency type A/D converters. Successive approximation machines are noted for their speed.

11. Because of the V/F converter's smooth, bow-type linearity characteristic, all bits over its full range are almost exactly the same size (1 LSB) and the differential nonlinearity is very nearly zero.

12. Choices **b** and **c** are true in many cases, but **a** is the best choice. A VCO is basically linear over a limited range of output frequency and does not operate down to zero frequency.

13. The best answer is "all of the above." We might add that for a given resolution (≥10 bits), V/F based and integrating A/D's generally cost less than successive approximation types.

14. This question involves some computation. At the output of the multiplier the squared sine wave has an amplitude of +1.6V and an average value of +0.8V. Since it is ON only half the time, the actual average is +0.4V. This voltage produces an average output frequency of 400 Hz from a 10 kHz V/F converter. The maximum integration time in hours is then: $T = 10^{10}/(400 \times 3600) = 6944.4$ hrs. □

Author's biography

Eugene L. Zuch is a product marketing manager at Datel Systems, Inc., Canton, MA. He holds BSEE and MSEE degrees from MIT as well as a BS from MIT's Sloan School of Management. Gene has an extensive background in functional circuits and is a prolific author on the subject.

7. Glossary of Data Conversion Terms

Glossary of Data Conversion Terms

This glossary defines the most often used terms in the field of data conversion technology. Each of the terms has been described or referred to elsewhere in this book.

ABSOLUTE ACCURACY: The worst-case input to output error of a data converter referred to the NBS standard volt.

ACCURACY: The conformance of a measured value with its true value; the maximum error of a device such as a data converter from the true value. See *relative accuracy* and *absolute accuracy.*

ACQUISITION TIME: For a sample-hold, the time required, after the sample command is given, for the hold capacitor to charge to a full scale voltage change and then remain within a specified error band around final value.

ACTIVE FILTER: An electronic filter which uses passive circuit elements with active devices such as gyrators or operational amplifiers. In general, resistors and capacitors are used but no inductors.

ACTUATOR: A device which converts a voltage or current input into a mechanical output.

ADC: Abbreviation for analog-to-digital converter. See *A/D converter.*

A/D CONVERTER: Analog-to-digital converter. A circuit which converts an analog (continuous) voltage or current into an output digital code.

ALIAS FREQUENCY: In reconstructed analog data, a false lower frequency component which is the result of insufficient sampling rate, i.e., less than that required by the sampling theorem.

ALIASING: See *Alias Frequency.*

ANALOG MULTIPLEXER: An array of switches with a common output connection for selecting one of a number of analog inputs. The output signal follows the selected input within a small error.

ANTI-ALIAS FILTER: See *Pre-Sampling Filter.*

APERTURE DELAY TIME: In a sample-hold, the time elapsed from the hold command to the actual opening of the sampling switch.

APERTURE JITTER: See *Aperture Uncertainty Time.*

APERTURE TIME: The time window, or time uncertainty, in making a measurement. For an A/D converter it is the conversion time; for a sample-hold it is the signal averaging time during the sample-to-hold transition.

APERTURE UNCERTAINTY TIME: In a sample-hold, the time variation, or time jitter, in the opening of the sampling switch; also the variation in aperture delay time from sample to sample.

AUTO-ZERO: A stabilization circuit which servos an amplifier or A/D converter input offset to zero during a portion of its operating cycle.

BANDGAP REFERENCE: A voltage reference circuit which is based on the principle of the predictable base-to-emitter voltage of a transistor to generate a constant voltage equal to the extrapolated bandgap voltage of silicon ($\approx$1.22V).

BANDWIDTH: The frequency at which the gain of an amplifier or other circuit is reduced by 3 dB from its DC value; also the range of frequencies within which the attenuation is less than 3 dB from the center frequency value.

BCD: See *Binary Coded Decimal.*

BINARY CODE: See *Natural Binary Code.*

BINARY CODED DECIMAL (BCD): A binary code used to represent decimal numbers in which each digit from 0 to 9 is represented by four bits weighted 8-4-2-1. Only 10 of the 16 possible states are used.

BIPOLAR MODE: For a data converter, when the analog signal range includes both positive and negative values.

BIPOLAR OFFSET: The analog displacement of one half of full scale range in a data converter operated in the bipolar mode. The offset is generally derived from the converter reference circuit.

BREAK-BEFORE-MAKE SWITCHING: A characteristic of analog multiplexers in which there is a small time delay between disconnection from the previous channel and connection to the next channel. This assures that no two inputs are ever momentarily shorted together.

BUFFER AMPLIFIER: An amplifier employed to isolate the loading effect of one circuit from another.

BURIED ZENER REFERENCE: See *Subsurface Zener Reference.*

BUSY OUTPUT: See *Status Output.*

BUTTERFLY CHARACTERISTIC: An error versus temperature graph in which all errors are contained within two straight lines which intersect at room temperature, or approximately 25°C.

CHARGE BALANCING A/D CONVERTER: An analog-to-digital conversion technique which employs an operational integrator circuit with a pulse generating feedback loop. Current pulses from the feedback loop are precisely balanced against the analog input by the integrator, and the resulting pulses are counted for a fixed period of time to produce an output digital word. This technique is also called *quantized-feedback.*

CHARGE DUMPING: See *Charge Transfer.*

CHARGE INJECTION: See *Charge Transfer.*

CHARGE TRANSFER: In a sample-hold, the phenomenon of moving a small charge from the sampling switch to the hold capacitor during switch turn-off. This is caused by the switch control voltage change coupling through switch capacitance to the hold capacitor. Also called *charge dumping* or *charge injection.*

CHOPPER-STABILIZED AMPLIFIER: An operational amplifier which employs a special DC modulator-demodulator circuit to reduce input offset voltage drift to an extremely low value.

CLOCK: A circuit in an A/D converter that generates timing pulses which synchronize the operation of the converter.

CLOCK RATE: The frequency of the timing pulses of the clock circuit in an A/D converter.

COMMON-MODE REJECTION RATIO: For an amplifier, the ratio of differential voltage gain to common-mode voltage gain, generally expressed in dB.

$$CMRR = 20 \log_{10} \frac{A_D}{A_{CM}}$$

where A_D is differential voltage gain and A_{CM} is common mode voltage gain.

COMPANDING CONVERTER: An A/D or D/A converter which employs a logarithmic transfer function to expand or compress the analog signal range. These converters have large effective dynamic ranges and are commonly used in digitized voice communication systems.

COMPLEMENTARY BINARY CODE: A binary code which is the logical complement of straight binary. All 1's become 0's and vice versa.

CONVERSION TIME: The time required for an A/D converter to complete a single conversion to specified resolution and linearity for a full scale analog input change.

CONVERSION RATE: The number of repetitive A/D or D/A conversions per second for a full scale change to specified resolution and linearity.

COUNTER TYPE A/D CONVERTER: A feedback method of A/D conversion whereby a digital counter drives a D/A converter which generates an output ramp which is compared with the analog input. When the two are equal, a comparator stops the counter and output data is ready. Also called a *servo type* A/D converter.

CREEP VOLTAGE: A voltage change with time across an open capacitor caused by dielectric absorption. This causes sample-hold output error.

CROSSTALK: In an analog multiplexer, the ratio of output voltage to input voltage with all channels connected in parallel and off. It is generally expressed as an input to output attenuation ratio in dB.

DAC: Abbreviation for digital-to-analog converter. See *D/A Converter.*

D/A CONVERTER: Digital-to-analog converter. A circuit which converts a digital code word into an output analog (continuous) voltage or current.

DATA ACQUISITION SYSTEM: A system consisting of analog multiplexers, sample-holds, A/D converters, and other circuits which process one or more analog signals and convert them into digital form for use by a computer.

DATA AMPLIFIER: See *Instrumentation Amplifier.*

DATA CONVERTER: An A/D or D/A Converter.

DATA DISTRIBUTION SYSTEM: A system which uses D/A converters and other circuits to convert the digital outputs of a computer into analog form for control of a process or system.

DATA RECOVERY FILTER: A filter used to reconstruct an analog signal from a train of analog samples.

DATA WORD: A digital code-word that represents data to be processed.

DECAY RATE: See *Hold-Mode Droop.*

DECODER: A communications term for D/A converter.

DEGLITCHED DAC: A D/A converter which incorporates a deglitching circuit to virtually eliminate output spikes (or glitches). These DAC's are commonly used in CRT display systems.

DEGLITCHER: A special sample-hold circuit used to eliminate the output spikes (or glitches) from a D/A converter.

DIELECTRIC ABSORPTION: A voltage memory characteristic of capacitors caused by the dielectric material not polarizing instantaneously. The result is that not all the energy stored in a charged capacitor can be quickly recovered upon discharge, and the open capacitor voltage will creep. See also *Creep Voltage.*

DIFFERENTIAL LINEARITY ERROR: The maximum deviation of any quantum (LSB change) in the transfer function of a data converter from its ideal size of $FSR/2^n$.

DIFFERENTIAL LINEARITY TEMPCO: The change in differential linearity error with temperature for a data converter, expressed in ppm/°C of FSR (Full Scale Range).

DIGITIZER: A device which converts analog into digital data; an A/D converter.

DOUBLE-LEVEL MULTIPLEXING: A method of channel expansion in analog multiplexers whereby the outputs of a group of multiplexers connect to the inputs of another multiplexer.

DROOP: See *Hold-Mode Droop.*

DUAL SLOPE A/D CONVERTER: An indirect method of A/D conversion whereby an analog voltage is converted into a time period by an integrator and reference and then measured by a clock and counter. The method is relatively slow but capable of high accuracy.

DYNAMIC ACCURACY: The total error of a data converter or conversion system when operated at its maximum specified conversion rate or throughput rate.

DYNAMIC RANGE: The ratio of full scale range (FSR) of a data converter to the smallest difference it can resolve. In terms of converter resolution:

Dynamic Range $(DR) = 2^n$

It is generally expressed in dB:

$DR = 20 \log_{10} 2^n = 6.02n$

where n is the resolution in bits.

EFFECTIVE APERTURE DELAY: In a sample-hold, the time difference between the hold command and the time at which the input signal equalled the held voltage.

ELECTROMETER AMPLIFIER: An amplifier characterized by ultra-low input bias current and input noise which is used to measure currents in the picoampere region and lower.

ENCODER: A communications term for an A/D converter.

E.O.C.: End of Conversion. See *Status Output*.

ERROR BUDGET: A systematic listing of errors in a circuit or system to determine worst case total or statistical error.

EXTRAPOLATIVE HOLD: See *First-Order Hold*.

FEEDBACK TYPE A/D CONVERTER: A class of analog-to-digital converters in which a D/A converter is enclosed in the feedback loop of a digital control circuit which changes the D/A output until it equals the analog input.

FIRST-ORDER HOLD: A type of sample-hold, used as a recovery filter, which uses the present and previous analog samples to predict the slope to the next sample. Also called an *extrapolative hold*.

FLASH TYPE A/D CONVERTER: See *Parallel A/D Converter*.

FLYING-CAPACITOR MULTIPLEXER: A multiplexer switch which employs a double-pole, double-throw switch connected to a capacitor. By first connecting the capacitor to the signal source and then to a differential amplifier, a signal with a high common-mode voltage can be multiplexed to a ground-referenced circuit.

FRACTIONAL-ORDER HOLD: A type of sample-hold, used as a recovery filter, which uses a fixed fraction of the difference between the present and previous analog samples to predict the slope to the next sample.

FREQUENCY FOLDING: In the recovery of sampled data, the overlap of adjacent spectra caused by insufficient sampling rate. The overlapping results in distortion in the recovered signal which cannot be eliminated by filtering the recovered signal.

FREQUENCY-TO-VOLTAGE (F/V) CONVERTER: A device which converts an input pulse rate into an output analog voltage.

FSR: Full Scale Range.

FULL POWER FREQUENCY: The maximum frequency at which an amplifier, or other device, can deliver rated peak-to-peak output voltage into rated load at a specified distortion level.

FULL SCALE RANGE (FSR): the difference between maximum and minimum analog values for an A/D converter input or D/A converter output.

F/V CONVERTER: See *Frequency-To-Voltage Converter*.

GAIN-BANDWIDTH PRODUCT: The product of gain and small signal bandwidth for an operational amplifier or other circuit. This product is constant for a single-pole response.

GAIN ERROR: The difference in slope between the actual and ideal transfer functions for a data converter or other circuit. It is expressed as a percent of analog magnitude.

GAIN TEMPCO: The change in gain (or scale factor) with temperature for a data converter or other circuit, generally expressed in ppm/°C.

HIGH-LEVEL MULTIPLEXING: An analog multiplexing circuit in which the analog signal is first amplified to a higher level (1 to 10 volts) and then multiplexed. This is the preferred method of multiplexing to prevent noise contamination of the analog signal.

HOLD CAPACITOR: A high quality capacitor used in a sample-hold circuit to store the analog voltage. The capacitor must have low leakage and low dielectric absorption. Types commonly used include polystyrene, teflon, polycarbonate, polypropylene, and MOS.

HOLD-MODE: The operating mode of a sample-hold circuit in which the sampling switch is open.

HOLD-MODE DROOP: In a sample-hold, the output voltage change per unit of time with the sampling switch open. It is commonly expressed in V/sec. or µV/µsec.

HOLD-MODE FEEDTHROUGH: In a sample-hold, the percentage of input sinusoidal or step signal measured at the output with the sampling switch open.

HOLD-MODE SETTLING TIME: In a sample-hold, the time from the hold-command transition until the output has settled within a specified error band.

HYSTERESIS ERROR: The small variation in analog transition points of an A/D converter whereby the transition level depends on the direction from which it is approached. In most A/D converters this hysteresis is very small and is caused by the analog comparator.

IDEAL FILTER: A low pass filter with flat passband response, infinite attenuation at the cutoff frequency, and zero response past cutoff; it also has linear phase response in the passband. Ideal filters are mathematical filters frequently used in textbook examples but not physically realizable.

INDIRECT TYPE A/D CONVERTER: A class of analog-to-digital converters which converts the unknown input voltage into a time period and then measures this period.

INFINITE-HOLD: A sample-hold circuit which converts an analog voltage into digital form which is then held indefinitely, without decay, in a register.

INPUT DYNAMIC RANGE: In an amplifier, the maximum permissible peak-to-peak voltage across the input terminals which does not cause the output to slew rate limit or distort. Mathematically it is found as

$$\text{IDR (Input Dynamic Range)} \frac{SR}{\pi GB}$$

where SR is the slew rate and GB is gain bandwidth.

INSTRUMENTATION AMPLIFIER: An amplifier circuit with high impedance differential inputs and high common-mode rejection. Gain is set by one or two resistors which do not connect to the input terminals.

INTEGRAL LINEARITY ERROR: The maximum deviation of a data converter transfer function from the ideal straight line with offset and gain errors zeroed. It is generally expressed in LSB's or in percent of FSR.

INTEGRATING A/D CONVERTER: One of several types of A/D conversion techniques whereby the analog input is integrated with time. This includes dual slope, triple slope, and charge balancing type A/D converters.

INTERPOLATIVE HOLD: See *Polygonal Hold.*

ISOLATION AMPLIFIER: An amplifier which is electrically isolated between input and output in order to be able to amplify a differential signal superimposed on a high common-mode voltage.

LEAST SIGNIFICANT BIT (LSB): The rightmost bit in a data converter code. The analog size of the LSB can be found from the converter resolution:

$$\text{LSB Size} = \frac{FSR}{2^n}$$

where FSR is full scale range and n is the resolution in bits.

LINEARITY ERROR: See *Integral Linearity Error* and *Differential Linearity Error.*

LONG TERM STABILITY: The variation in data converter accuracy due to time change alone. It is commonly specified in percent per 1000 hours or per year.

LOW-LEVEL MULTIPLEXING: An analog multiplexing system in which a low amplitude signal is first multiplexed and then amplified.

LSB: Least Significant Bit.

LSB SIZE: See *Quantum.*

MAJOR CARRY: See *Major Transition.*

MAJOR TRANSITION: In a data converter, the change from a code of 1000...000 to 0111...1111 or vice-versa. This transition is the most difficult one to make from a linearity standpoint since the MSB weight must ideally be precisely one LSB larger than the sum of all other bit weights.

MISSING CODE: In an A/D converter, the characteristic whereby not all output codes are present in the transfer function of the converter. This is caused by a nonmonotonic D/A converter inside the A/D.

MONOTONICITY: For a D/A converter, the characteristic of the transfer function whereby an increasing input code produces a continuously increasing analog output. *Nonmonotonicity* may occur if the converter differential linearity error exceeds ±1 LSB.

MOST SIGNIFICANT BIT (MSB): The leftmost bit in a data converter code. It has the largest weight, equal to one half of full scale range.

MSB: Most Significant Bit.

MULTIPLYING D/A CONVERTER: A type of digital-to-analog converter in which the reference voltage can be varied over a wide range to produce an analog output which is the product of the input code and input reference voltage. Multiplication can be accomplished in one, two, or four algebraic quadrants.

MUX: Abbreviation for multiplexer. See *Analog Multiplexer.*

NATURAL BINARY CODE: A positive weighted code in which a number is represented by

$$N = a_0 2^0 + a_1 2^1 + a_2 2^2 + a_3 2^3 + \ldots + a_n 2^n$$

where each coefficient "a" has a value of zero or one. Data converters use this code in its fractional form where:

$$N = a_1 2^{-1} + a_2 2^{-2} + a_3 2^{-3} + \ldots a_n 2^{-n}$$

and N has a fractional value between zero and one.

NEGATIVE TRUE LOGIC: A logic system in which the more negative of two voltage levels is defined as a logical 1 (true) and the more positive level is defined as a logical 0 (false).

NOISE REJECTION: The amount of suppression of normal mode analog input noise of an A/D converter or other circuit, generally expressed in dB. Good noise rejection is a characteristic of integrating type A/D converters.

NONMONOTONIC: A D/A converter transfer characteristic in which the output does not continuously increase with increasing input. At one or more points there may be a dip in the output function.

NORMAL-MODE REJECTION: The attenuation of a specific frequency or band of frequencies appearing directly across two electrical terminals. In A/D converters, normal-mode rejection is determined by an input filter or by integration of the input signal.

NOTCH FILTER: An electronic filter which attenuates or rejects a specific frequency or narrow band of frequencies with a sharp cutoff on either side of the band.

NYQUIST THEOREM: See *Sampling Theorem.*

OFFSET BINARY CODE: Natural binary code in which the code word 0000 . . . . 0000 is displaced by one-half analog full scale. The code represents analog values between $-FS$ and $+FS$ (full scale). The code word 1000 . . . . 0000 then corresponds to analog zero.

OFFSET DRIFT: The change with temperature of analog zero for a data converter operating in the bipolar mode. It is generally expressed in ppm/°C of FSR.

OFFSET ERROR: The error at analog zero for a data converter operating in the bipolar mode.

ONE'S COMPLEMENT CODE: A bipolar binary code in which positive and negative codes of the same magnitude sum to all one's.

PARALLEL TYPE A/D CONVERTER: An ultra-fast method of A/D conversion which uses an array of $2^n - 1$ comparators to directly implement a quantizer, where n is the resolution in bits. The quantizer is followed by a decoder circuit which converts the comparator outputs into binary code.

PARALLEL TYPE D/A CONVERTER: The most commonly used type of D/A converter in which upon application of an input code, all bits change simultaneously to produce a new output.

PASSIVE FILTER: A filter circuit using only resistors, capacitors, and inductors.

POLYGONAL HOLD: A type of sample-hold, used as a signal recovery filter, which produces a voltage output which is a straight line joining the previous sample value to the present sample. This results in an accurate signal reconstruction but with a one sample-period output delay.

POSITIVE TRUE LOGIC: A logic system in which the more positive of two voltage levels is defined as a logical 1 (true) and the more negative level is defined as a logical 0 (false).

POWER SUPPLY SENSITIVITY: The output change in a data converter caused by a change in power supply voltage. Power supply sensitivity is generally specified in %/V or in %/% supply change.

PRECISION: The degree of repeatability, or reproducibility of a series of successive measurements. Precision is affected by the noise, hysteresis, time, and temperature stability of a data converter or other device.

PRE-SAMPLING FILTER: A low pass filter used to limit the bandwidth of a signal before sampling in order to assure that the conditions of the Sampling Theorem are met. Therefore frequency folding is eliminated or greatly diminished in the recovered signal spectrum.

PROGRAMMABLE GAIN AMPLIFIER: An amplifier with a digitally controlled gain for use in data acquisition systems.

PROGRAMMER-SEQUENCER: A digital logic circuit which controls the sequence of operations in a data acquisition system.

PROPAGATION TYPE A/D CONVERTER: A type of A/D conversion method which employs one comparator per bit to achieve ultra-fast A/D conversion. The conversion propagates down the series of cascaded comparators.

QUAD CURRENT SWITCH: A group of four current sources weighted 8-4-2-1 which are switched on and off by TTL inputs. They are used to implement A/D and D/A converter designs up to 16 bits resolution by using multiple quads with current dividers between each quad.

QUANTIZATION NOISE: See *Quantization Error.*

QUANTIZATION UNCERTAINTY: See *Quantization Error.*

QUANTIZED FEEDBACK A/D CONVERTER: See *Charge Balancing A/D Converter.*

QUANTIZER: A circuit which transforms a continuous analog signal into a set of discrete output states. Its transfer function is the familiar stair-case function.

QUANTIZING ERROR: The inherent uncertainty in digitizing an analog value due to the finite resolution of the conversion process. The quantized value is uncertain by up to $\pm Q/2$ where Q is the quantum size. This error can be reduced only by increasing the resolution of the converter. Also called *quantization uncertainty* or *quantization noise.*

QUANTUM: The analog difference between two adjacent codes for an A/D or D/A converter. Also called *LSB size.*

R-2R LADDER NETWORK: An array of matched resistors with series values of R and shunt values of 2R in a standard ladder circuit configuration.

RATIOMETRIC A/D CONVERTER: An analog-to-digital converter which uses a variable reference to measure the ratio of the input voltage to the reference.

RECONSTRUCTION FILTER: See *Data Recovery Filter.*

RECOVERY FILTER: See *Data Recovery Filter.*

REFERENCE CIRCUIT: A circuit which produces a stable output voltage over time and temperature for use in A/D and D/A converters. The circuit generally uses an operational amplifier with a precision Zener or bandgap type reference element.

RELATIVE ACCURACY: The worst case input to output error of a data converter, as a percent of full scale, referred to the converter reference. The error consists of offset, gain, and linearity components.

RESOLUTION: The smallest change that can be distinguished by an A/D converter or produced by a D/A converter. Resolution may be stated in percent of full scale, but is commonly expressed as the number of bits n where the converter has 2^n possible states.

SAMPLE-HOLD: A circuit which accurately acquires and stores an analog voltage on a capacitor for a specified period of time.

SAMPLE-HOLD FIGURE OR MERIT: The ratio of capacitor charging current in the sample-mode to the leakage current of the capacitor in the hold-mode.

SAMPLE-MODE: The operating mode of a sample-hold circuit in which the sampling switch is closed.

SAMPLER: An electronic switch which is turned on and off at a fast rate to produce a train of analog sample pulses.

SAMPLE-TO-HOLD OFFSET ERROR: For a sample-hold, the change in output voltage from the sample-mode to the hold-mode, with constant input voltage. This error is caused by the sampling switch transferring charge onto the hold capacitor as it opens.

SAMPLE-TO-HOLD STEP: See *Sample-to-Hold Offset Error.*

SAMPLE-TO-HOLD TRANSIENT: A small spike at the output of a sample-hold when it goes into the hold mode. It is caused by feedthrough from the sampling switch control voltage.

SAMPLING THEOREM: A theorem due to Nyquist which says if a continuous bandwidth-limited signal contains no frequency components higher than f_c, then the original signal can be recovered without distortion if it is sampled at a rate of at least $2f_c$ samples per second.

SAR: Successive approximation register. A digital control circuit used to control the operation of a successive approximation A/D converter.

SCALE FACTOR ERROR: See *Gain Error.*

SERIAL TYPE D/A CONVERTER: A type of digital-to-analog converter in which the digital input data is received in sequential form before an analog output is produced.

SERVO-TYPE A/D CONVERTER: See *Counter-Type A/D Converter.*

SETTLING TIME: The time elapsed from the application of a full scale step input to a circuit to the time when the output has entered and remained within a specified error band around its final value.

This term is an important specification for operational amplifiers, analog multiplexers, and D/A converters.

SHORT CYCLING: The termination of an A/D conversion process at a resolution less than the full resolution of the converter. This results in a shorter conversion time for reduced resolution in A/D converters with a short cycling capability.

SIGNAL RECONSTRUCTION FILTER: A low pass filter used to accurately reconstruct an analog signal from a train of analog samples.

SIGN-MAGNITUDE BCD: A binary coded decimal code in which a sign bit is added to distinguish positive from negative in bipolar operation.

SIGN-MAGNITUDE BINARY CODE: The natural binary code to which a sign bit is added to distinguish positive from negative in bipolar operation.

SIMULTANEOUS SAMPLE-HOLD: A system in which a series of sample-hold circuits are used to sample a number of analog channels, all at the same instant. This requires one sample-hold per analog channel.

SIMULTANEOUS TYPE A/D CONVERTER: See *Parallel Type A/D Converter.*

SINGLE-LEVEL MULTIPLEXING: A method of channel expansion in analog multiplexers whereby several multiplexers are operated in parallel by connecting their outputs together. Each multiplexer is controlled by a digital *enable* input.

SINGLE-SLOPE A/D CONVERTER: A simple A/D converter technique in which a ramp voltage generated from a voltage reference and integrator is compared with the analog input voltage by a comparator. The time required for the ramp to equal the input is measured by a clock and counter to produce the digital output word.

SKIPPED CODE: See *Missing Code.*

SLEW RATE: The maximum rate of change of the output of an operational amplifier or other circuit. Slew rate is limited by internal charging currents and capacitances and is generally expressed in volts per microsecond.

SPAN: For an A/D or D/A converter, the full scale range or difference between maximum and minimum analog values.

START-CONVERT: The input pulse to an A/D converter which initiates conversion.

STATIC ACCURACY: The total error of a data converter or conversion system under DC input conditions.

STATUS OUTPUT: The logic output of an A/D converter which indicates whether the device is in the process of making a conversion or the conversion has been completed and output data is ready. Also called *busy output* or *end of conversion output.*

STRAIGHT BINARY CODE: See *Natural Binary Code.*

SUBSURFACE ZENER REFERENCE: A compensated voltage reference diode in which avalanche breakdown occurs below the surface of the silicon in the bulk region rather than at the surface. This results in lower noise and higher stability. The reversed biased diode is temperature compensated by a series connected, forward biased signal diode.

SUCCESSIVE APPROXIMATION A/D CONVERTER: An A/D conversion method that compares in sequence a series of binary weighted values with the analog input to produce an output digital word in just n steps, where n is the resolution in bits. The process is efficient and is analogous to weighing an unknown quantity on a balance scale using a set of binary standard weights.

TEMPERATURE COEFFICIENT: The change in analog magnitude with temperature, expressed in ppm/°C.

THREE-STATE OUTPUT: A type of A/D converter output used to connect to a data bus. The three output states are logic 1, logic 0, and off. An *enable* control turns the output on or off.

THROUGHPUT RATE: The maximum repetitive rate at which a data conversion system can operate to give specified output accuracy. It is determined by adding the various times required for multiplexer settling, sample-hold acquisition, A/D conversion, etc. and then taking the inverse of total time.

TRACK-AND-HOLD: A sample-hold circuit which can continuously follow the input signal in the sample-mode and then go into hold-mode upon command.

TRACKING A/D CONVERTER: A counter-type analog-to-digital converter which can continuously follow the analog input at some specified maximum rate and continuously update its digital output as the input signal changes. The circuit uses a D/A converter driven by an up-down counter.

TRANSDUCER: A device which converts a physical parameter such as temperature or pressure into an electrical voltage or current.

TRANSFER FUNCTION: The input to output characteristic of a device such as a data converter expressed either mathematically or graphically.

TRIPLE-SLOPE A/D CONVERTER: A variation on the dual slope type A/D converter in which the time period measured by the clock and counter is divided into a coarse (fast slope) measurement and a fine (slow slope) measurement.

TWO'S COMPLEMENT CODE: A bipolar binary code in which positive and negative codes of the same magnitude sum to all zero's plus a carry.

TWO-STAGE PARALLEL A/D CONVERTER: An ultra-fast A/D converter in which two parallel type A/D's are operated in cascade to give higher resolution. In the usual case a 4-bit parallel converter first makes a conversion; the resulting output code drives an ultra-fast 4-bit D/A, the output of which is subtracted from the analog input to form a residual. This residual then goes to a second 4 bit parallel A/D. The result is an 8 bit word converted in two steps.

UNIPOLAR MODE: In a data converter, when the analog range includes values of one polarity only.

V/F CONVERTER: See *Voltage-to-Frequency Converter.*

VIDEO A/D CONVERTER: An ultra-fast A/D converter capable of conversion rates of 5 MHz and higher. Resolution is usually 8 bits but can vary depending on the application. Conversion rates of 20 MHz and higher are common.

VOLTAGE DECAY: See *Hold-Mode Droop.*

VOLTAGE REFERENCE: See *Reference Circuit.*

VOLTAGE-TO-FREQUENCY (V/F) CONVERTER: A device which converts an analog voltage into a train of digital pulses with frequency proportional to the input voltage.

WEIGHTED CURRENT SOURCE D/A CONVERTER: A digital-to-analog converter design based on a series of binary weighted transistor current sources which can be turned on or off by digital inputs.

ZERO DRIFT: The change with temperature of analog zero for a data converter operating in the unipolar mode. It is generally expressed in μV/°C.

ZERO ERROR: The error at analog zero for a data converter operating in the unipolar mode.

ZERO-ORDER HOLD: A name for a sample-hold circuit used as a data recovery filter. It is used to accurately reconstruct an analog signal from a train of analog samples.

This is Datel-Intersil

In April, 1979 Datel Systems was acquired by Intersil, Inc. and became Datel-Intersil. Datel-Intersil is an established international leader in the design and manufacture of data conversion circuits and systems. Intersil, Inc. is a forward integrated, multi-technology company which designs and produces a broad line of semiconductor components and systems including add-on and add-in memory systems; it ranks among the 10 largest independent semiconductor companies in the U.S.

With the growing importance of data acquisition systems in industrial, military, and commercial applications, the combination of Intersil and Datel product lines results in one of the broadest lines of data acquisition products in the industry. Further, a steady stream of significant new products is assuring a leadership position in supplying the demand for the high performance data acquisition devices of the 1980's.

These products are manufactured by one or more of the following technologies: monolithic CMOS, monolithic bipolar, thin-film hybrid, and discrete component circuits. Many new products employ a combination of technologies to achieve the desired performance.

The present data-acquisition product lines of Datel-Intersil include: A/D and D/A converters, sample-holds, analog multiplexers, operational and instrumentation amplifiers, V/F converters, voltage references, temperature sensors, digital panel meters, digital panel printers, data loggers and readers, data acquisition systems, computer analog I/O boards, digital voltage calibrators, power supplies and DC-DC converters.

For information on any of these products, please fill out a Request for Information form and send to:

DATEL-INTERSIL, INC.
11 Cabot Boulevard
Mansfield, Massachusetts 02048
Telephone: (617) 339-9341

Credits

ORDER FORM

Please send to

Attn: Marketing Dept.
11 Cabot Boulevard
Mansfield, MA 02048

Please send additional copies of
DATA ACQUISITION
AND CONVERSION HANDBOOK:

No. Copies	Price Each	Total
	$4.95	
Shipping and Handling*		
Amount Enclosed		

*Outside U.S. and Canada add $2.75 per copy for air shipments and handling.

NAME _____

COMPANY _____

M.S. DEPT. _____

STREET _____

CITY _____ STATE _____ ZIP _____

Enclose check or money order in U.S. dollars
(no cash or stamps) made out to:
DATEL-INTERSIL, INC.

REQUEST FOR INFORMATION

Please send to

DATEL
INTERSIL

Attn: Marketing Dept.
11 Cabot Boulevard
Mansfield, MA 02048

Please send technical data on the following product areas:

☐ Active Filters
☐ A/D Converters
☐ Analog Multiplexers
☐ Computer Analog I/O Boards
☐ D/A Converters
☐ Data Acquisition Systems
☐ Data Loggers and Readers
☐ DC-DC Converters
☐ Digital Panel Meters
☐ Digital Printers
☐ Digital Voltage Calibrators
☐ Op Amps & Instrum. Amps
☐ Power Supplies
☐ Sample-Holds
☐ Temperature Sensors
☐ V/F Converters
☐ Voltage References

NAME _____

COMPANY _____

M.S. DEPT. _____

STREET _____

CITY _____ STATE _____ ZIP _____

TELEPHONE: ( ) - _____

My interest is: ☐ Immediate
☐ Future   ☐ File only

ORDER FORM

Please send to

Attn: Marketing Dept.
11 Cabot Boulevard
Mansfield, MA 02048

Please send additional copies of
DATA ACQUISITION
AND CONVERSION HANDBOOK:

No. Copies	Price Each	Total
	$4.95	
Shipping and Handling*		
Amount Enclosed		

*Outside U.S. and Canada add $2.75 per copy for air
shipments and handling.

NAME _____

COMPANY _____

M.S. DEPT. _____

STREET _____

CITY _____ STATE _____ ZIP _____

Enclose check or money order in U.S. dollars
(no cash or stamps) made out to:
DATEL-INTERSIL, INC.

REQUEST FOR INFORMATION

Please send to

DATEL
INTERSIL

Attn: Marketing Dept.
11 Cabot Boulevard
Mansfield, MA 02048

NAME _____

COMPANY _____

M.S. DEPT. _____

STREET _____

CITY _____ STATE _____ ZIP _____

TELEPHONE: ( ) - _____

Please send technical data on the
following product areas:

☐ Active Filters
☐ A/D Converters
☐ Analog Multiplexers
☐ Computer Analog I/O Boards
☐ D/A Converters
☐ Data Acquisition Systems
☐ Data Loggers and Readers
☐ DC-DC Converters
☐ Digital Panel Meters
☐ Digital Printers
☐ Digital Voltage Calibrators
☐ Op Amps & Instrum. Amps
☐ Power Supplies
☐ Sample-Holds
☐ Temperature Sensors
☐ V/F Converters
☐ Voltage References

My interest is: ☐ Immediate
☐ Future   ☐ File only

ORDER FORM

Please send to

Attn: Marketing Dept.
11 Cabot Boulevard
Mansfield, MA 02048

Please send additional copies of
DATA ACQUISITION
AND CONVERSION HANDBOOK:

No. Copies	Price Each	Total
	$4.95	
Shipping and Handling*		
Amount Enclosed		

*Outside U.S. and Canada add $2.75 per copy for air shipments and handling.

NAME _____

COMPANY _____

M.S. DEPT. _____

STREET _____

CITY _____ STATE _____ ZIP _____

Enclose check or money order in U.S. dollars
(no cash or stamps) made out to:
DATEL-INTERSIL, INC.

REQUEST FOR INFORMATION

Please send to

DATEL INTERSIL

Attn: Marketing Dept.
11 Cabot Boulevard
Mansfield, MA 02048

Please send technical data on the following product areas:

- ☐ Active Filters
- ☐ A/D Converters
- ☐ Analog Multiplexers
- ☐ Computer Analog I/O Boards
- ☐ D/A Converters
- ☐ Data Acquisition Systems
- ☐ Data Loggers and Readers
- ☐ DC-DC Converters
- ☐ Digital Panel Meters
- ☐ Digital Printers
- ☐ Digital Voltage Calibrators
- ☐ Op Amps & Instrum. Amps
- ☐ Power Supplies
- ☐ Sample-Holds
- ☐ Temperature Sensors
- ☐ V/F Converters
- ☐ Voltage References

NAME _____

COMPANY _____

M.S. DEPT. _____

STREET _____

CITY _____ STATE _____ ZIP _____

TELEPHONE: ( ) - _____

My interest is: ☐ Immediate
☐ Future   ☐ File only